The Living World

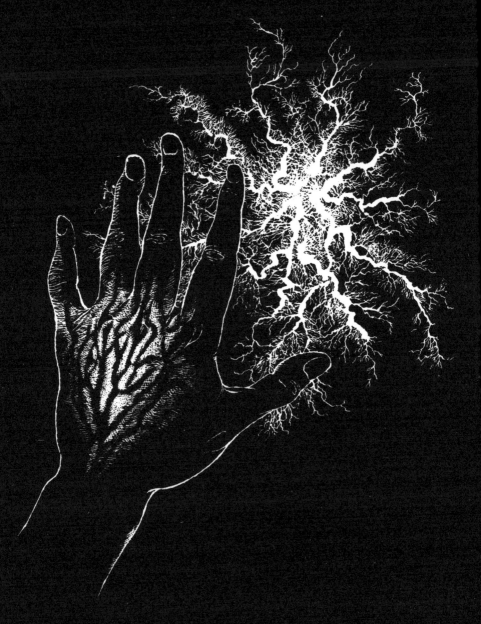

BERNARDA
BRYSON   PLATE I

THE
LIVING WORLD

The Miracles of Creation
revealed in
the World around us

By
RUTHERFORD PLATT

Drawings by
BERNARDA BRYSON

Souvenir Press · London

First published by Simon & Schuster,
New York, as *The River of Life*
First British edition published 1964
by Souvenir Press Ltd., 34 Bloomsbury
Street, London, W.C.1

" The Nations in the Tree " is reprinted by
courtesy of the Grolier Society, which
published this chapter in a slightly
different version in *The Book of Knowledge
Annual* © 1955 by the Grolier Society, Inc.

The author wishes to express his appreciation
to Shirley Sarnoff for her help in the
research for this book.

Made and printed by offset in Great Britain by
William Clowes and Sons, Limited,
London and Beccles.

➤➤➤➤➤➤➤➤➤ CONTENTS ⫷⫷⫷⫷⫷⫷⫷⫷⫷

v

Part Three
ANIMATED TOOLS AND EQUIPMENT

Part Four
SECRETS OF SURVIVING

⟫⟫⟫⟫⟫⟫⟫ POSTSCRIPT ⟪⟪⟪⟪⟪⟪⟪

Now that I have finished this book I find myself trapped in a maze of mirrors. Crowds of flag animals, dancing bees, whirligig beetles, rabbit eyes, and ant lions stare at me from thousands of reflections. This is like Alice's experience when she peered behind the looking glass and found herself conversing with a lot of animals who were very busy, wise, and serious in a timeless, topsy-turvy world.

But if you will explore this world with me, we shall discover that it is stranger than Alice's and at the same time has a mysterious unity. It becomes apparent that every body is made with counterparts of every other body. All eyes register light with the same kind of impulses whether they are the thousands of tiny eyes of a bee or the big round globes of the horse and the owl. Muscles all have the same sort of action whether in the dogfish, centipede, sparrow, or ape. Limbs of a mouse turn into wings for a bat, hind wings of a bee turn into halteres for a housefly, forelegs of a dog become arms for a man, nose and jaw merge and elongate to make a trunk for an elephant, the segments of a spine lengthen, without increasing their number, to make a tail. The fundamental body parts of the turtle, sea gull, hippopotamus, and donkey are similar. When living things came out of the sea to live on land, fins turned into legs, gills into lungs, scales into fur. Every living body is the same phenomenon.

Increasing the awe and wonder of the unity of life is its rhythm. Every move of a free and healthy animal has harmony, whether swimming, flying, crawling, running, or merely turning its head. This is seen even in the combat and violence of living, in the spring of a lion on its prey, or the power dive of a gannet after a fish. A similar rhythm is revealed in the centers of daisies, the spiraling of pine cones and tendrils, and in the eccentric twistings of driftwood. Out of the dynamic spirals of life arise countless melodies. And each melody is unique. One is never exactly repeated all through the ages because the combinations of the rhythms of the air and the oceans are infinite.

The beings encountered in our adventure are revelation after revelation of an urgent inner force devoted to making each thing live in its own way. In the changing ages protoplasm has exercised supreme wisdom, fresh skills, unique ingenuity to enable its creatures to meet new situations as they arise. Was this amazing potential inherent in protoplasm at the beginning? Or as time rolled along has guidance been given to protoplasm from an outside source? Either way, life is very far from being automatic in the way living forms have anticipated distant futures. We do not have the least hint of the purpose behind this genius of the living cell, but we must admit that it's a miraculous phenomenon on the level of a divine creation.

Part One

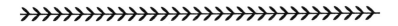

JUST
OUTSIDE THE WINDOW

>>>>>>>>>>>>>> 1 <<<<<<<<<<<<<<

An Exciting Animal

IF YOU WILL come with me early on a spring morning to the willow at the foot of my hill, I will show you an exciting animal. The night shadows still lingering in low places are melting away, and the day shadows are shortening in unison. You can see the earth revolve simply by holding out your hand and watching a shadow move across it. As the shadow glides off, you feel the warmth of sunlight deliciously increase on your skin.

This is the time and place, if you are in the mood, to see events that weave the fanciful fabric of life over land and sea. Every square inch of the landscape is filled with life, which dwells in a soft, gently responsive substance in a multitude of forms. Each is ready to absorb its portion of this day's energy coming in from across sky space—at eleven million miles per minute. These receptors of light energy are as different in their sizes, structures, and systems as a green leaf, a flower, an aphid, a caterpillar, a bird's egg in a nest, a rabbit, or you and I watching a tassel on a willow. All are interdependent and all are acting in unison with the moving shadows. Each pulses with light that imparts motion to everything it touches, even to the granite bones of the earth.

Yesterday's sunlight called out this willow tassel from its bud, by setting in motion water, causing it to flow upward against gravity and squeeze through the thread of the twig into the bud. The bud had been made ready to respond to this water in a certain way; it had the right amount of elasticity to expand to a point and then burst. The red tassel appeared out of a silent explosion.

The opening of a bud is similar to the phenomenon of birth which causes an egg to break and a bird to appear at the moment it is ready, a baby to burst out of its mother's womb, fruits to crack when their seeds are ripe. Every living event occurs at just the right time to make ready for the next event and often, as with the bee and the willow tassel, for one individual to meet another precisely at a time and place.

The emergence of the tassel happened at this spot yesterday. This morning we see today's sunlight continue this smooth flow of life where yesterday's left off. The tassel is stippled with red lumps in pine-cone spirals, and now these are opening in succession, beginning at the tip and following the spiral course around and around to the base, like a sparking fuse. When the lumps crack open golden pollen grains spill out, turning the tassel yellow before our eyes. This is a signal for the bee. At this spot this moment the Plant Kingdom is summoning the Animal Kingdom to touch it and help itself to these crystals of packaged sunlight.

Somewhere in the vastness of the outdoors a beehive is hidden deep in the shadows of the night. At the moment the first rays of sunshine brush the hive, the hugging, sticky population heaves with a low, rumbling buzz. Then, in concert with the melting shadows, twenty-day-old bees are roused to go out and search spring jungles for the sun energy stored in pollen and nectar. Orders are precise; not all the bees in the hive can go out and gather sunlight, but only those on whom the sun has risen at least twenty times. They alone have the power and equipment to fly miles and fetch great loads.

Nectar of flowers is often mistakenly spoken of as honey; but it does not become honey until it has been fortified with saliva and worked over in a bee's stomach. Bees boil down nectar to make honey for the same reason we boil down sap to remove the water when making maple sirup. Standing on the rims of reservoir cells, the bees buzz their wings like electric fans, blowing sun-dried air across the watery fluid.

Maple sap was not invented for man to make sirup, but apparently nectar was invented for bees to make honey. A flower has no personal use for its nectar, which, indeed, even has an odor different from the flower's own fragrance. Drops of the stuff sparkle like diamonds on the floor of the flower so placed that when a bee stoops to pick them up its body knocks against the flower's organs. This seems to be a haphazard kind of copulation, but fields of flowers prove that it is a reliable way to spark ovaries, and thus flowers unable to run to each other can fertilize their seeds.

A flower makes no nectar for use directly in its own life but only to present the nectar to a bee at a time and place and in such a manner that the bee will help the flower to reproduce. Thus the bee is an extension of the flower, serving as one of its organs of reproduction. This is the keynote of the legend of bees and flowers, yet, romantic as this is, it falls short of telling the true wonder of the relationship of the flower and the bee. The most awe-inspiring part of the tale is what pollen does to bees, not to flowers. In a sense it makes the bee a form of flower!

A pollen grain is the male germ of a plant. It carries the potency to reproduce its plant according to an exact pattern that is imprinted in the pollen grain. The astonishing fact is that this pollen, powered to reproduce a flowering plant, can also reproduce bees! It is not a substitute for the bee male germ, but it is a miracle drug which bees use to reproduce themselves.

Bees collect great quantities of both flower products—pollen and nectar—but they collect them in different ways and make different kinds of foodstuffs out of them. Nectar is swallowed and carried in the bee's stomach, while pollen is swept together and packed into baskets outside its body, where it is carried in big bundles on its hind legs as conspicuous as the bundle on the head of a Burmese woman. This pollen load is flown back home and turned over to young bees on whom the sun has risen for nine days.

A young bee that has absorbed sun energy for eight days, whether overcast or clear, builds up the power of its head glands so that, on the ninth day, these will produce a certain kind of chemical. On that day bees are handed baskets full of freshly gathered pollen, which they chew without swallowing, mix with the chemical, and turn into pollen mush. This mush is fed to all newborn babies—those one or two days old. Pollen mush is rich in protein and strongly acid, powerful food for babes, yet this pollen potency that ripens a seed also ripens the tiny white worm that comes out of a bee egg and turns it into the elaborate and complex mechanism that we call a bee—in just two days.

The wonder of protein is veiled behind the familiarity of the word. Protein is a combination of carbon, nitrogen, oxygen, and hydrogen, familiar enough elements, but when combined in protein they have the power to drive life forces in fore-ordained directions at the right moments. This life stuff is not a thing, it is a power: the peculiar power of living matter that designs living systems so varied, so harmonious, so precisely synchronized that our file labeled "protein" seems to hold the special secret of an inventor.

Protein pollen mush turns the little white worms that come out of the bee eggs into busy, buzzy bees, equipped with pollen baskets on their after legs, nectar stomachs, wax glands for comb building, multi-telescope eyes for seeing flowers in the sunlight, instruments for polarizing light to fix a course on long trips to and from flowers, and a power plant to drive them

II. *The bee does a contortionist act in mid-air—*
splashing pollen, packing pollen into the baskets
on its hind legs.

PLATE II

BERNARDA
BRYSON

through the air like flying boxcars. These are standard specifications for a sensational animal.

ASTOUNDING ACROBATICS

You and I were left at the foot of my meadow watching a willow tassel gush pollen. This glitter of gold is drawing bees like a magnet from miles around. They are scouting the area, traveling with empty pollen baskets at fourteen miles per hour, each with 12,600 eyes wide open for a swaying or quivering object.

The first bee zooms in and stops short about two inches from the tassel to catch its odor. After a second's pause it does a belly flop on top of the catkin and splashes in the pollen like a child in surf. In two seconds pollen crystals are sticking all over the bee, on hairs that grow out of its eyeballs, the back of its neck, its hairy chest, abdomen, legs—every spot on its body except on the wings, which are smooth and polished. Wings must not be encumbered with pollen or the bee will sink like an airplane with wings heavily iced. The polish of bee wings is a bit of the ineluctable logic of living things.

After splashing, the bee suddenly rises straight up a few inches above the tassel and stops at a spot in mid-air. This feat of defying gravity is done with the easy economy of effort and offhand manner of a great artist.

Promptly the bee does a contortionist act like a little man putting on his coat in a high wind. It scrapes off pollen from its face, chest, and head with its front legs; from its abdomen and back with its middle legs—which calls for peculiar leg hinges and adroitness in order to scrape on top. As pollen is scraped, it is passed aft from front legs to middle to hind legs without a grain being lost. Almost before you can turn around, the body of the bee is cleared, and a wad of pollen is neatly packed into each basket on the hind legs.

Another plunge into the tassel and repeat. If its baskets are not full when pollen is gone from stamens on top of the tassel, the bee makes a somersault dive, zooms down, curves up steeply, and grabs a pollen box on the underside of the tassel with one toe. It hangs there, swaying deliciously. The elasticity and strength of the stamen are exactly calculated for the weight of the bee.

From our viewpoint this looks like fun—hanging by one toe and splashing pollen with the others. Probably the bee enjoys it instinctively as this is an opportunity for a beautiful job of splashing pollen dust. The contortionist act in mid-air follows, and the bee has its baskets loaded in three minutes.

Somehow, as you stare at this peculiar performance at a fixed spot in mid-air just above the tassel, the act, like so many things we see in nature, appears isolated, complete in itself. We do not usually consider the chain of events that have led up to this ritual and other events that now will lead away from it. It is true that the spectacle of a tassel of pollen crystals, lustrous and rich, must loom great to a bee and catch its eye in the sunlight. But the encounter of tassel and bee is not so haphazard as that, and events that lead up to the contact of the bee and the pollen grains are not coincidental. Else in the long run bees would not score enough goals to win the game. The early-morning hours on this particular day—not yesterday, not tomorrow—when this tassel effervesces with ripe pollen, are the single opportunity for this tassel and this bee to meet. And they do meet, for the law of averages with which nature works insures this necessity.

CELESTIAL NAVIGATION

The bee which appears before our eyes may have come from a mile beyond the village, perhaps three or four miles away from across the meadows on the other side of the lake. Though the tassel is big and conspicuous to a bee confronting it, the trip is a long one indeed for such a tiny traveler. In proportion to its size, two miles is to the bee what a trip from New York City to Richmond, Virginia, is to a man. Imagine flying such a long way across a pathless countryside you have never traversed before, with only your senses to guide you, to the Virginia State House and then back to the street address from which you started, and you have a hint of the size of the problem which the bee easily solves.

The willow, the landscape, the angle of the sunlight, the breeze that vibrates the tassel, the inner stress of the hunger of the hive, and the special capacities of the thousands of eyes in the bee's head, plus many conditions and forces, all fall into place, are all synchronized to produce the result. While we merely see the bee appear, splash, pack pollen, and vanish.

No book is big enough to analyze for our finite minds all the details and calculations of this commonplace achievement of the bee. The science of hitting the willow tassel at the right instant is true life metaphysics, combining physics, chemistry, dynamics, electronics, mathematics, biology, and mysterious influences.

Consider the details of the bee's equipment. Instead of a single wide-angle lens like that of the human eye, each of the two eyes is a compact bundle of 6,300 long-focus telescopic lenses directed at slightly different angles, forming a curved surface with telescopes pointing up, down, right, left, so that a bee can scan a wide area without moving its head. A mariner who swings his telescope to search the sea is scanning in the same way, except that the bee uses thousands of telescopes fixed at the various angles instead of turning its head.

In addition to its two bundles of telescopes, the bee has three separate, extra-powerful telescopes near the top of its head. These are sight boosters. They add to the stimulation of the 12,600 eye pieces. With elaborate equipment such as this, the bee can pick up little objects fast. Twelve thousand six hundred telescopes for seeing all around at the same time, enhanced with three super-telescopes, are apparatus to find what you are looking for across the vast phantasmagoria of a landscape. It sounds like a supernatural idea.

Its eyes pick up the pattern of lights and shadows from trees silhouetted against the sky, from water and rocks, and they are particularly sensitive to the vibrations of colors from the pin points of flowers. As these bright spots move across the lattice of many lenses, the flashing off and on of a certain color excites the bee's attention. The more contrast of light and shadows across its broad eye lattice, the better the bee sees. An inquisitive scientist extracted one of the multi-telescope eyes and looked through it—even photographed through it. The print revealed an image made by black and white dots like a printer's half-tone plate.

Such an eye picks up flicker fast—as when a willow tassel quivers in the slightest breeze. With flexing form and the way it dangles from an elastic stem, it whispers to the bee. So also flowers with broken outlines and with vividly contrasting lines and spots are more conspicuous running across the lattice of lenses. White, light green, or yellow flowers, which do not have the color contrasts of dark flowers, send out strong ultraviolet signals. For a long time it was hard to figure out why noncontrasting, light-colored flowers had such a powerful attraction for bees, because ultraviolet is invisible to our eyes.

Our willow tassel had filtered out the ultraviolet rays of the sunlight and shot them into the air, where they caught the eyes of the bee. These rays drew the bee closer until the swaying and vibration of the tassel incited the bee's optic nerves, and that was the signal to halt in mid-air. The bee steered to within two inches of the tassel, where its antenna picked up the smell of pollen—and it dived in.

How peculiar color is! No one can ever say whether you and I have the same mental images of color. We can agree that we receive the same length of light rays, which we call red or blue, but the visible image of the mind's eye can never be compared.

However, in the *emotion* of color we have a chance for some slight understanding of the bee's viewpoint. Colors are not merely a description of an object. The pigment of a painting, the tint of a dress, the tints and tones of interior decorating, are some of the ways that color is used as an emotional element rather than a descriptive one. Color touches secret springs of feeling, and we can suppose that color produces a highly emotional reaction in a bee.

A bee a-wing across the landscape is spurred by the alternation of shade and brightness. You and I have a feeling of well-being in the splendor of things basking in sunshine. Doubtless a bee also has a sense of well-being and relaxation of nerve stress through observing that the territory is right, the season is right, and time of day is right—for pollen. As it wings its way, the bee's tremendous batteries of telescopes pick up the gleam from the surface of a pond, the dark and light of trees against the sky, the quivering of flowers. Its mood at this time, early in the spring, when the hive's stores are low after winter, when new babies should be a-borning in greater numbers each day, is keyed to respond to that particular kind of vibration and that particular intensity of ultraviolet which the willow tassel offers. The willow is literally broadcasting signals to which the inner tensions of the bee are, at that very moment, all attuned. The wave lengths of the colors are all that matters. Neither we nor the bee need call traffic lights green, yellow, and red where everybody feels and reacts in the same way to certain vibrations.

The Custom-Made Queen

NATURE TAKES REPRODUCTION very seriously and usually sets aside about half of the population especially equipped to bear babies and eggs. But not so with bees. They are made to fetch and carry and serve and work relentlessly, with no leisure for courtship and with no organs capable of producing bees. Yet, since we see many bees around, it is obvious that their problem of reproduction has been solved in some way.

Just one bee is enough to maintain a population of fifty thousand or more and keep bees coming into the world at the rate of more than a thousand a day. This calls for a superlative mother, who, incidentally, has no time for sexual intercourse after eggs start coming out of her assembly line.

This mother is custom-made, when the need for an egg-layer arises, by the simple expedient of keeping one of the regular babies on pollen mush after the second day instead of switching it to honey. All baby bees get pollen mush their first two days, and after that they are usually given a diet of honey for the rest of their lives. Workers, the vast majority of the hive, are fed in this way. The one-in-fifty-thousand bee selected to become a queen is kept on pollen, which works a weird miracle in the body of that bee. Its jaws are shortened, its head grows rounder, its abdomen grows longer, projecting far out behind, and it acquires a terrific curved stinger. This large female summoned into being by pollen mush has no pollen baskets, no honey stomach, no wax glands, no daylight navigation instruments; her eyes will be smaller and a different shape; she will have a different kind of flight mechanism.

Usually, an animal is all taped out when the egg is fertilized. This goes for a centipede, horse, housefly, man, or practically any animal you can think of. An embryo is foreordained to develop step by step, with only the addition of food, water, and oxygen from outside itself, into its particular kind of animal. The queen bee is a startling exception. The nature of a baby already born is deliberately altered by its associates simply by feeding it different food from the others.

Baby-feeders are only five days old and have never flown. They are baby-feeders because they have tangled threads in their foreheads which bear a thousand tiny knots like strings of beads. Unraveled, end to end, these would stretch three times as long as the bee's body. These strings of beads produce chemicals which convert pollen into pollen mush. Every bee mysteriously acquires these beads on the fifth or sixth day of its life and thus becomes a baby-feeder.

The need for a new egg-layer arises as an emergency when the old queen dies or goes on a slowdown strike in producing eggs because she is about to take off with a swarm (or is removed by a man who wants to see what will happen). The emergency is obvious first of all to the twenty-two bees who are feeding the queen pollen mush every twenty-five minutes. Their excitement is contagious, and it causes bees to open cracks between the segments of their abdomens, squeeze out wax, and start building an extra-large cell. The egg layer is an extra-big bee and the ordinary cell that snugly fits ordinary bees is not nearly large enough. Her special cell will be set apart, where it looks like a peanut dangling from the comb.

If the old queen is still hanging around, she will drop an egg into the big cell as well as into the other cells. When this hatches, the baby in the big cell gets pollen mush for the rest of its life. The baby-feeders touch the big cell with their antennae, feel its dimensions, and that is their signal—the baby in the big cell is not to be shifted to honey. But if the emergency was caused by the death or disappearance of the old queen and she is not around to drop in a routine egg, the nervous bees will lug over an unhatched egg from a regular cell and put it in the big cell. Or they may bring a conventional baby from another cell and put it in the big cell, provided the infant is not over two days old and still on pollen mush.

THE QUEEN'S MEN

It takes a poet to do the queen's mating justice. A Frenchman, Jules Michelet, overwhelmed by its rhapsody, exclaims, "One brief moment, a moment announcing the approach of death, the grand festival of love . . . they lavish with royal magnificence their last days. Wherefore should they economize, when tomorrow they die? Break forth then, O life of splendor! Let that incandescent ardor, that torrent of existence be poured out!" What more can you say? This outdoes the legend that bees are a kind of funny little people happy in the service of their queen. Ordinary words just can't describe the fantastic ritual of the mating queen.

Matching the fairy tale of a custom-made queen is the magical act of the queen when she desires to summon up a male.

The queen is well supplied with spermatozoa for producing conventional bees. When she wants a male, she simply turns an internal faucet that closes a valve shutting off a sperm from reaching an egg. Then, lo and behold, a big male bee with extra-huge eyes and powerful smellers is procreated from this unfertilized egg! How and when did she get the sperm?

Man has been interested in bees since before history, but the question of how the queen becomes stocked with a lifelong supply of male sperm has been a deep mystery through the centuries. A daring explanation was advanced by one of the greatest insect authorities of the eighteenth century, the Hollander Jan Swammerdam, who, observing that male bees give forth a strong odor, supposed that the queen was impregnated by this scent, which he called *aura seminalis*.

Today we piece together the story from the take-off of the queen into the sky pursued by males, her return to the hive, and a few eyewitness accounts. These are only quick glimpses and impressions, for such events cannot be staged as a laboratory experiment. The queen and males will not mate in a room, or even in a big cage. They may be induced to take off, with males in pursuit of the queen, but the whole experiment ends abruptly when sensitive antennae touch walls or ceiling. They must rush upward freely in the open air, the clear sky, and with the late afternoon sun around four o'clock.

The potency of pollen mush that grows a bigger bee and a complicated egg-laying machinery inside her also hastens her maturity. Six days after a queen is born she is ready for mating. On the same day a few hundred trigger-happy males from nine to twelve days old (an exclusive coterie in a population of fifty thousand) are alerted by the odor of the queen.

In fair weather an explosive exit occurs when the sun is slanting from the west. If it is raining the queen and the males pace the hive, impatiently waiting for another day. This can go on for a week in a spell of overcast weather, while the queen waits as glum and helpless as a fogbound schooner. It is important to get going, time's awasting, for if bad weather keeps her waiting until she is twenty days old, even though the old lady then goes on a mating flight, she will bring forth only unfertilized eggs, all males.

The males have no social life; they do not even lead the life of a bee. They exist solely to take the one great flight that inspired Michelet and die. The chance for one male's success is slight, with one queen pursued by hundreds of males. Only a fraction of one per cent of the bee males ever hit the bull's-eye. When this happens, the male wins the race only to fall to the ground and have his body torn to pieces by the queen and die. The males who failed return to the hive, where the same bees that had waited on them devotedly before the exciting contest, bringing them an abundance of honey, now refuse to have anything to do with them. The frustrated males are set upon and beaten if they so much as look at honey, so they soon starve, and their bodies are pushed out of the hive to become fertilizer for future flowers for future bees.

Yet male bees are superbly equipped as missiles to pursue a nimble target. We observed that the pollen and honey collectors who go out daily to spot flowers have 12,600 telescopes to scan the horizon. The male bee who flies for half an hour on a single afternoon in all his life has twice as much see-power. A patient Englishman named Dr. Cheshire counted 26,180 eye telescopes on the head of the male. Look the different kinds of bees straight in the eyes and you will see how differently they stare back at you. The ordinary bee with no sex has eyes that bulge like big cheeks. But the male peers at you with great hemispheres extending from under his chin around the side of his head until they meet at the top. Moreover, the three big booster telescopes on the top of the head of the ordinary bee are bigger on the male and placed in the middle of his forehead so that he can fix the queen with his gaze when she flies straight ahead of him into the sky.

Odors are the spoor and signs of the bee world. The regular bee gets odor instructions through 4,800 tiny oval disks on its antennae. These give adequate smell power to the ordinary workaday bee. But the superb male, who just eats and waits until he's sprung, has 75,600 smelling disks on his antennae to alert him when the great moment comes.

This prodigious male bee is a vivid example of the lengths to which nature goes to populate the earth. He is given superb equipment and power to complete a dexterous mission in a split second of his life. He has no other duty to perform. Yet the chances are more than a hundred to one that this magnificent animal will be wasted. Such prodigality recalls how nature creates myriads of golden pollen grains so that a few of them may be sure to spark ovaries, and scatters countless seeds so that a few may take root and preserve life.

Mating in the Sky

THE SKY IS BLUE, the wind is gentle, the hour is 4:00 P.M. The six-day-old queen comes out on the threshold of the hive. Inside, the drones are going through elaborate cleaning operations of their huge eyes and their antennae gear. They waggle their heads, brush and brush with the forelegs, polishing up the lenses and the smell receptors.

She's off! The queen mounts vertically, dives, turns like crazy. She circles the sky with a broad sweep, the pack of males after her. Once in a while a male takes a spurt, shoots up behind and a little above the queen, misses, takes his place again in the pack. At close to the highest point of the flight the virgin is not so quick to dodge. Suddenly a male strikes her. He mounts her back, and the two swirl through the air together. It's over in a few seconds, and, embracing, they fall to the ground.

The queen is primed with enough sperm to last her all the rest of her life. That could be five years—so vital and long-lived is bee sperm. Although regular bees die in six weeks, this egg-layer has an entirely different life cycle; this souped-up queen mechanism can go on laying eggs year after year. Four million sperms are packed into her little sperm bag, which gives her a lifetime supply even though she turns out eggs at the rate of a thousand or two per day.

Strangely, the eggs to be fertilized inside this queen, with her storage of pollen through the months and years ahead, are not yet developed. She will manufacture them on the interior assembly line fresh each day. They will have tough plastic shells, impermeable to the sperm, but each coating is pierced with one of the smallest holes imaginable. As an egg parades down the assembly line it revolves until this ultra-microscopic pinprick exactly meets the spout where the sperm comes out of the internal faucet.

Each sperm is an animal universe in itself. Sizes of living things are as relative as time itself. There is no large or small; there is the mysterious abstraction that is the flow in the River of Life. We catch this glimpse of it inside the bee who has mounted to the sunlight in the fresh air, and, there touched by another bee which promptly dies, is able to fertilize thousands upon thousands of eggs for years to come.

We have had a glimpse of a female bee, the only one in a population of fifty thousand fit to be a mother, circling higher and higher pursued by a pack of males like a handful of pebbles someone has flung at her. This is the first time in her life she has tried her wings, yet as the others approach she maneuvers with the aplomb of an expert pilot. The males follow every turn, each keeping its twenty-six thousand telescopes on the target, while they gradually close in, circling, passing, darting, swooping, looking for the split-second chance to jump the queen.

As this peculiar turbulence hurtles along over the country-side, it is joined by more males from other hives hidden around the landscape. Bees are intolerant of strangers who do not have the colony smell unless the strangers are males. One sniff of a foreigner and they sting it right out of their lives. But a male can move from hive to hive, and any male in smell shot of a chase is free to join the hue and cry. This permit is the sole privilege of the male bee, who has no hope of ever settling down to a happy marriage. Waited on by baby-feeders and wallowing in banquets until the queen takes off is no privilege; the male is being fattened for the kill.

The freedom of the males to join the chase may be nature's way of strengthening the race of bees by mixing chromosomes from outside the family circle. But while strange males are ignored and can hang around in any hive, bees will tolerate only one queen and she must have the regimental odor. If a stranger queen drops in she is offered the hospitality of a lethal sting.

The incumbent queen is hysterically affected by having another queen around. She, who is a slave most of the time, asserts herself ferociously when another queen appears on her horizon. That horizon is the hexagons of the cells at the end of her nose, where she is putting eggs. Occasionally the cell builders get a little confused and set up more than one baby for a queen. Then the queen who encounters more than one baby being brought up as a queen tears the extra baby apart, stings the superfluous princess to death. She tolerates only one to supplant herself. When the one daughter being raised to succeed her grows to be a big girl ready for her flight into the sky, the old queen usually is considerate enough to quit the hive, taking along some of the population in a swarm to settle elsewhere. Otherwise, when the new queen returns the two of them fight it out to the death.

Suppose a second queen, not brought up in the hive, so she smells foreign, comes into a hive by mistake. This violation of etiquette stirs a commotion in which all the bees vie with one another to sting her to death. This is a problem for the bee-keeper who wants to introduce a fresh queen to increase honey production. One way to meet the dilemma is with peppermint candy.

The new queen is installed in the hive in a little cage with an opening to the outside so that the man can keep her fed for three days while the others are refusing to bring her food. The bees are foiled by a wire mesh from throwing her out, although they can poke antennae through it for exchanging odors. One wall of the cage is made of peppermint candy two and one quarter inches thick. (Any hard candy except cinnamon will do.) Bees eat good candy at the rate of three quarters of an inch per day, so in three days the wall is eaten away, the new queen steps out and is greeted with open antennae because in those three days she acquired the regimental odor.

In six weeks even the bees which were one day old when the queen started her job of laying will be dead, so the entire population of a hive can be replaced with another queen's offspring. The beekeeper has to wait only those six short weeks for his better breed of bees, although, to all appearances, it is the same hive with the same odor. This kind of immortality is little appreciated.

I can find no report as to whether the old queen sulked during those three days following the arrival of the new queen with her candy. But the old prima donna must be removed before the candy is gone or she will sting the well-bred queen to death whatever her odor.

Our smelling apparatus is so mediocre compared to the enormous numbers of sensitive instruments for sending and receiving odors that stud the bee's body that it is difficult for us to appreciate what odor is to a bee. Bees use odors as though they could touch and handle them, and perhaps hear them. Bees are stone-deaf according to our kind of hearing, but perhaps they hear a flower sending out fragrance as vibrations, the way we hear musical notes.

Although bees are peculiar in many ways, there is nothing extraordinary in the idea of a female pursued by males. In life's greatest sporting event the female may flee by swimming, flying, running, dodging—or she may just act coy—whatever it

2

takes to be hard to get. The practice is especially exciting in the case of rats and mice, which plunge into dark holes and in and out of a maze of hiding places. Squirrels play the game with great aplomb, tearing around in circles waving tall tails, hiding behind trees and peeking out, rushing out on limbs. The shrew is so adept at escape and capture that it may well be called "shrewd." Cats, rabbits, and the roebuck deer are graceful artists in hairbreadth escape and capture.

On the other hand, the solitary queen bee circling and streaking high above the landscape pursued by hundreds of high-powered males about to die has lyrical quality. It is abstract beauty, revealing color, fancifulness, spontaneity, and strength of life in the face of death. And when the female is caught the pair do not pause in their headlong course. Procreation is achieved on the wing.

There are a few other exciting matings when speeding through the air, and perhaps many that we do not know about.

THE MYSTERY OF THE MOSQUITOES

So delicate, so slender, the mosquito was a tantalizing mystery for many years. How can a creature whose life hangs by a thread be such an aggressive nuisance and even a contender against men for ownership of parts of the earth's surface? Whence come such enormous numbers?

Various attempts have been made to tag individual mosquitoes. It is almost impossible to hold one without injuring it, and its body is so incredibly slender that the wonder is it can hold a full set of organs properly arranged to operate the creature. The method of marking bees with paint spots doesn't work with mosquitoes because there isn't enough area on the body on which to put a suitable dab of paint.

A fairly good way to tag a mosquito, in case you're interested, is to blow gold, silver, or bronze powder (the kind that printers use) at it with a bean shooter. The light dust does not interfere with mosquito activity and the different colors identify different starting points for the experiment. Then you catch them by the good old-fashioned slapping method and examine the bodies with a lens to see the color of the dust. This procedure has turned up the surprising fact that mosquitoes travel a long distance *against* the wind as well as down the wind. In a high wind they hide and wait.

The most exciting fact about mosquitoes which blowing powder at them through a bean shooter has revealed is that they mate in mid-air. Some people might say that is of interest only to another mosquito, but Darwin said, "My work has impressed me with the importance of trifling facts."

Mosquitoes swarm, and then, to use the words of a solemn scientific report, "grappling pairs fall out."

At first the swarm is composed entirely of males, which lurk all day among the grass and bushes, in the shadows of leaves, around stables—there are billions of little hiding places for billions of male mosquitoes. So utterly self-effacing is the male that what he eats is still a mystery and what he does most of the time is unknown. But just after sunset, or just before, if the sun goes behind a cloud, when the light is dim (twelve foot-candles of illumination is just right) the males gather above a church steeple, tree, bush, points conspicuously silhouetted against the twilight sky. Their fabulous numbers form such a dark, curving swarm over a church steeple that it has caused people to turn in a fire alarm. The words of the firemen on such occasions are unreported, but doubtless they were not speaking of the haunting mystery of the nuptial dance of male mosquitoes.

The mosquito swarm has the practical result of multiplying one male's tiny hum until it swells into a penetrating buzz that can be heard by the females far and wide in the grass, bushes, shadows among the trees, and in the stable. A mosquito vibrates its abdomen as a tiny tuning fork to produce a hum in middle C, and when the volume is increased by the vibrating of a million abdomens, the pitch of middle C is exactly right to fill female mosquitoes with great longing. There is no pursuit: the females rise from here and there to join the dance of the male swarm, and afterward all that happens is that grappling pairs fall out.

THE CARNIVAL OF THE MAY FLIES

May flies stage an exhibition dance of great charm and with countless hordes. But this is regarded as a nuisance by people who get the insects in their eyes, mouths, ears, and hair, and who have to start windshield wipers to drive through the swarm, or who see May flies peppering a picnic salad, or crunch them underfoot near a porch light. May flies are appreciated only by people interested in mating in the air or by fishermen who use them as models for fly-tying because of their beautiful, slender, curving bodies, alert wings, and the liveliness, so luscious to fish, of their demeanor.

May flies are misnamed, although a few appear in May, because their height-of-the-season dance rises toward sundown late in the summer. It is the males who are showing off with an astonishing vertical jig. A May fly flies straight up thirty inches. Then, using its wings as a parachute, it drops down slowly thirty inches on exactly the same line. At the bottom point it mounts again straight up. As the air is filled with countless numbers, it would seem inevitable that some of the dancers would collide, but each May fly follows its own straight path without deviating. Still there would not be room for all the May flies that want to dance at the same time unless some vertical lines overlapped. So frequently a thirty-inch path of one drops halfway down the path of the one just below. When May flies find themselves in this situation—exactly in line with each other—they co-ordinate their rhythms so that both are going up at the same time and both are going down at the same time, and there is no collision.

May-fly wings are polished and flash with highlights in the setting sun. Their bodies are transparent golden yellow, and they are as buoyant as bubbles. The wonderful dance and the sparkling in the twilight of the males draw the females to join the bouncing.

The life of this aerial fantasy is but a day, though the animal has existed for several years in another form. All that time it was a worm which breathed with gills, like a fish, grubbing around among sticks and stones in the darkness under water— until this last day of its life when the worm comes to the surface, splits its skin along its back, and unfurls a pair of exquisite wings. For some secret reason this first pair of wings will not do. They are soon shed, along with a transparent plastic covering in the shape of the whole body, and returned to the element store without being used. A second pair of wings exactly like the first is produced in a short time out of a new plastic cover that now hardens on contact with the air, and the May fly is ready for its one day of glorious life.

After the mating dance the female skims the water and shoots eggs onto the surface from parallel twin jet pipes extending from her rear end. She is the only insect that has two egg pipes, but when these are empty her wings come off and she flutters down and dies. Billions of her fellows, both male and female, are dying all around. A creature that has only one day to live in the sun needs two egg pipes to get through her job before the curfew. On the other hand, she needs no mouth, no intestines, no form of defense for survival. This is the world's rarest creature which is not on the go for food and is completely defenseless. The May fly has no time to eat, and it isn't intended that she should survive.

THE JIG OF THE MIDGES

Compared to the massive mist of May flies, dancing midges are like a puff of bright red sparks shaking up and down in mid-air. You can see them only by looking directly into the sun, which catches their transparent red bodies and gives them a pink glow. Who hasn't caught sight of this fairy dance and wondered how small an insect can be and why it jiggles that way? I can see them any warm, still evening in early summer jiggling beside my cabin in the country. The position of the swarm, exactly where it will catch the rays of the setting sun, is part of the plan to transform otherwise invisible creatures into red sparks visible to their mates.

The whole swarm dances in unison. When there is a breeze these red sparks, lighter than dust, will fly into the wind at just the right rate to hold a fixed position in the air. How do countless thousands in open formation hit the same beat? What are they in step with? The baton of sunlight? Or does each separate body have precisely co-ordinated impulses? It takes a lot of practice and orchestra music for the Rockettes at Radio City Music Hall to step in unison. When do midges practice?

I was reminded of the dance of the midges when Dr. Vincent Schaefer showed me a certain chemical freezing in the cold tank at the General Electric Research Laboratory. Its crystals separate at equal distances, form in long perfect ranks, and then vibrate in precise unison. This dance of inanimate crystals is controlled by an electronic impulse. Why not the same explanation for midges? The name of the chemical that dances like midges is pentaerythritol. That should explain the whole thing.

THE ZOOM OF THE DRAGONFLIES

Dragonflies have been on earth a long time. Their ancestors in the Coal Age were two feet long. All that time they have been successful with mating in the air though they have reduced their size to three inches during 250 million years. Their preference is for personal, individual flight instead of organizing a ballet.

It is true that dragonflies sometimes appear in swarms like the famous swarms of locusts when they are moving out of an overcrowded place, but this is not a mating flight. Because they fly in single pairs, dragonflies look more romantic than May flies, midges, and mosquitoes. They are big and fly low so you can easily see their marvelous pursuits. After a chase, dragon-flies zooming in tandem bounce up and down as though travel-ing swiftly over waves in the air. Nothing could be more free, open-airy, poetic, while they flash iridescent reds, purples, and metallic blues in the sunlight.

Controversy still rages around this beautiful mating a-wing. Nobody is positive whether, after all, the male dragonfly isn't just capturing a mate and running off with her to settle on a leaf. There is no proof coming up in the foreseeable future be-cause dragonflies are the third fastest insects in the world, ex-ceeded only by the hawk moth and the horsefly. A dragonfly in Australia has been clocked at sixty miles per hour. This dragonfly could give a good race to the fastest four-footed run-ner in the world, the cheetah—the hunting leopard of India—which has clocked sixty to seventy miles per hour. Because of its great speed the moment of coition of the dragonflies has not yet been observed. This is one of many fascinating subjects yet to be investigated.

ANT AIR ARMADAS

We were marveling at the way bee sperm remains potent for years in the sperm bag of the queen. Three or four years is normal, and there is a record of one queen who kept sperm potent for seven years of egg-laying. The ant tops this by laying eggs for twelve to seventeen years after a single mating in the sky.

Unlike queen bees, egg-laying ants are not just an occasional production to meet an emergency. They appear in the ordinary course of events by the thousands, and males appear in equal numbers down in the dark underground galleries of an ant community. There, among crawling ants, certain individuals mysteriously grow wings and these turn out to be egg-layers and their future mates. The rank and file are wingless.

Comes a day in July and August, the winged ants are drawn

by sunlight to the entrance of their tunnels. The mere wearing of a set of wings begets the drastic change of attitude from seeking darkness to seeking light. If one of these winged ants, male or female, about to crawl out into the daylight, has its wings clipped it promptly runs back underground.

The winged ants wait around the entrance until all weather conditions are precisely right—humidity, wind, sunlight. If there are days of waiting all the ants are restless. Down in the galleries the ants that will never fly run around aimlessly, coming up repeatedly to peek out at the weather, and are just as upset at the delay as the big ants, male and female, standing around with wings quivering.

The mating flight is a mass movement, with egg-layers and males flying off together high and wide. At the same time other winged ants are taking off from many other colonies far and near. Ants seem to have an identical sense of moisture, temperature, wind, else what signal for this spontaneous jump-off is given and by whom over a wide area? Aggregations of male and female ants rise and join forces from countless underground populations over the landscape. They are not so dense that they darken the sky as the smoky trails of traveling termites darken tropical skies, but they are legion. Ants go high and few people notice their flight until they fall back to earth. Then it is not grappling pairs you see, but males falling from the sky in their death struggle, for they have finished the job of reproduction for which they were designed.

After her single stratosphere (from the insect viewpoint) flight, the female ant is ready to produce for years to come. She drops to earth but does not return to her home-town community. Instead, as soon as she touches ground, she tears off her wings, runs around looking for an opening under a stone or in the grass-root jungles to tunnel underground, and starts a fresh colony of her own. This massive mating in the sky, followed by hundreds and thousands of new ant communities, reveals why ants are so populous in our world—or is it ours?

Bee Talk and Other Secrets

WE WERE WATCHING a bee arrive at a willow tassel at the foot of my meadow and perform an outlandish acrobatic act. Wait a few minutes and you will see eight or ten more bees arrive to load up on tassels that dangle all over the same tree. The length of time from the disappearance of the first bee to the arrival of the others depends on the distance to the hive; you might wait ten minutes or an hour. Later, these will be followed by more and more, steadily drifting in individually, until many are diving, splashing, and packing pollen among the tassels on the same tree. The new arrivals are all from the same hive as the first bee. They were not led to the spot personally, yet here they are, and somehow the first one must have told the others about it.

This is true. It did tell the others back at the hive in a conversation so remarkable that the man who proved it exclaimed in his report, "No competent scientist *ought* to believe these things!" It took super-patience, ingenuity, and years of experimenting for Karl von Frisch to breach the barrier of understanding between himself and these marvelous little creatures.

2*

You dissolve powdered artists' pigments in alcohol and shellac and apply the mixture to the bee with the smallest camel's-hair brush from which all but three hairs are plucked. With this you can stick a speck of color to a bee that dries instantly. Yellow, red, or green spots are then applied to front or rear of chest or abdomen, and if you have a system in which location and color represent numerals you can give thousands of bees identification tags with their own numbers.

This was the first step toward tuning in on bee conversations and discovering how one bee tells others that it has found pollen and in what direction to go for a wealth of the golden grains. Information is spelled out for compass course, distance, the exact kind of flower, and the abundance of pollen or nectar that is waiting to be plundered on that very day. The place where the willow tassel was discovered is pin-pointed in the outdoors so precisely that the others can go straight to the spot and load up.

The human animal also attaches instinctive meanings to words and colors. This is the art of the orator, the expression of music, and the suggestions of odors. Brain washers have discovered the sinister power of changing instinctive meanings through sheer repetition. So far as we know, there are no brain washers in the bee world, where every bee through generations of undeviating stereotypy agrees on the exact meaning of color, signs, odor, language. After all, this is true of every animal— the dog digging for a bone, the lofty giraffe reaching up at the fluttering green leaves against the blue sky, the whale opening its mouth wide as it rushes through a krill-filled sea. The secret signs are always there and understood by the particular animal who must use them to live.

The bee message is conveyed with two kinds of dancing—a figure eight and a wig-wag dance.

The figure eight is used only for pollen or nectar in nearby flowers. Bees fly so fast and examine so much area with their thousands of telescopes sweeping an arc of 270 degrees that it is unnecessary to waste time giving a compass course when the source of pollen or nectar is within 150 feet of the hive. In this case a space is cleared in the crowd of bees on the surface of the comb, and here the bee who made the original discovery runs around in the figure eight, circling to the left and then to the right. Excited bees crowd up, touch the performer with antennae to pick up the fragrance of the flower from the hairs on its body, and as soon as the scent is obtained off they go.

They fly in expanding circles around the hive, keeping within 150 feet, and soon pick up the exact scent which they are carrying around with them. The first bees back with a load perform the figure eight for other excited bees awaiting their turn to touch the dancers, and these pick up the odor for identifying the right flowers and are off. The figure-eight dance says, "Plenty all around, fellows. Go and get it!"

The wig-wag dance is for long-distance trips. The dancer runs straight forward, turns to the right, goes about to the starting point, runs straight forward again on the same path, turns to the left, goes about, repeats. This action right and left is emphasized by the wig-wagging of the dancer's abdomen. The performance electrifies the audience.

The straight line of the wig-wag dance gives the compass direction for the flowers to be visited. You and I might think that it would be very difficult to point out a direction with a line on a vertical wall, as on the face of a honeycomb which stands vertically in a hive. But the bee solves this mathematical problem easily by using gravity as a compass.

The straight line of the bee dance is at an exact angle to a plumb line, and that angle is the same as the angle which a bee is to fly in relation to the direction of the sun. If the flower with ripe pollen is directly into the sun from the hive, the wig-wag dance will have its center line straight up and down. "The place is in the same direction as the sun!" Or if the bee line of the wig-wag dance points straight down, "The place lies directly away from the sun!"

Shadows pivot all day long, changing every minute with the revolution of the earth, and so also does the line of the bee dance change its angle from the vertical, paced with the sun moving across the sky!

A curious man thought he would fool the bees by laying a comb flat, with its face horizontal, so it would be impossible for the bee to use the straight line of gravity for its compass. With scarcely a pause, the bee ran forward along the line, headed straight toward the flower burgeoning with pollen out yonder. When it must run on a horizontal surface the bee no longer changes the line of the wig-wag dance with the angle of the sun but points directly at the target.

Bees measure distance in flying time—the way airlines measure distance these days—and the wig-wag dancer tells the distance by the speed of its run-around. Nine circles in fifteen seconds, says that the flowers are 330 feet from the hive; four and one half circles, five eighths of a mile; two circles in fifteen seconds, three and seven tenths of a mile. You take it from there and see how bees talk to each other. Then try to imagine where their protoplasm learned all this.

In the figure-eight dance, where distance doesn't matter, the bee lays the facts on the table by doing its figure eights faster and with more energy if there is lots of pollen or nectar; slowly, halfheartedly, if they are in limited supply. When the dance is energetic more bees hie forth to find the flowers. Only a few go forth if the dance is halfhearted, and the others seem to figure that it isn't worth the trouble as they will probably find the supply exhausted before they get there.

Both the distance and the abundance of the booty are spoken of in the wig-wag dance. The rate of speed of circling right and left calls the flying time exactly, while the vigor or languor of abdomen wagging spells out a plentiful or limited supply. This steps up the efficiency of the business of the hive, especially when a number of bees that have been exploring the landscape in various directions return about the same time.

Then the one that shouts the loudest—that is to say, dances most energetically—dispatches the most bees to its flowers. The bee we were watching on the burgeoning willow tassel must have put on a furious performance back at the hive.

Spotting the particular kind of flower recommended by the returning scout is important to bees because they like to stick to one kind of pollen or one kind of nectar each day. Without clear information about the particular flower which a bee has been told to collect from, it could arrive at the right location only to find many kinds of flowers blooming there. On the twenty-first of June, the Festival of the Summer Solstice, I have counted forty-seven species of flowers blooming in a compact area. Little and big flowers are sprinkled like confetti over the ground. But the bees go straight to their work on the flowers which they have been told to collect from on that day because each carries in the eighth segment of its antenna a sample of that flower's odor picked up from the scout's hair.

Even a bee can miss its scent cue if it has to depend entirely on odor picked up from the hairs of a scout's body. Delicate scents are snatched from the hairs when they are exposed in a rush of fresh air over a long distance. So insurance is provided. The long-distance searcher, instead of letting the others pick up the scent by touching a hair, will hand over a particle of pollen dust or droplet of nectar which it has held in its mouth out of the wind all the way back. The recipient takes this particle in its mouth and thus carries on its trip a package of odor.

The recent translation of bee talk has been a great surprise. Nothing like it has ever been discovered among insects, birds, fishes, or animals, but it makes you wonder whether members of all the tribes of the Animal Kingdom may not be talking to one another all the time. And who can say that the plants may not talk among themselves just because they do not have nerve systems? The communication used by the bee in haranguing its fellows and giving them clear instructions is very different from the conventional communications of other animals with sight, sound, and odor. We have all been ordered around in unmistakable terms by birds, snakes, dogs, or skunk. But that is just saying *shoo!*

A rhinoceros talks that way to other rhinoceroses when he stakes out his territory with no-trespassing signs by using piles of dung as surveyor's stakes. Crows squawk harshly to announce the discovery of carrion to other crows. As for the universal subject of mating, birds unfurl brightly colored feathers, fireflies flash lights, paradise fishes blow bubbles, the blue-behinded ape shows a blue behind to entice a pursuer, swans whistle, and the howler monkey howls. All this is on-the-spot, impulse communication and cannot be compared with the bee's announcements of news headlines concerning fortuitous situations that lie ahead.

What the bees do as soon as they have received the information is as incredible as the bee talk. Every airport serviceman knows that running out of fuel brings a crash landing. Bees never crash land. The flying distance, which takes account of head winds that call for more fuel or tail winds that call for less, is brought back by the scout and known in advance. Whereupon the bee, before it takes off, somehow calculates the precise amount of fuel it will need and then helps itself from the hi-octane honey tanks of the hive, sucking up more honey for a long flight, less for a short flight, or only a pinhead speck of honey, which will give enough mileage if the flowers are in the immediate vicinity. For a quarter of a mile another half pinhead is added. And if the orders are to fly to a flower a mile away the bee, before starting, will suck three pinhead specks into its honey sac.

Despite this careful weighing of the situation, followed by intelligent action, the bee is truly a puppet in an inflexible commune. Bees are never so lazy that they visit flowers closer rather than farther if the word is that the farther place has more booty. They never refuse to work, never sulk, never talk back. They are the most efficient and hard-working living machines on earth. And these furry little ovals smaller than the tip of your little finger are sparked by microscopic knots of nerves which can calculate a situation.

Before taking off, not only does this creature carefully measure the fuel needed to reach the flower but it also measures it for the *kind* of trip this is going to be. Let me explain.

Nectar is a potential fuel. It is watered-down honey which, mixed with certain chemicals in the bee's head, can be used for fuel in a pinch—not hi-octane, such as the fully processed honey in the storage cells of the comb, but a satisfactory low-grade fuel. Thus the bee avoids wasting one fraction of a pinhead speck of the precious processed honey belonging to the commune by taking only enough for the outward trip to the flower, if it has been told that it is to collect nectar at the goal, or both pollen and nectar. It knows that there is a fuel pump at the other end, so that it can get nectar at the destination to convert into fuel to use on the return trip.

As a flying boxcar a bee has an impossible load factor. A load of pollen on its hind legs plus nectar in its stomach equal to its body weight must be lifted into the air and transported. Full baskets of pollen are about one third of its body weight, and two thirds are the honey fuel and pay load nectar in its honey sacs. The bees that came to the willow tassel, which delivers pollen only, from three or four miles away, must have started with full tanks of honey in order to have enough fuel to get there *and back* with a pollen load.

The question as to whether the mission is for pollen only, nectar only, or both was answered by the dancer when it handed over the minute parcel of nectar or a grain of pollen, as though they are keys to the flower. The arresting point of the story is the way the bee acts for maximum efficiency—that is, maximum pay load. Knowing that honey taken for fuel from hive supplies is a loss to the hive, he acts to keep its fuel to a minimum and repay it with a profit on its return.

Bees also make decisions after arriving on the scene. They pause as though taking a fraction of a second to think; they hover, they look, they touch and smell with antennae, they taste with their feet, and then take appropriate action. On-the-spot decisions such as this are common with all sorts of animals. It is the decisions that bees make *before* they go forth that are so extraordinary.

We have already dredged out of the bee's weird world another case of decision that makes us wonder whether a bee can think. It takes something out of the ordinary course of events to summon a male into being. It is up to the queen herself to "decide" when to have males around. She carries a bag of sperms with a valve that opens and closes to let the sperms out one at a time to fertilize each egg as it comes parading down the assembly line that is inside her. This smooth-running mechanism makes it possible for her to people the hive at the rate of one or two thousand babies per day. But the internal valve is under her control and cannot operate automatically according to outside conditions such as temperature or moisture, but only according to the emotions of the queen. If she elects not to open the valve and an egg slips by without being united to a sperm—the result is a male!

The queen's intention in this matter is unpredictable. She may permit one egg in five hundred to go unsparked and bring forth a male, or again she may choose to conjure up several dozen males in quick succession. In this respect the queen is a female of moods.

Scientists, naturally, recoil at the idea that insects are capable of voluntary acts involving intelligence, and it is interesting to find a profound statement of the late Frank E. Lutz, Curator of Insects at the American Museum of Natural History, about the praxis of this queen who can abolish or summon up males at will: "If a queen bee has to think about the sex of her offspring every time she lays one or two thousand eggs a day, in addition to thinking about all the other things that concern her, she must do a lot of thinking."

Of course we are always ready to defend intelligence as our prerogative, but isn't it a question of semantics? If intelligence is a relative word for a phenomenon of life in the way that voice or mobility is relative, we can be comforted that our intelligence is superior for us and their intelligence is superior for them. Both ours and theirs have qualities of intuition, genius, faculty for doing the right thing at the right time, keen senses to guide impulses. Beyond this there are two kinds of intelligence—that of action and that of thought. Our intelligence has special qualities of wisdom and understanding (or can have)—and above all imagination. Imagination is our mind's dominant power.

Bee intelligence is limited to the bee world. I suppose they never suspect that any other kind of animal lives on earth. Although referred to as the only domesticated insects, I believe that they are not the least bit tamed and that man channels this wild power to his desires only because bees can perform the miracle of changing sap into honey.

A rose is just as sweet by any other name and a flower is just as attractive for ransacking whether it grows in an orchard or hedgerow, in garden or meadow. A series of hexagonal wax cells built in a wooden box to the exact dimensions of a bee's abdomen feel just as good as those built in a hollow tree. I am confident that, far from being domesticated and tamed, bees have never seen a man or exchanged glances as a man does with his dog. What the bee sees is probably a vague, huge shape of no more interest than a big rock, tree trunk, or building. If the huge shape interferes with the bee's routine it gets stung whether it is cow, dog, or man.

When bees zoom at you with blazing eyes to stab you, surely it is not because they have it in for a man, woman, or child, and they do not cry, "There blows a man—sting him!" Their marvelous multi-thousand telescope eyes are not designed to tell a man from a tree. But take one step that disturbs their precious prerogative for pillaging a flower or intrudes on the ritual of the hive and they don't have to recognize you. Blind impulse drives them to protect their rights to food and home. So they have no imagination and cannot see beyond their tight little world, while we, with imagination, can enjoy this glimpse into the bee world in the morning sun as well as ponder the stars and life on other planets.

Memory is not imagination, although it is an ingredient of imagination. Bees have a curiously keen memory for certain things, one of which is the direction of light at a particular time of day. This has been put to the test again and again with great astonishment. When bees have discovered a lush source of pollen or nectar that is located northeast by east of the hive, if during the night when the bees inside are all snoring (the low buzz sounds like that) you slyly shift things around so that the plunder lies southwest by west, the next day they will set their course northeast by east and wander around thwarted and bewildered. It is not the visual landmarks that they recall —these have all been changed by the trick—it is the direction of the sun's rays at a certain time of day that they remember.

They remember not only direction but also time. If certain flowers offer pollen at a certain time of day as determined by the angle of the sun, they will return at that time of the next day. Often flowers open pollen boxes at certain hours or even minutes, and bees catch on to this and somehow remember to go to the exact pin point of a spot in the vast landscape at precisely the right time when the flowers are delivering the most pollen.

You and I might suppose that the bee gets its time cue from the direction of sunlight, just as we tell time by a sundial. It seems to go without saying that bees which orient their flying according to the constantly changing direction of sunshine and shadows would take their cue for leaving the hive from the

III. *Bees diving deeply into fruit blossoms for nectar.*

BERNARDA
BRYSON

PLATE III

BERNAR
BRYSO

PLATE IV

same source—namely, the direction of the sun that is so easily observed by their big eyes. But the more you look into the life and times of the bee, the more surprises you stumble across.

Although the bee, after it is in the air, holds its course on the target by remembering the direction of the sun in relation to the flowers, an infallible memory starts it off. The bee is triggered by an internal alarm clock that ticks off exactly twenty-four hours. This astonishing bit of information was revealed by a trick of international dimensions planned by the American Museum of Natural History and the University of Paris.

An unsuspecting group of bees in Paris was given the opportunity of getting nectar only at one time of day—twelve noon, let us say. So they got the habit of going out only when the clock was striking twelve mid-day. When this rhythm was established the bees were given a ticket on an air line and went to New York between the hours of their summons. In New York, at exactly the twenty-four-hour interval, out they came, oblivious of the strange scenery, and buzzed around looking for food. None was to be found for three days, during which they kept right on schedule, emerging every twenty-four hours when their internal clocks struck twelve noon—though the sun's rays in New York said it was seven o'clock in the morning.

Another group of bees acquired their internal clocks in New York, and they also stuck to their twenty-four-hour interval, paying no heed to the fact that everybody around was speaking French and that twelve noon had passed five hours earlier.

Skill is not imagination, although doubtless it is a subconscious ingredient of imagination. The bee is a sensational acrobat. As a flyer it outdoes man with its swift perfection of adjustments in turbulent air and holds to its course through random encounters of wind velocity and direction changes. A bee, like a strong-minded expert, carries out a fixed purpose to fly straight and level, up and down, or to make such and

iv. *The bee's head is formed by two domes of eyes. Part of its brain is wrapped around its neck, part is at the base of the wings, and part is at the attachment of the legs.*

such a turn. A man has to learn these things and then reaches great heights of skill in flying, playing tennis, typewriting, driving a car. It is flexibility in the subconscious meeting of an unpredictable situation in a flash that distinguishes skills from habits. Bees are more skillful in their pursuits than men; however, they never had to learn their skills. They are bee kinds of skills, and they can't learn any different kind, and they can't stop doing it.

The bee certainly has a kind of brain, a wonderful brain for a bee. It is not bunched together in a cranium, but part of it is wrapped around the throat where it catches the nerve impulses from the antennae, co-ordinates these, decides what the situation calls for, and then gives stop-and-go signals to the busy throat with its chemical equipment. Another part of the brain is at the base of the wings where it makes them operate with split-second control and a third brain section is at the attachment of the legs. One result of this is that the bee can fly or run around without its head. But it takes a head brain to regulate the starting and the stopping.

The volume of a brain in relation to the size of an animal is considered a measure of intelligence. Some of the prehistoric monsters that vanished into fossils had tiny brains in proportion to their colossal weight of bones and muscles, and we call them stupid.

It is astonishing how, in the long run, the size of a brain varies according to the complications of each creature's life. This is true even among the same kind of creatures. The ordinary bee, which goes through the timetable of baby feeding, hive building, pollen collecting, comb building, has a larger brain than the big queen and the lazy male. This ordinary bee's brain is 1/174 the size of its body. Your brain and mine is 1/50 the size of our bodies. We win by a landslide according to this test of intelligence.

There is one more test of bee's intelligence. How adaptable is it? Bees appear to be adaptable in the way they accept a man-made hive for a home instead of a hole in a tree, but this shows lack of imagination. It's all the same to them. A bee-keeper's hive is ever ready to swarm and go off and establish itself in a hole in a tree or vice versa. In other words, instead of being intelligent about living in a man-made hive and using wooden combs, the bee is just easily fooled—a little dumb, shall we say. As these conditions simulate its wild conditions it is always wild. In this respect the bee is as dumb as the zebra in a zoo who perks up when he is given a cement cone imitation of a termites' nest on which to rub himself.

Intelligence is inherent in protoplasm. It is part of the same phenomenon that makes an amoeba flow by extending and withdrawing its fingers like lobes and then wrap itself around food; or causes a mushroom living in underground blackness to elevate an umbrella for throwing out its spores in the sunshine and wind; or gives the willow tassel elasticity to quiver in the breeze as though it had the idea of attracting more bees that way. Every living thing must have its own brand of intelligence to cope with its own problems. The bee is peculiarly fit in this respect.

The Bee Animal

To THIS POINT in our tale we have been catching glimpses of a fascinating and curious way of life. Some actions are inspired by other actions as though the whole sequence had been carefully planned, as in the case of the scout who struck gold and then went straight back to town, gathered a crowd and harangued the others all about it. Other activities are filled with rhythm, excitement, and tenacity of purpose, as in the case of the buoyant bees swaying on tassels and the pack pursuing the virgin queen into the sky.

But don't you feel something unsatisfactory in all this, and a little disquieting? The story doesn't make sense. The life of the bees is loaded with death. Every day when the hive is in full swing there are one thousand two hundred funerals on the average, and, true, there are about the same number of births, but why the big turnover? This is a horrible speed-up of T. S. Eliot's *Murder in the Cathedral:* "We wait, we wait for another October . . . from generation to generation the same things happen."

Life force is misspent. Death lingers in the gentian and willow. It overtakes the male at the height of his savage vigor. It whispers to the fertile queen as she sees her children dying by thousands around her. It obliterates—after the last trip on the forty-first day—the faithful pollen and nectar gatherer and all the elaborate equipment developed for its purpose. Death is automatic and nobody cares.

Can this horror be resolved simply by saying that after all there are various life spans and each has its own fulfillment? Our three score and ten is the bee's six weeks, and the bee's is the May fly's single day. This is to say that the bees in relation to their length of life are vanishing no faster than my class at Yale. Are our lives more worth while for that reason? Is the mountain more worth while because it looks down on generation after generation of men before it too is flattened and disappears at its appointed time in ten thousand years?

The baby-feeders, the hexagonal cell builders, the pollen and nectar ransackers are the bulk and body of the hive. Everything is set up for these to do their work, but for what and for whom are they working? Surely not for themselves, for tomorrow they will be gone. Yet they work relentlessly, condemned to perform with never varying precision operations of never varying monotony to no end except to their repetition in the future.

Having peered closely at bees to see wonders beyond compare, we are loath to spoil the inspiration of so much color and rhythm in the warm heart of the sunlight with such lack of faith and vision. The trouble with rationalization is that it looks for reasons for living in terms of science, and those terms are strictly limited to man's senses and experience. Surely no one can see a flower open, or a bee going about its perfect business, or gaze at the Milky Way without admitting that there are relative life spans and relative comprehensions, each with its own mysterious fulfillment. The senses and experience of a fish are not those of a bee; a bee's are not those of a man.

But the fish and the bee cannot imagine anything beyond the limits of their own lives, any more than can a man.

Faith is not such an abstract and difficult-to-grasp value as many people think. It may be the one realistic quality which the human animal can have that other animals cannot have. Look again at the mountain and consider how, though it is doomed to level out in ten thousand years, the chances are good that bee animals will be buzzing around in the vicinity, May flies will still be dancing, and willow tassels still trembling in the breeze and burgeoning with golden pollen through the centuries—and perhaps even when the mountain is gone.

The bee, then, is life, not death. Because it possesses the basic fact of life—reproduction—it lives on and on. This is the primal distinction between a living and nonliving thing. That nonliving beeswax, wood of the tree, a boulder outcropping in the field, the skeleton of the body, a city skyscraper, vanish in their time as truly as the shadows they cast, while the bee animal is buzzing and dancing in the same way for millenniums.

Draw away a little distance and look at the honey bees as a whole, and the form of a living unit emerges like a rough sketch of a most interesting animal. At the beginning of this story I promised to show you an exciting animal, and this compact, breathing, humming assemblage is it.

The bee animal is a coalition of fifty thousand bees. Each individual bee is a component of this animal in the same way that each cell is a component of every animal and plant body. The bee animal is put together by the same principle as the cell-renewal plan, for just as cells are constantly dying and being created in droves so is this weird ball of buzz.

It has no skeleton, but that is not a criterion of an animal; it does not necessarily have to have a skeleton. The jellyfish, earthworm, flying squid, to mention a few of nature's imaginative creatures, have no skeletons. The bee animal is not contained within an over-all skin, but this is not necessary for this peculiar animal because its component bees have an enormous area of skin that serves the whole animal. It does not have a head or tail, but neither does a starfish, sponge, amoeba, volvox, and countless other creatures.

The bee animal is put together according to nature's basic plan of forming big living things by combining small living things. The first many-celled animals came into existence when single-celled creatures adhered to one another and divided up the work of the various parts of the bigger body among themselves. The volvox, an underwater animal shaped like a ball, is an especially good example of this principle. Some of its individual members are earmarked to reproduce and others are the swimmers that work collectively to make this curious living ball roll over and over.

Microscopic members of the dictyo at first run around separately and then merge to build the dictyo mushroom. The sponge animal is made in the same way—by a merger of separate cells that divide up the work of the big animal so that their various groups act like organs. Once the components are put together they lose their independence. They must stay together to survive. This is just as true of honey bees because no one of them is able to exist a day by itself.

The bee animal is not a rigid form and in this respect it is like so many of the flexing early animals. In general it takes the form of an oval about eighteen inches long. The hexagonal wax cells, indissoluble in water, are not only a home but also serve as a substitute for a rigid skeleton. Similarly the nautilus octopus emerges far out of its shell, reaches this way and that to collect food, and then withdraws into the stunning geometry of its dynamic spiral.

It is wonderful to peer underneath the sights of life and discover consonance and unity. Both the chambered nautilus's shell and the bee animal's hive are produced for equal needs— a home to dwell in, store food in, reproduce in, and the rigid protection and support of an outside skeleton. The surprise comes when we see how these products, so differently styled for different animals, are wrought by the same forces acting in a similar way.

Shell and cell are tailor-made perfections with dimensions, proportions, coefficients, and tolerances that exactly fit the peculiar bodies and ways of life of their respective animals. Each creature is endowed with a sort of creative genius that also gives direction and control of its motions so that it conjures up without ado this right thing for itself. One has glands on its foot that can separate dissolved lime out of sea water and turn it into soft cement which the animal spins round and round on the lip of the shell, where it quickly hardens to the finest porcelain. The other has glands on its abdomen that can separate oil out of pollen grains and turn it into soft wax which the animal pats on at the right spot to add the next cell and turns round and round to fashion a cylinder; then it pushes and pushes the soft cylinders of wax against one another until they turn into hexagons. This they must do if they are pushed long enough according to the law of physics for getting the most cells into the least space with the least amount of material. This is the same as the law of crystallization that gives a snowflake six points, that made the stones of the Giants' Causeway hexagonal, and that causes soap bubbles to join themselves together with six-sided surfaces instead of round surfaces.

Both the chambered nautilus's spiral and the bee's hexagons are such marvels of geometric design that it is as though they have a divine gift. This is true; it is the gift of life. They are only fulfilling the relentless orders of their genes, as do all living things. Nature uses different ways to accomplish the same purpose for different creatures. Each is an equal masterpiece, in the creation of which the animal is only the brush and the hand.

A spectacular feature of the bee animal is the way it can reach. Every animal at large in the open must reach out in its own way to supplement its running, crawling, or flying. A bird reaches by a lightning stroke of its flexible neck; a snake by coiling its body like a taut spring and then letting go while lengthening its reach with a flashing fang. Elephants have trunks to reach with; thus energy is spared in moving the ponderous head and body. The neck of the giraffe is a beautiful landmark of an animal reaching skyward. The tongue of a chameleon reaches far out from its body faster than a mercurial fly can take off. A spider is the cleverest of all reachers in that it avoids all the effort of reaching by spinning a web which extends roundabout like a sort of radar screen while the tiny spider sits in the center and waits for the signal. This comes as a jerk on a silk thread tells the spider a prey has been reached.

Of all animals the bee animal is the farthest reacher and the most nimble-fingered. Its parts that go out reaching are connected with the rest of the body no less vitally than the fingers on a hand. Individual honey bees never thrust themselves out to grasp food for their individual selves but always to bring the pollen or nectar back to all the bees of the bee animal.

Moreover, this food is swallowed by the hive and put into circulation from mouth to mouth, so that this distribution among all the bees of the bee animal functions as food borne on a blood stream distributed to all cells of a body. Moreover, the bees are instructed just before they reach out which flower to touch and what to take, a process similar to mind or instincts directing a hand where to reach and fingers where to touch.

So deft is the touch of the bee animal that it never hurts the delicate flower it reaches to for food. So skilled are its fingers (or so cleverly designed the flower!) that they leave a flower healthier than before it was touched. Animals which paw, crush, grope, or, like the aardvark, thrust a snorting nose into an anthill are terribly awkward compared to the swift and buoyant long-distance reach of the bee animal.

The results of the touch of the bee animal are so fruitful that a profitable industry has sprung up renting them to farmers and fruit growers, who place them in apple orchards or alfalfa fields. In this industry bee animals are trucked around according to climate and installed where and when an orchard or an alfalfa field is about to flower.

The first living units of every animal and plant are soft, flexible cells of colloidal jelly all looking like the same kind of thing. Yet each possesses a code which foreordains it to take a certain shape and size and act out the life of the body in which it lives. The appearance of the blob of colloidal jelly changes according to the age of the animal or plant and according to where it is located in the body. Some cells make the tissue of a heart, lung, or brain, or supply a tongue, a tooth, or a toenail. Great throngs amalgamate to give an animal strength and rigidity with muscles and bones, or a plant with fibers and wood. To be transformed into these nonliving structures they must die. Other blobs will change their form into the living tissue of eating apparatus, or running and flying structures, or a blood stream, or miles and miles of nerve communication lines, or procreative organs.

Under the direction of the same life controls the bee animal develops its organs in an amazingly similar manner. Baby bee components start their lives all alike in size, appearance, and behavior, and then, to carry on the life of the body in which they live, they change step by step in equipment of glands and are grouped together to carry out utterly different divisions of labor. They have turned into insects which now play the roles of cells by amalgamating to create the body of the big bee animal and keep it in operation.

The cell-insects are transformed in multitudes and according to age. The babyhood of an individual bee unit is two days; from the third to the fifth day it is assigned the job of cell cleaning and keeping things neat around the premises where the bee animal lives; on the sixth to eighth day of its life it turns to baby-feeding and condescends, if it encounters males, to feed them too, while twenty-two are chosen to feed the queen, and that is some job if she is going to lay her weight in eggs every day. Around the sixteenth to eighteenth days the scales on the bottom of the abdomen loosen, wax oozes out, and at that point the bee turns to hive building.

It is a vital necessity of the bee animal always to have enough wax cells for living space. If more cells are needed in an emergency than the bees of exactly the right age can build, they will call for extra help from others a little younger who will be stimulated to squeeze out wax ahead of time, or from some a little older who had closed up their wax works but now open them again. The body of the bee animal is flexible enough to take care of all its needs and expected emergencies, as are the cells of your body which jump to the special job of healing your finger when it is cut or knitting a bone when it is broken.

After a couple of days of heavy wax production and cell building, the eighteen- to twenty-day-old bees stand on the threshold of the hive and vibrate their wings like electric fans to ventilate the premises. Then comes the final stage in the organic transformations of cell-insects of the bee animal. From the twentieth day to the end of their lives on the forty-second day, bees are the reachers and gatherers of their animal.

The bee animal does not change outwardly, as conventional animals do, by growing up, giving birth, dying off, and growing up again. Its growth is internal; it permeates the animal— again this is like living cells. The bee animal is forever young and forever mature. It is always being reborn, always renewing its stature, always ready for a well-rounded life, with many bees available for its various parts and functions, at all ages, at all times. Far from living on the brink of perpetual death the bee animal never grows old.

Conventional animals are converted once when their cells take various shapes as the animal grows. But the strange bee animal enjoys a double conversion. First, ordinary cells of its components are converted in the usual way into insects, and then these in turn are reconverted to make the bee animal, in which some supply food, some build, some reach, and some are converted into the genitals of the animal.

The bee animal is a sedentary creature, preferring to stay in one place indefinitely. But there comes a time when, because of overcrowding or scarcity of food, it must move on. So part of it moves on and becomes another bee animal exactly in the manner of cell division or an amoeba dividing.

This flight of a hunk of the bee animal to find another location where there is less crowding and more food is rather awkward and is accomplished by a great to-do. The big ball holds together, using thousands of tiny wings of its thousands of units to move itself. A bee animal in flight is a great, swaying, jerking ball of buzz. While concentrating on the moving operation, a bee animal is fairly helpless; its units stick together and do not dart off alone, so it doesn't sting. However, a bee animal on the move scares people and birds out of their wits. The animal's confusion and vicious sound provide its security—similar to the threat act of squawking birds or a dog's growling and its hair standing on end. Animals are much given to empty gestures and sounds to terrify enemies. Buzzes, hisses, snarls, roars, are all very effective without involving any further effort.

A bee animal on the move got a four-column headline in the New York *Herald Tribune* when it successfully competed with a major-league baseball game on television. "BEES KEEP CUSTOMERS RACING IN AND OUT OF BAR." This bee animal invaded upper Manhattan, the heart of New York City, where it attached itself to the limb of an elm thirty feet above the sidewalk. The customers of the bar and grill were torn between watching the appalling sight of the bee animal or the Yankees playing the Dodgers. The barkeeper, not the bees, went after small boys who were throwing things at the animal. "If they knock that down in front of my door, they'll wreck my business. Those bees would chase everybody a mile."

This predicament of the bee animal is like that of the deer that wanders into town, or the whale that ran aground in San Francisco harbor, or the bear that created a panic in downtown Spokane. The bee animal that rolled on a thousand wings into uptown Manhattan, tired of looking for a hollow tree or a beekeeper's hive, came to rest on the elm—where the bark at least felt and smelled good. Then scouts went forth according to custom and brought back the information that their animal need reach only two blocks to Fort Tryon Park for pollen and nectar. This bee animal was also richly rewarded with sugar for making honey. It could reach across the street where grapes were laid out on a fruit stand—but that rich find, which must have been announced back in the hive with a most vigorous figure-eight dance, lasted only two days because after that the fruit-store man was too scared to display grapes. With the barkeeper on its side protecting it from sticks and stones, the bee animal out on a limb got along very well for a few weeks. Cold weather finally killed this lonely wild animal caught in the big civilized city.

The Dytiscus

WHEN NIGHT FALLS the bee animal pulls in its reachers and hides its heaving mass in the dark depths of the hive. There, unseen through the night, this weird creature performs its secret rites of converting the populations of its organs to different tasks than those they had performed the day before, so that everything is on schedule and the bee animal is ready for the next sunrise with fresh, young vigor.

But there is much other life in the neighborhood that does not coast to a halt with the setting sun. Many animals switch on stored sun power and take over the living world by night. These creatures awaken in the darkness and go after food and a mate. By night also plants carry on their greatest activity of growing; it is then that they increase in height and branches lengthen, saving their bud opening and flowering for sunlight.

On a moonlit night little one-and-a-half-inch submarines circle the sky a few hundred feet overhead until, one after another, they drop straight down and disappear into a pond. There is a good chance that one pond into which they splash is in your neighborhood. Should you happen to be in a greenhouse or under a skylight or in a shack with a bright tin roof (all of which reflect moonlight the way water does), you may hear them hitting like pebbles falling out of the sky.

If you pick one up next day, you will find yourself holding a living mechanism stunned to silence. Its hard, smooth surface is polished, oiled, slippery to the touch. Its color is rich, ripe-olive, with narrow yellow lines curving along its length, sharp and clean as though drawn with drafting instruments. Its form is not that of a torpedo tapered at each end but the broad, flat oval of a fish turned on its side. This is the design of our first atomic submarine, the *Nautilus*, whose engineers calculated her lines for the utmost maneuverability under water.

The *Dytiscus* is not a visitor from outer space, although the mystery of its flight, control, and mechanical design lends an unreality as though it were. The dytiscus beetle comes from an ordinary pond in the neighborhood, where it spends most of its life as a submarine. Then suddenly in the dark of night it takes a running start, shoots up through the surface of the water, and breaks out wings along the yellow lines of its hull. This happens after it has fished out a pond and an overpowering appetite drives it to find another, or perhaps the population of the pond has become too great and dangerous and it is thwarted by competition. These are the same urgent needs that drove the bee animal to travel.

The dytiscus has legs, but they are shaped like oars and could hardly carry him to another pool fast enough. He finds it awkward to walk on land. Moreover, it is easier to spot another pool from the air than down in the grass-root jungles, especially when the reflections of moonlight signal where another pond is. The dytiscus was invented before tin and glass roofs, and he hasn't yet found the answer to them.

Both the dytiscus and man are air-breathing animals. But man must take in oxygen through holes in his face, keep his lungs supplied with it every second, and then expel poison gas without asphyxiating himself. Doing this calls for complicated arrangements if a man wants to stay under water. Jules Verné hung these arrangements on the outside of his men in *Twenty Thousand Leagues under the Sea,* so that they looked like monsters enclosed in an enormity of helmets, tanks, valves, and hoses. The man could walk on the bottom of the sea wearing this massive poundage because of his buoyancy under water, but he could not cavort like a fish. Such a man is not in the same league with the dytiscus.

Recently man has invented a human version of the dytiscus's equipment, called Scuba (self-contained underwater breathing apparatus). This consists of a heavy metal tank with one hundred forty atmospheres compressed into it carried on the back and rubber shoes like webbed duck feet for paddling. Just below the surface the Scuba man, or girl if it is in a movie, has an hour to live under water, while if he goes deep, his time is reduced to ten minutes. He is buoyant like other underwater animals, is swayed by waves, carried by currents, and this is the nearest a man comes to acting like the dytiscus.

The dytiscus dives, holding a single bubble of air caught by a quick wink of a wing just before going under. This bubble is squashed against his back under the wing. The air bubble is not under pressure but merely a modest parcel of ordinary air. The final snapping closed of his heavy body wings imprisons this bubble. We might say that it snaps on its Scuba bottle. The broad blades of hind legs, their rowing surface increased by bristles along their edges, are the web shoes, and this is the nearest the dytiscus comes to acting like a human being.

The dytiscus can stay below for thirty-six hours. Much of the time it's a swimming mechanism vibrating from stem to stern with energy. Instead of paddling with gentle kicks as do a leisurely Scuba man's, the dytiscus's legs are as busy as an outboard motor. If he had to depend on the oxygen of one bubble for so much energy, he would drown in a few seconds, but nature solves this problem quietly and easily.

The air bubble functions more as a pump primer than a

v. *The three forms of the dytiscus: as a flying machine, an atomic submarine, and, in its larval stage, a water tiger.*

PLATE V

reserve of air. It sets in operation a system for absorbing oxygen from the water. As quickly as oxygen in the bubble is used up, it is replaced with oxygen from the water. The bubble is squashed under the wings against portholes in the skin leading into a network of short tubes that deliver the oxygen fuel instantaneously to the nearest muscle or organ. These tubes are so fine they can be seen only with the highest-powered microscope. One twenty-five thousandth of an inch in diameter, they are exceeded in smallness only by the liquid-filled tube of a nerve fiber. Nothing is too small, too complicated, too delicate, but that life can put it together and make it work —when something must live. Thus the dytiscus breathes not through mouth or nostrils but through holes distributed over its body.

Its blood is pale green and carries only food. The dytiscus has no red blood corpuscles to carry oxygen in a slow liquid flow but possesses a far more speedy method of ventilating its body by blowing oxygen through short pipes. However, the borrowed bubble of the dytiscus gradually loses its force. Then the dytiscus must come up near the surface to renew the bubble after a few hours. It simply sticks the tip of its tail end-up through the surface, gives a click of its wings, and has a fresh bubble.

In this way, an air-breathing animal with no gills like a fish's is able to pursue most of its life under water. It is designed to submerge instantly, still breathing air. When flying, its portholes take in air directly from the air in which it flies. The dytiscus continues to breathe air easily whether in flight, under water, or walking on the ground.

As the dytiscus doesn't use its face for breathing, its mouth can be used solely for eating. If the Scuba man while submerged tried to gulp a shrimp or an oyster, he would drown. But the dytiscus is one of the mightiest eaters in a pond.

Appetite drives the dytiscus appallingly. It can only be satisfied in a pond which teems with meat and vegetables. Among pastures of pond weeds float millions of tiny clear plastic boxes filled with green leaf material. These plants, the diatoms, appear automatically, grow without cultivation, and fill a pond with food more delicious to the underwater animals that enjoy them than pumpkins and tomatoes.

The meat and vegetables of the pond pull on the dytiscus when he flies high in the moonlight, just as hay and oats in the barn pull on a horse when his head is turned toward home. This idea is so closely associated with silvery reflection from the surface of quiet water that its glint causes the dytiscus to cut his engines, tip forward, and plunge. When he vanishes through the center of expanding ripples, he is in his own kingdom.

At the bottom of his dive, the dytiscus pauses to take account of hunting conditions. He holds onto water grass or a sunken leaf or stick to keep the breathing bubble from bobbing him up to the surface. While near the bottom, he may catch sight of the phantom larva.

THE PHANTOM LARVA

The phantom larva spends its entire time under water although it is the child of parents who are half fly and half mosquito and spend their entire time in the air. The phantom larva looks like a glass tube; it is a half inch long, transparent except for eyes and the shadows of two ballast tanks fore and aft. It vanishes by holding still. It moves mysteriously by fanning gently with a Victorian lace fan attached in the position of a ship's rudder to the tip of its tail. It fans this right and left, while the transparent abdomen pulses in synchronization, and thus the phantom larva moves as lightly as a bubble.

With its ballast tanks the phantom larva can stop perfectly still wherever it will. These expand and contract as gas in its body is pumped into the ballast tanks or out of them. Thus the phantom larva can rise or sink vertically without swimming—

just by thinking about it. With a ballast gas tank forward and another one aft, it can hold its body horizontal when the front end is weighed down by a heavy prey just captured. And it can hold motionless, compensating for different pressures at various depths. The phantom larva has the most serene equilibrium of any living thing on land, sea, or in the sky.

This gives the phantom larva a unique secret of life. It can dwell in safety where the voracious dytiscus is king because it is as transparent as water and can vanish without the moving of a muscle. This remarkable act of survival under water insures also the lives of the weird descendants of the phantom larva, peculiar insects up in the air which are mosquitoes and flies at the same time, called *Chaoborus*, "flesh-of-chaos."

If, after waiting a while, nothing is to be seen below (the phantom larva having made itself invisible), the dytiscus swims up to the top story of the pond where there is always more activity. Here he can hunt meat without the effort of swimming and using up his bubble. Turning upside down, he thrusts his rear end up close to the surface until a few oiled hairs poke up through the surface film. He now dangles head-down, hooked to the plastic ceiling of the pond. The oil of the hairs on his behind displaces enough water so that a dimple is open to the air, and this is refreshing, like opening a window to let plenty of fresh air into the room. He can loosen his wings and dispense with the bubble while still completely submerged.

THE NEPA

By chance, somebody else may be similarly occupied near by. This is the nepa, which you would take for a little waterlogged leaf, about three quarters of an inch long, hanging from a slender twig. The twig consists of two half tubes pressed tightly together, so tightly fitted, in fact, that they form a watertight pipe. With this the nepa punctures the surface film and, while suspended well below the surface, can suck in air

3*

as through a straw. The nepa knows whose meat he is, so if the dytiscus happens to hang himself up on the surface film nearby, he takes off in a panic, clambering over debris to hide in mud at the edge of the pond.

On the other hand, the nepa can find plenty of beef smaller than he is, and to handle this his two front legs are converted into scissors. End segments are hinged so as to fold back tightly and cut up the meat with sharp edges. In addition to these scissors, the nepa has an extra heart in each wing. This is putting furniture into an abandoned room because the nepa's wings have lost their flying power. Underneath the wings, now forever folded, there is a second pair of delicate wings, pink with bright red veins. And beneath these the hind end of its body is red with black bands. If it could lift its wings and fly, the nepa would flash with color. Such brilliance must have been used by the nepa's ancestors in the open air to catch the eye of a mate. Once upon a time the nepa must have been a flier.

Today the nepa owes its life to good legs. It still has four land-running legs after having turned two into scissors. Although it lives most of the time under water breathing through the long straw, when it comes to outwitting the dytiscus it turns into a runner and heads for land.

THE AESCHNA

A flying submarine cannot pursue a running animal into mud. Neither can the dytiscus with all his furious swimming overtake the *Aeschna* (pronounced eeshna), a green and yellow one-inch torpedo, second only to the dytiscus himself as a swift and skillful hunter. With six legs held firmly against its sides, this cigar-shaped body jerks, shoots, and darts around under water, possessed with some kind of magic of motion that has long puzzled people who have studied it.

Now it can be told that the aeschna uses jet propulsion and

has been operating in the pond long before we ever caught on to this possibility for shooting around. The aeschna has a bladder in its behind attached to a funnel, with the small end pointed straight back. This bladder-and-funnel device is the terminal of the alimentary canal, and that is arranged so the full length of the animal through head, stomach, and intestine is used to build up great pressure. The aeschna literally puts his whole self into a sudden and powerful poop that shoots him forward. The mechanism is controlled by the aeschna's nerves so that he can shoot around as quickly and easily as the phantom larva holds still—and with nothing moving on the outside.

Before making a squeeze play, the aeschna appears to be thinking as he lies in ambush fixing a prey with his eyes. His big eyes occupy most of his head, and they have an hypnotic stare with which he follows the prey no matter how slowly it moves. Once in a while he gives a jerk to test the situation. If this jerk paralyzes the prey with fear, the aeschna's lower jaw flashes out like the tongue of a chameleon. The creature struck by this lightning is then seized in pincers which the aeschna carries on his lip.

The aeschna's body must be well fed because down deep in the pond it is slowly turning into the body of a big dragonfly. The aeschna is the underwater child of the swiftest and most beautiful flyer in the world. High up there in the sunlight, the dragonfly flashes with iridescent blue as it zooms on superb wings almost sixty miles per hour. The swift darting and the big eyes of the dragonfly are the only reminders of its childhood spent as a jet-propelled aeschna under water.

If the pond is not too deep and the bottom is light colored, the dytiscus can see some tantalizing shadows as he hangs from the ceiling. These are the shadows of animals who walk on top of the surface film of the pond.

One is the shadow of a stick moving very slowly, with three little round shadows keeping pace on each side. This is the water measurer, the thinnest animal in the world. It is so thin it appears impossible that heart, lungs, stomach, and intestines can be lined up in such a straight, narrow line with room to operate. Appropriate to this architecture, its head is shaped like a needle with two bulging eyes placed halfway back. The little round shadows are cast by the dimples of its footsteps on the surface of the water. Its toes consist of waxy hairs which hold a little air between them. The light-footed water measurer tiptoes along with far-reaching steps, slowly and carefully forever pacing off the pond.

THE WHIRLIGIGS

The whirligig beetles stir up froths of pinwheels over the surface. These black, shiny, seedlike creatures have flat legs with long fringe on their edges which more than double their rowing surfaces. Whirligigs have never told anyone why they row so madly in circles. But their ancestors survived by doing just that, so they do it too. This whirling commotion is enough to confuse or scare off almost anybody.

Let an insect fall on the surface and the whirligigs stop their gyrating long enough to fight over the meat. They have an eye also for underwater food. Whirligig beetles have bifocals. The lower half of a whirligig's eye sees under water and the upper half sees in the air—a perfect arrangement for a creature which is half under water and half above. The bifocal eyes are located most precisely to be divided by the straight line at the surface of the water. The whirligig gets wetted on the underside of its body where there are no air-carrying hairs, while its upper side is covered with a down of oily hairs that are buoyant. Thus, it rides high like a canoe.

Although it takes blind hunger to drive a frog or bird to go after whirligigs for dinner, when this does happen it is disastrous because whirligigs gyrate in crowds and many can be bagged with one shot. Another animal of the pond surface, the back swimmer, avoids this threat to existence by zigzagging, not as a ballet chorus, but by darting this way and that, albeit back swimmers get so excited they often collide.

The back swimmer's curving, shiny back is neatly keeled. When diving, eating, carrying on his life, there is nothing unusual about him except that he is a neat replica of a rowboat. But let him catch sight of the dytiscus or the aeschna, and he makes for the surface, breaks through the plastic ceiling, flops upside down and describes Zs over the pond. He really puts his heart into it. The back swimmer has an extra heart in his hind legs which beats vigorously only when needed on occasions such as this. This uninhibited ham has discovered that with the extra heart in his hind legs, he can do all right with those alone, and so he holds the other four legs up out of the water. The creature is then trimmed as though one person seated in the back of the rowboat were doing all the rowing.

THE WATER STRIDER

The water strider casts the most playful shadows. He not only skates and runs but also leaps upon the surface of the water, and, if alarmed, he can take off lightly and fly away. He is built on the plan of a daddy longlegs, a hard seed suspended from astonishingly long, slender legs.

The wonder is that semi-rigid, sharply tipped wire legs can support the animal's body without piercing the surface of the water, but of course that is no problem for the creative impulse which designed the water strider. He accords with the law of hydrodynamics which says that the strength of a surface film is increased when pressed down at widely separated points. This explains why the water strider can skate around without piercing the surface film when his long, thin legs are spread far apart—in fact, they are almost horizontal to the knees.

Also, his feet are shod with a short pile of oily hairs that the water cannot penetrate. His feet are oval to make a trough-shaped dimple in the surface film which supports him like a tiny canoe. Finally, the water strider does not lift his feet when he hurries; he keeps six points of support by holding the fore and aft pairs of legs still, while spreading the midship pair like outriggers and sculling with them. This sends him rushing over the water with six wakes streaming out Vs behind.

A six-point support is necessary only when moving swiftly or when needing support to leap or take off into the air. When standing still, the water strider can lift legs three at a time to clean off dust particles while balancing on a slender tripod, the tips of which never prick through the surface to let him down. This cleaning procedure is a dignified and deliberate routine that takes about ten minutes. If disturbed before the routine is completed, the water strider sculls off with an angry sound, seething. When he resumes his toilet, he does not take it up where he left off but starts again at the beginning of the routine. The emotions of a virtuoso admit no partial measures.

With all his marvelous mechanism for living as a flying submarine, with all the respect paid to him by the nepa, the aeschna, the phantom larva, and the back swimmer, the dytiscus has a cross to bear in the person of his own son.

He begat the lad in an off moment. His life had been spent mostly as a bachelor—hunting, living well, diving, flying. He had given scarcely a thought to mating until one day in well-fed middle age he found himself taking up music. He began to make violin notes by scraping a leg across the edge of a plate on his abdomen, making it vibrate. This was so pleasing he played around with the hobby until he found a way to make a second note by rubbing the edge of one of his tough wings against the edges of his abdomen plates and thus producing a kind of harmony.

The dytiscus is nearsighted under water. He can see only about six inches, and what he sees is blurred. This is fortunate in that it gives the others in the pond a break. But now, while he is fiddling, the blurred form of another dytiscus draws near. It is small, appealing, evidently charmed by the magic of the music. He rushes at her, but, for the first time in his life, he does not grab this vision in his jaws and eat it. What is more, the dytisca does not flee or make a commotion. At this point the dytiscus discovers that not only has his music cast a spell but also he possesses two *acetabula,* which is dytiscan for "swellings on front legs covered with suction cups." Acetabula offer great possibilities for a most remarkable embrace. The dytiscus can clasp the dytisca between these suction-cup pillows and they can go swimming and diving together through the pond, with no fear of being separated. A few weeks later the lonely dytisca staggers out upon wet wood and mud at the edge of the pond looking for a spot to hide her eggs.

Doubtless the dytiscus has long since forgotten the episode and little suspects that the water tiger which one day swoops into sight is his own son. This water tiger, the larva of the dytiscus, is strong, streamlined, handsome in his way. No wings, but six powerful legs enlarged with stiff bristles give him banks of oars the like of which have never been seen in these parts before. He is built for speed, power, direction. He has a broad head bearing two long, sickle-shaped hooks that snap together, seize, pierce with the strength of an iceman's tongs.

These tongs are not only sharp but also hollow. When they have clamped and punctured prey, the water tiger pumps digestive juices from his stomach through the tongs into the catch, and after a short time sucks it all back, in this way drinking the soup. This sounds cruel to us, because we don't eat soup the same way. A duck, deer, oyster, and many others might regard us as being just as terrible as the water tiger's prey regards the water tiger. The fact is the water tiger and everybody else in the pond is doing just what we are doing— enjoying dinner.

At sight of the water tiger that is two inches long, and bigger than his sire, the dytiscus does not stop to greet his son but takes off with all his might. He dives into the water weeds with the water tiger after him, and it's nip and tuck who will eat whom.

The meadow pond, the still waters among the reeds in a bay of the lake, the pool of a brook, are not rare and faraway places. There are millions of such places; they are everywhere. They are beautiful silver in moonlight, and blue and green in the sunlight. They seem so still.

The kingdom of the dytiscus is only a few cubic feet of life, but it is a curious blend of the forces of life. Here are five levels, with five atmospheres for living. The air above, the transparent surface film, the upside-down layer just below the surface, the mid-region under water, and the bottom. Just as the sunlight pours through all these layers, so also many inhabitants pass easily up and down, living in all the layers. Others, who may live only below or above, are way stations of the light that sweeps through them, often making the deepest dwellers in the pond related to the highest flyers in the sunlight. These few cubic feet are but a crumb of the dynamic crust of the earth. Yet this small room is fully furnished for living. Here are ample supplies of the elements, and plants to convert them into food, and a motley population eager to eat that food, to survive, and to procreate.

This is a replica of every living place.

Part Two

>>>>>>>>>>>>>>>>>>>>>>>>>>>>>>>>>>>>>>

EVENTS BEYOND TIME

Chapter 7

Curtains of Mystery

JUST IMAGINE that nothing like the bee animal, the dytiscus, and the hobgoblins in the pond has ever been seen, that they never existed. Then try to imagine them back to life. You can't do it. They are too unreal. You couldn't even draw them on paper with any idea that such caricatures could live. Much less could you imagine the way they act—the bee animal stopping in mid-air and then dancing on the hive; the dytiscus diving out of the night sky and catching a bubble to breathe with at the instant it vanishes in the middle of a circle of ripples; the mother of the high-flying flesh-of-chaos that lives under water where it can appear and disappear without moving a muscle; the whirligig beetles that describe circles like outboard motor boats gone crazy; the water strider skating with its legs far apart on the water without falling in; and the terrible water tiger that drinks blood like soup through a pair of hollow ice-man's tongs.

All this is a fairy tale in which outlandish beings pursue impossible lives. Yet you well know that these creatures and their cavortings are no more unreal than all the rest of life. They are not more peculiar than elephants around Lake Chad, or animals on a farm, or mice and men in a city.

How can such things be? Where did they come from?

The question reveals the first marvelous fact about life on earth—namely, that it had a beginning. There was an old theory that life on earth had no origin here, that when the earth cooled to the point of being hospitable it was colonized by seeds from interstellar space. This was a sensible deduction when there was alchemy instead of organic chemistry and all that could be observed on the subject was the dust of spores and seeds borne on the wind to colonize the land. Strangely, today we can say that this no-origin theory may be close to the truth, if the seeds are atoms or their electrons which carry the power to put together life.

Another time-honored theory is that life originated on earth as a supernatural event. Surely the word miracle is broad enough to include life. We can see a thousand miracles around us every day. Why is science continually rejecting the supernatural? What is more supernatural than the tide coming in and going out? To say that this is due to the law of gravity makes it no less supernatural. Or what is more supernatural than an egg yolk turning into a chicken?

I think that neither of these old theories is outdated by modern science. They are no less symbols of the great mystery of truth than the hieroglyphics of today's laboratories. They all add up to the same fact—that life on earth had a beginning. It is a universal fact that all the living objects we see around us have their beginnings and endings, and the evidence indicates that the whole show also had a beginning.

The second marvelous fact about life on earth is seen when we regard the earth's life in relation to the whole cosmos. All life is exceedingly minute in space and time. Even on earth its activity is confined to a thin surface area.

This modicum hurling through blackness and lethal cold is a hint that life is the result of a highly improbable event. Yet, given enough time and suitable materials, this event was almost certain to happen. No matter how small the chance, it is possible to calculate the probability that an event will take place.

There is perhaps nothing else exactly like earth's bizarre living cargo in all the universe. It is unique because it has been shaped, sized, and equipped to fit into the depths of the sea, the heights of the mountains, beaches and jungles, caves and treetops, and all the varieties of climates and soils that exist on earth. These living places have been hammered out on the anvils of endless violence, of winds and rains, volcanic explosions, fire, glaciers, baking drought, bending rocks, floods of lava, and the pushing up and pressing down of land and seas. To live in these many living places, there are many different animals and plants.

We find ourselves in the midst of bees and dytiscuses, earthworms, ants, hummingbirds, kangaroos, cats, dogs, lamellicorns, eagles, sea arrows and porpoises, spiders that spin miles of silk out of tiny bodies, rabbits that scare off pursuers by bobbing white cotton balls, blue-behinded apes, elephants—and giraffes that are obviously absurd. These fellow inhabitants of our earth, living in the same age that we live in and try so hard to own, are our traveling companions on an incredible journey. We all cling to the same ball as we go spinning and rushing through space. In the last three seconds we covered another 180 thousand miles on the way from nowhere to nowhere.

There are so many of us that we are unable even to arrive at final limits for the groups of bacteria, insects, fishes, starfishes, shellfish, reptiles, and mammals that suckle their young. For example, no place has ever been found for the animated little powerhouses called viruses. It can be argued with equal bewilderment that they are alive or that they are nonliving specks of matter. Some living things, including bacteria, cannot even be called plants or animals. They sometimes behave

like plants in the way they move and reproduce, sometimes
like animals.

The greatest wonder of all this is not the immense variety
but the underlying identity of a skunk cabbage and a firefly,
an earthworm and a walrus, a mushroom and a hippopotamus.
Each is a different sum of the same elements. Each is tied to
the same circuit of energy. All the beings of the two kingdoms
of life have the same urges, the drive for food, the fight for time,
and the impulse to procreate. For us this is the most thrilling
drama ever staged; it is as fictional as any story that can ever
be written, as fantastic as any dream that can ever be dreamed.

Life comes into focus between two curtains of mystery.

Beyond the farthest star lies a mystery so impenetrable that
we cannot describe it with any word of our physical vocabu-
lary, nor contemplate its nature with all the powers of imagination. It is sometimes referred to as blackness and emptiness,
as though the mystery beyond the stars is void of the radiant
energy of light, or a vacuum lacking the tiny electric particles
which fill all space on this side of it. That area beyond is an
awesome barricade to knowing—a barricade that has a curious
nature. No matter how far we may strive to push it back, it
scarcely moves.

It is impossible for us to explore with a telescope what
Haydn's *The Creation* calls "the gloomy shades of ancient
night." The Mt. Wilson Observatory has an enormous eye that,
from its mountaintop a mile above the garish lights of Holly-
wood, peers out into space a billion light-years away. There it
picks up a farthest star and beyond that nothing but black mystery. The farthest star appears as a faint speck of light on a pho-
tographic plate that has been exposed for hours, and when this
is greatly enlarged it turns out to be not a single star but a
hundred billion stars. We are seeing them not as they are today
but as they were a billion years before the seas and soil of the
earth came alive. To map the entire heavens in this way would

take five thousand years. We can only peer into a few scattered spots to take samples of what lies out beyond. But this is not the main frustration in the search for the beginning.

In 1948 Mt. Palomar's giant eye—two hundred inches in diameter—cast a glimpse out there twice as far as the Mt. Wilson eye. Instead of seeing another farthest star two billion light-years away it saw something incomprehensible that has been kept as a deep secret from all except a few insiders. Final proof may take generations and even more complicated arrangements than the five-hundred-ton Palomar telescope that has a twenty-ton mirror so perfectly ground it does not distort a reflection as much as 1/250,000 of an inch while rotating with the earth as smoothly as a zephyr. There is a hint of a new dimension as startling as the discovery that the earth was not flat but round. It appears to confirm Einstein, that there is no such thing as a straight line out into space, that two lines cannot be parallel on the scale of the cosmos, and that Euclid's geometry applies only on the small scale of our planetary system.

The evidence is strong that the cosmos—that is, all creation to us—is not infinite but may be measured. In fact, it is about two billion light-years across. When man builds an eye that can see twice as far as Palomar, he will, theoretically, be able to see all the way around the cosmos and back.

However, he will not see the back of his neck as he looks through the telescope because the light rays entering the telescope will have traveled four billion light-years round trip. What will be observed taking place no one can say. Perhaps he will see the earth being torn out of the sun.

Even this not-purely-fanciful situation leaves us with a farthest star and beyond that the impenetrable mystery. For if the cosmos is an ellipse that contains all reality, including interstellar space, what is beyond the cosmos? What then is the cosmos suspended in?

Just as the telescope stops at the curtain of mystery beyond the "farthest star," the microscope stops at the curtain of mystery beyond the electron, which is called at this moment the "fundamental particle," as though there is nothing smaller. Suddenly we find that this smallest particle contains the mightiest power! So we encounter another curtain of mystery within, as impenetrable as the one beyond.

But there is scope enough between the curtain of mystery without and the one within. All the teeming world we know is concentrated in a veneer of air, earth, and sea only as thin in proportion to the earth as the coating of wax on the skin of an apple. Nevertheless, that is depth enough for flying, diving, burrowing, running, and fighting.

Among apparitions greeting the eyes of astronomers using super telescopes are splatters of starlight called spiral nebulae, millions of light-years away. A light-year is a unit of distance coined to extend miles-per-hour through the Milky Way and beyond. It begins where miles-per-hour leaves off, with the speed of light, the fastest velocity known in the universe—186 thousand miles per second. When that is translated into the number of miles light travels per year, we can use this unimaginable unit of distance to talk about nebulae; then suddenly time and space become the same mystery.

Arithmetic is an unlimited tool of understanding, so we multiply the light-year by a million and there, at that distance, we vaguely detect nebulae like *our* Milky Way. Two million of them are already within reach of the telescope and they are scattered over the sky in all directions. Their light that has finally reached into our telescopes left them a million years before, so we are looking at things that have vanished long ago! It is a unique opportunity to see events that occurred a million years ago. And what do we see? Island universes in the form of flattened spiraling shapes like pinwheels.

Those which do not appear as spirals may be presented edge-on as seen from our observation platform; or they may be recent explosions which have not yet been disciplined to make spirals; or possibly some dim splatters are traces of cyclonic systems that have almost spent their energies, so that their fires are cool and they are on the verge of disappearing.

The Irishman, William Parson, who first picked up the whirlpools in the sky a hundred years ago, was greatly excited because he recognized the spirals in nature that are phenomena of growth, movement, change. He proclaimed that the dynamic law of life was "almost within our clasp." What Mr. Parson did not know was recently confirmed at Palomar—that the Milky Way surrounding the earth is itself a spiral nebula, and our Solar System is located in one of its whirling arms, on which we are literally whipping around in a superb snap-the-whip game through space.

Counterparts of these spiral galaxies are reflected everywhere in matter. Molecules make material substance such as rock by crystallizing, and they form spirals when they crystallize. All around us among living things, we see spirals wherever we look—in the curve of the ocean wave just before it topples, in the perfection of the shell of the chambered nautilus, in pine cones and tendrils of wild cucumber, in beaver's tooth and claw and the elephant's tusk.

The creative power which generates pinwheels with stars and spirals with molecules makes merry-go-rounds with solar systems. There are thousands of solar systems and they are all acting in the same way, with planets circling suns, satellites circling planets, wheels within wheels.

Peer through an electronic microscope into any atom, whether it be in your blood, in granite, or in the oceans of water or air. The nucleus of the atom plays the part of the sun, and the electrons revolving around it are the planets. This act, so infinitesimal that it cannot be seen with the ordinary microscope but only with electronic instruments, has the same general proportions as our Solar System. The ratio of the diameter of the earth to its distance from the sun is that of the size of an atom's nucleus to the distance of the encircling electrons.

If an atom were enlarged to the size of a barn, we could yet scarcely see its nucleus, which would then be about the size of this o. Gravity is the force that holds the sun and planets in their places; magnetism holds the nucleus and electrons in their places. But words like gravity and magnetism explain nothing at all. No one knows what gravitation is, although it is supposed to be a kind of electromagnetism, which is another word that brings us up against the black curtain. However, if their forces are the same, as they seem to be, it confirms the unity between those solar systems in the sky and the solar systems in your body.

Thus, between curtains of the unknown we catch glimpses of a haunting unity and control throughout the universe. In such a setting life began as an inherent product of sun and space.

THE ELEMENTS MAKE READY

Until recently attempts to explain the origin of life in physical terms have been considered heresy. On the other hand, some scientists and philosophers have been guilty of many absurdities, such as the spontaneous appearance of frogs and worms in mud, and a recipe for producing mice from decomposed grain and a dirty shirt, or consigned life's origin to other heavenly bodies from which it was somehow delivered to earth by a sort of interstellar parcel post in particle packages.

Today, electronic science and modern chemistry are turning up revelation after revelation, yet, as we proceed, the whole vast universe surrounding this living spark of earth grows ever more overwhelming and mysterious. But as confusion lessens, the realization of order grows. When you stand apart from a tapestry the separate threads and the way they are twisted in the warp and woof vanish, while the pattern emerges.

The same kind of rhythm and activity is over all. Every minuscule of life in its own existence has utility, fitness, and economy that are qualities of art. We see how materials and energies are brought together in well-chosen proportions and then processed by an orderly sequence of events. In this we can feel the sense of a life force as clear and primeval as that which the sun worshipers felt, but with more reverence, less fear. We too are watching processes just as early man watched the rising and setting of the sun. Seeing them work is far from knowing who or what makes them work and why. But in the processes of atoms, in crystal building, and in showers of cosmic rays, there may be a parallel to the Bible story that "God created."

The universal power of the atom, working with inanimate elements, extends natural phenomena on the level of formal invention. This is seen in the evolution of such equipment as the antenna of an insect, or the mind of a man.

Making animals and plants calls for raw materials plus power to do the work, just as does the making of any product. The raw materials for life are abundantly stored in rocks, water, and air, where they are tapped by life in precisely the quantities that are needed. Power is supplied in great surplus by sunlight, which delivers energy at the rate of over 100 thousand calories per square foot per hour. A spectacular example of one kind of receptor life has set up to catch that energy is seen in leaves on a tree, exposed at certain angles in mounting terraces to give each leaf the most sunlight and least shade. Leaves are so carefully placed for the best result that a single mature maple tree occupying a few square feet of land spreads out an acre of leaf surface to the sun.

Considering the bodies of creatures and plants, with their complicated tools and equipment, whether the fly's eye, the elephant's trunk, the moist pollen jewelry in the splendor of an orchid, we might suppose that a countless number of different kinds of raw materials would be required for their manufacture. To the contrary, in all the universe there are fewer than one hundred different kinds of elements and of these you can count on your fingers the elements used to make living bodies.

One of the most astonishing secrets of life is that the basic materials are few in number, and it is the ratios and the way they are combined that make all the differences. This is more startling than a rabbit out of a hat; it is a million animals out of the same hat.

When we look for when and where life began we get lost in the woods. We discover a trail that leads us to a landmark which we hail with satisfaction and then must figure out which of many ways to take into deeper woods. Such a landmark was the discovery around 1600 that everything is not merely liquid or solid, but that there is another quality called gas that arises from burning or evaporating. The Dutchman, Van Helmont, who discovered this, called it *geest*, Dutch for "ghost," hence the word "gas."

Around 1700 a false landmark was hailed, but probably no more "false" than many of our concepts will turn out to be. This was phlogiston, an essence given off by fire. Dry wood and gas absorb it from the air like a sponge and give it up to the air when they burn. When the air is saturated with phlogiston, there can be no further combustion. Plenty of evidence was found to prove this, and it was common parlance in chemistry until around 1800, when oxygen was hit upon. Today, phlogiston is an unknown word, and both it and the "ghost" seem naïve. Even the meaning of the word oxygen seems naïve. It is "acid-generator," from the Greek *oxus* for acid, and *gen* for being born. The first word given to it by its German discoverer was *Sauerstoff*, "sour stuff." Today our landmark to end all landmarks is the atom. Doubtless that will be considered naïve and will even be forgotten by our grandchildren's children, who will have other perceptions.

THE ATOM

Even inspired imagination cannot take us beyond physical reality. That is why we see bigness to the farthest star and smallness to the electron and not one light-year or millimicron farther. Nevertheless, the discovery and use of the atom could be as great an opportunity for man to travel his next mile on the road to infinity as was man's discovery and use of fire. Moreover, like fire, the atom is a phenomenon of the whole universe. That we should know this gives us a bigger adventure than befell the cave man. His control of fire was as local as a campfire, while forest and prairie fires were feared as the fire and brimstone of hell.

Compared to the atom, fire is incidental. Everything, be it fire itself, a bird's feather, a hound's tooth, sunlight, craters on the moon, or the air in your lungs—everything is the peculiar work of atoms. I say peculiar, because only the atom has the power to render all existence. It is a power—*and yet it is material substance.* An atom is so real it can cast a shadow!

Though we may not see the atom directly or feel it with any of our senses, yet it is observed somewhat as we see wind by the quivering of poplar leaves or by the shimmer of ripples on the surface of water. The shadows and echoes of an atom show that it is far less capricious than the wind; it is never erratic. So by detecting its effects and its works, a clear picture of a strictly organized and rhythmic object emerges.

If the atom is material, we can talk about it in ordinary words. So now forget that you are a super-colossus in proportion to an atom and think of it as the size of any convenient object, like a ball of string with strands wound around in all directions. What do you find this unit of matter to be like?

The atom consists of three kinds of particles. Two of them are held tightly together to make its nucleus. Think of these as two very heavy grains of sand, a white one and a black one.

The white is called a proton and is magnetized with a positive charge of electricity. The black grain, called a neutron, is not electrified—it is inert, dead weight. Nevertheless, it plays an exciting role. The third particle is extra-lightweight and whirls around the other two at high speed. Think of this swift light particle as an electric spark held to its orbit by the magnetic attraction of the white grain in the nucleus. This whirling particle of every atom is famous today, going by the name of electron. All three particles spin about their axes as does the earth.

Since the circling electron is at a great distance from its nucleus (in the proportion of the earth from the sun), it follows that the bulk of an atom is mostly open space, or nothingness. This is one of the weird facts of existence.

What kind of materials these particles are that we have likened to grains of sand and an electric spark is a secret kept by the atom, but they are different from any substance we know in heaven and earth. Our comprehension starts with the structures that atoms create. What atoms are doing is more important than what they consist of. We find that this doing is an activity of great power that produces astonishing results. These results all stem from one kind of operation—namely, the whirling of the spark around the grains. A very slight change in the angle or distance of the orbit produces an utterly different result. For infinite possibilities nature adds more grains and more sparks, whirling in the three-dimensional space that we have visualized as a ball of string in which the paths of the whirling sparks are the string. Every time another white grain with its spark is added, a different element occurs!

In this simple one-two-three way all elements can be numbered, starting with atom number one—hydrogen—which has one spark whirling around one white grain, to atom number ninety-two—uranium—with ninety-two sparks circling ninety-two white grains. Such a sequence gives a glimpse of how the elements may have evolved from hydrogen, number one, the chief element of water, the original material of existence. Nature doesn't need more than ninety-two to work all the miracles of heaven and earth. Moreover, all ninety-two elements are made of the same kind of particles; it is only the numbers of these particles that determine whether the material is oxygen or gold.

The higher-numbered atoms—that is, those with many grains in the nucleus and an equal number of electrons whirling around them—don't stick together strongly, and white grains from the nucleus break off and fly away, and their outer electric sparks go with them. Since the exact number of white grains and electrons determines the element of an atom, when some of these are lost the element changes. This is why we say that the high-count elements are radioactive. Grains of the nucleus zoom off with terrific force and what is left then forms a different element. Thus radium, after losing four grains of its eighty-six, has eighty-two left. That is the number for lead, so it has turned into lead.

It is a paradox that an atom which consists of vast open spaces can build hard substances like granite or the enamel on your teeth. The circle described by a propeller with one blade is mostly space, but when that blade revolves fast, it doesn't feel like empty space when you come up against it. Two blades would make it harder still. The atom is a round ball because electrons are whirling on different planes, and where there are a number of electrons, they are at different distances from the nucleus, some whirling inside of others. This explains why gases such as hydrogen and helium that have only one and two electrons respectively are very light compared to iron, which has twenty-six electrons and so is heavy.

Another bit of atomic logic is its weight. The heavy grains in the nucleus are always the same weight, whether they are white or black. The precision of their equal weight exceeds all the skill of technology to equal. It is an ultimate perfection, an invariable, hidden behind the hits and misses of the creative law of averages. This should make an element that has two white grains and their two electrons twice as heavy as hydrogen, the number one element with one white grain and one electron. This would be true except for the addition of the black grains, which add weight without electrons. Black grains give atoms a chance for a greater variety of weights and more scope in building more enduring things without exceeding the limit of ninety-two electrons.

As was just said, the black grains are inert—at least they don't share in the electrical activity. They are like sandbags for ballast, but we can imagine that without them nature would never have gelled a star or a planet; and black void would have been broken only by tiny electric particles, positive and negative, wandering aimlessly in solitude.

Black grains (neutrons) added and subtracted in a nucleus do not make another element. That is determined by the number of electrons and the equal number of protons. The black grains do make the same element heavier. So iron is not twenty-six times heavier than hydrogen; it is fifty-six times heavier because the kind of iron most abundant on earth has added thirty black grains to its nucleus. Uranium is not ninety-two times heavier than hydrogen but two hundred and thirty-eight times heavier because it is loaded with one hundred and forty-six black grains. As was said before, when the nucleus is loaded too heavily, it tends to break up, so that the heaviest elements, which include radium and uranium, are loosing their nucleuses and shooting off their radioactivity. Small amounts of these metals were still left on earth by the time we came along to play with them.

The maximum load an atom can carry permanently is that of lead, with eighty-two electrons and the extra ballast of one hundred twenty-six black grains making it two hundred and eight times as heavy as hydrogen, the atom with one electron. That is why the high-count radioactive elements, when they lose electrons and are reduced to lead, stop losing electrons at that point, and stay lead. Gold, number seventy-nine, is close to lead, being almost two hundred times heavier than hydrogen. If the innate force of the atom hadn't overreached itself and had stopped with lead, we would have had a comfortable existence without atomic bombs, which came out of Madame Curie's discovery in 1910 of radium and the way it hurls off electrons.

Even though lead can hold itself together, it is not very stable. The best permanence is reached at fifty-eight times the weight of hydrogen, where we find nickel, with twenty-eight white grains plus thirty black grains. Up to that point the power that binds the particles of the nucleus increases as the nucleus grows heavier. Iron, which is fifty-six times heavier than the first and lightest element, is close by and is one of the most permanent elements in the universe.

In flaming suns electrons fly away, atoms fuse to become molten lead and iron, their weight and power is built, and energy is discharged, making immense heat. In this fiery cauldron some elements are heavy, others are light, but always the elements are standard throughout the universe. Even though the atoms are tortured by thirty-six million degrees of heat, as in our sun, so that they cannot crystallize, they are gradually separated according to weight. The heavier elements sink toward the center and the lighter gases are left around the outside, some of them escaping into space. It is that way on our sun. On earth the process has gone farther, so that nickel and iron are the elements that make the central core and the lighter elements in the form of gas are around the outside, becoming the air we breathe.

And so—the elements made ready for life on earth.

4

A Splash of Sun Fire

NOBODY WAS RUNNING AROUND with a notebook and pencil when it happened, so we have only circumstantial evidence. There are many theories, but whatever actually happened must have been no less fabulous and dramatic than the theory that our sun barely missed a head-on collision with a star that came roaring in from outer space.

Colossal suns hurtling across the sky have rare chance for collision. Though this chance is one in millions, in the course of time some sun is foredoomed to be that "one." This is what almost happened to ours.

The near-hit, the miss, is what counts. The incoming star was about the same size as our sun, and a collision would have shattered both these beautiful powerhouses into a miniature Milky Way. This one in a billion, billion chance of existence for the bees and the dytiscus and you and me would have exploded into a super-nova, an immense bright flare, possibly noted with a shrug by queer astronomers on weird worlds out there in the universe.

On the other hand, the close approach of the stars caused

a great tidal wave in the molten stuff of the sun, exactly as on a small scale the pull of a full moon raises up a tide on earth. The pull was so violent that the sun stuff was drawn far out until the outer end with less sun gravity holding it back shot out toward the passing star. The center mass was elongated but remained the thickest, while the inner end held by the strongest attraction of the sun was pulled out, tapering to the last contact with the sun. A spindle is formed in this way when you drop the viscous white of egg from its shell. The elongated mass tapers at both ends just before it breaks loose. I have tried it.

Although this portentous tidal wave of sun stuff finally pulled away, yet the sun won the titanic tug of war. Its mighty gravity reached across space to hold on leash the detached fragments of the viscous spindle. The star that had brushed by, causing this rumpus, retreated into space, pulling the spindle apart and attracting the fragments just long enough to set up their circling all in the same direction around the sun. The seething lumps, because of their smaller sizes, then lost their fiery nature, their elements condensed as they cooled, and today we see the planets strung out in the plane of the visiting star's direction as it roared away.

The outline of the spindle is suggested by the way the planets are lined up according to size. Mercury, the nearest to the sun, is small—only three thousand miles in diameter; Venus, next in line, is 7,600 miles in diameter; then comes Earth, nearly eight thousand miles in diameter. Just beyond us, Mars is smaller instead of larger than the Earth—which may tell an exciting tale, as we shall see. Mars is located in a wide gap; it is 341 million miles from Mars to Jupiter. Jupiter holds the central position in the family and is by far the biggest, with a diameter eleven times that of Earth. Next to Jupiter, and almost as big, is Saturn. The planets farther out taper off with much smaller Uranus and Neptune, and finally, farthest out, Pluto is almost as small as Mercury at the other end of the spindle.

Something is missing. Why is Mars so small? Why is there an enormous gap in the spacing of the planets where the spindle calls for a big fellow comparable to Jupiter and Saturn?

In 1801, a little planet was discovered and named Ceres. A hundred years later, as telescopes improved around 1900, they began picking up real clues to answer the question of what became of the big vanished planet. Two little bodies, each one only twenty miles in diameter, with about the area of Rhode Island, were spotted close together and revolving around each other like eerie little fists shadowboxing in the sky.

This double whirligig is called the planet Eros, and, only sixteen million miles away, it is the closest to us of any other fixed body of the Solar System except the Moon. Sharp variations in light reflected from the surface of the little Eros lumps indicate irregular masses of rock. It is as though gigantic, craggy mountains like Mt. Everest had been torn out and hurled into space and became suspended between the gravity of the sun and the gravity of other planets and satellites round about.

Since Eros was discovered, hundreds of rocky masses have been spotted out there in the big gap, and they are named or numbered. One of the largest of the little planets is Ceres, with a surface about five times the area of California. Pallas is the size of West Virginia plus Texas. Juno equals Ohio. Vesta is a larger body, with enough square miles for New York, Pennsylvania, Ohio, and Kentucky combined. Many more of these bleak, craggy, sterile rock masses have been detected. Some are as small as ten miles in diameter. Smaller than that they become invisible. They travel in groups—there is a family of twenty-two and another of eleven—and all are in the gap between Mars and Jupiter. This is evidence of a collision, or explosion, and probably these are the fragments of the missing big planet that once occupied the center position of the spindle of the splash of sun fire. In that case Mars is the largest remnant.

Further evidence of the explosion of the missing planet may be some beautiful and peculiar jewelry picked up from the earth's surface that has piqued the curiosity of people for centuries. Without any scientific knowledge of its true nature, finders supposed that they had stumbled over fine glass made by prehistoric men in prehistoric melting furnaces.

This glass has a quality that is out of this world. It comes in translucent shades of green, amber, and brown. The surface is so smooth it is satiny, and it has fanciful shapes like ovals with ears, dumbbells, and teardrops. Pieces weigh from a fraction of an ounce to over a pound. This jewelry is called tektite, according to the dictionary "a glass of unknown origin."

Tektite gems have been picked up in Texas, Australia, the Philippines, Bohemia, and the Libyan desert. They are near-perfect glass and could only have been fused in a fierce 5,000° heat sustained over a long period of time, while highly fluid. The only conceivable way these conditions could be met would be as drops in the gases from the surface of a fiery newborn planet. These conditions were not met by primitive man, whose melting furnace was an armful of sticks.

Tektite jewels were said to be formed from the fusion of earth sediments at places where a meteor struck, but science says that no such perfect glass could be made by a flash of fire, regardless of its heat.

The one theory that explains the puzzle is that this glass must have been forged on a planet situated between Mars and Jupiter. This would have been a molten mass with a temperature above 5,000° after it had left the sun. When the planet broke up, its particles were spread through space, and thus arrived on earth as drops of glass.

What became of the Visitor that drew the planets out of the sun's fiery gases and molten stuff is not important. It is normal procedure for the roving sun which stirred up the ruckus to have vanished. Heavenly bodies come and go. Space easily swallows even whole galaxies. What really matters is that our earth, having carried off a full complement of the sun's elements, was equipped with all the raw materials necessary to produce a lot of life during three billion years of crust cooling.

Even in this moment of time we can see big things disappear in the sky. A comet swings in toward the sun with a long narrow orbit, pulled by the attraction of the big ball of fire as a moth to a flame. As it gets closer, the pressure of the sun's intense light breaks off crumbs from the head of the comet which pour back in space, forming the famous tail. The closer the comet gets, the greater its speed, so that at a critical point it curves away on its orbit and flies off with its tail not between its legs but streaming out ahead in triumph.

In 1682 Halley, a friend of Newton's who helped him figure out the law of gravity, identified a big comet as the same as one recorded with awe and wonder in 1531 and again in 1607. Halley predicted that it would return again in seventy-six years. Sure enough, since then it has kept its appointment with the sun three times and was last seen on schedule in 1910. Between visits Halley's Comet vanishes over the horizons of space to be gone for seventy-six years.

But comets are local; they are tied up with our Solar System. How much more should bodies which are sidereal—that is, belonging to the starry beyond—disappear. Such was the Visitor, a star itself, which, having caused the big splash, sped off beyond the black curtain, perhaps not to return near enough to be seen again for billions of years, if ever.

Though it can never be proved beyond dispute whether the earth was tossed out by a big splash of sun stuff or whether it was collected in space by magnetized space dust sticking together, the vital fact is that earth's rocks, seas, and air, as well as our bodies, consist of the same elements that make the sun and the planets. Everything on earth, living and nonliving, is of a piece with the cosmos. The different conditions on earth as compared to the fiery hurricanes on the sun are differences in the proportions of the same elements, and the way they are combined and act under enormous changes of temperature. The speed with which electrons whirl around in atoms depends on the heat. The same atoms at millions of degrees of temperature make pyrotechnic iron and nickel, and roaring gases of hydrogen, oxygen, and helium will, at the low temperatures of the earth, become solid metals and healthy atmosphere and water. Strange effects ensue when star stuff is released from its usual temperatures and permitted to cool—and the strangest of all is life.

Living and nonliving materials are made by the same process. Life is no more mysterious than gold or air made out of atoms. Atomically speaking, a flame, a block of granite, and a beating heart are equally wonderful. The same force makes mountains and organs of a living body. It is hard to put your finger on any substantial difference between living and nonliving nature. Controlled motion is not a peculiar property of life, or an atom would be alive, with its electrons whirling around a nucleus, and what is more, atoms organize spirals and solar systems with velocities that would make the swiftness of the hummingbird's wing appear to stand still in comparison.

Bewilderment as to what is living or not living was revealed recently in an adult class of graduate students of education, most of them schoolteachers, many with master's degrees. They were asked to state whether any of the following objects are living: a lighted match, an electric clock, the sun, the wind, gasoline, the ocean. The answers of 45 per cent said that one or more of these are living. This was so startling the examiners decided to ask another class, this time teachers of child psychology, whether the sun, clouds, sea, lightning, wind, stars, earth are living. The answers of 48 per cent said that one or more are living. Was it because the objects have motion or are active in some way?

Other questions were asked dealing with consciousness. "Ships are lost at the bottom of the sea. Do you think the sea itself knows where they are?" "This pearl was once in a shell in the sea. When the water moved, could the pearl feel the movement of the water?" Answers of one third of the class said that the sea or pearl or both were conscious. They reasoned, "Yes, the chemicals of the sea are aware." "Yes, the sea rules over the lost ships and knows them to be there." And the pearl felt "probably as a very young fetus might feel the effect of water in the mother's womb." Over 40 per cent attributed consciousness to the sea when asked, "Tides are caused by the pull of the moon. Do you think the ocean can feel the pull of the moon?"

Though the forces of life are identical in all existence, including the fierce fires of the sun and the sterile rock of the moon, the distinction is that something animate is sensitive, something inanimate is not sensitive. In this way life is a unique achievement of the atom's system of elements. We must know this if for no other reason than that you and I can think about atoms and animals, write about them, and read about them. The lighted match, the sun, and wind cannot do that. The pearl is not sensitive like a sparrow; and the electric clock, unlike a seed, cannot grow a tree.

If there is no substantial difference between living and non-living, the quality of sensitivity is all the more awe-inspiring; also the capacity of growth, and, in higher forms of life, the psyche of being. Are these qualities merely mechanical results of the revolution of electric particles around minute specks of matter in lots of one-two-three up to ninety-two? To say this is to surrender our quest.

The combination that brought about life on earth called for gleaning among an infinite number of possibilities with an infinite number of chances for a miss. The law of averages extending across infinity could do it, or it may have been designed by a creative spirit beyond our understanding. What has happened is like flinging a shuffled deck of cards into the air and seeing them fall to the table in the order of the suits. If you are looking for a special miracle, this is it.

The earth had to be a certain size, at a certain distance from the sun, traveling at a certain speed so that its centrifugal force would exactly counterbalance the gravity of the sun. Otherwise our globe would have zoomed back into the fiery cauldron long ago. If the traveling speed through space were too great, it would have shaken off the sun's pull and kept right on into the black deep-freeze of outer space. On the other hand, the earth's original impulse is never spent because it travels in frictionless space. Once set going by a primeval force (perhaps the tug by the Visitor), it keeps right on at the same speed. All bodies in space, whether a tiny meteorite or a huge sun, keep going at the same rate once they are set in motion, and only a collision can stop them. They do not drop as does a baseball when the original force of the fly is spent.

So it's good to have the earth just the right size and distance to suit us. No other planet has such a happy relationship with the sun. Only the earth has four seasons in a year of 365 days; only the earth has day and night in twenty-four hours. The rhythm of these seasons and days is the rhythm of life here.

Two other planets are close to this situation. Venus is the most exciting and will be the first planet visited when we get the space ships going. It is the nearest to us and about our size. Its year is shorter (225 days) because it is closer to the sun and, therefore, circles faster. Venus people would have more years than fourscore and ten without living any longer. Its day is the same length as our month, which makes an odd situation for living from our viewpoint. This would give it only 7½ days per year. Venus is hidden in clouds that never pull apart. But instead of water vapor, Venus's clouds are carbon dioxide, and there is no oxygen in her atmosphere. In this age of plastics, it can be seriously argued that Venus's clouds are a more or less firm plastic formaldehyde. If there is any life under those

4*

plastic clouds, it must be utterly different from the creations of protoplasm on earth.

Mars is on a track outside ours and therefore circles more slowly for a longer year of 687 days. Mars's trouble is not too much atmosphere but too little, with only a trace of water vapor and oxygen. Mars is half the size of the earth, so everything there weighs half as much as it does here. The heavy atmosphere which earth retained because it was big enough to hold it flew off into space from Mars while it was cooling. Mars has white polar caps that come and go with the seasons, but as there is so little water on Mars, these are thought to be frozen carbonic-acid gas. The surface of Mars is mostly a red desert of rusty iron ore. When iron rusts, it is oxidized, which means that it gathers in oxygen. This indicates what became of the oxygen of Mars's atmosphere that did not escape into space; it was absorbed into iron ore.

Most tantalizing on Mars are traces of green and brown patches and lines changing color with the seasons. It has recently been found that these patches of color have the same spectrum as lichens. Here on earth lichens have survived through the ages in the most harsh and sterile places. Lichens are the nearest plants to the North and South Poles, regardless of cold. They grow on the desert floor of Death Valley regardless of heat. They survive with the minutest amount of moisture and cling to bare rock without the need for nourishing soil. If it could be proved that we are looking at lichens on Mars, this would make big newspaper headlines as our first glimpse of life on other worlds. Moreover, judging by the resiliency of animal life on earth, as when a fairy shrimp egg survives sixteen years in dry dust and temperatures of 100 degrees below zero to 180 degrees above, there could also be things creeping around in the lichen jungles on Mars.

Lichens are part of the whole life system based on protoplasm. If lichens were alive on Mars, we should know that the protoplasm experiment has succeeded elsewhere in the universe. From that information it is plausible to suppose that other worlds teem with unimaginable forms of life. Then, given longer ages in which to develop, it would be impossible to suppose that supercreatures wiser than we do not exist.

All other planets are out of the competition. Mercury is the closest to the sun, and it could never condense an atmosphere in its terrific heat. Mercury's crust is volcanic rock like our moon's. On the far side, the big planets, Jupiter and Saturn, are too distant from the sun for necessary warmth. When their primeval fires cooled, the temperature on their surfaces plunged to a deep freeze of 184 degrees below zero. Their atmospheres consist of ammonia vapor and methane, which is our natural gas. In 1955 our astronomers detected the first radio waves found from another planet coming from Jupiter. This powerful electric agitation in Jupiter's atmosphere has been named "thunderbolts of Jove."

A weird fact about the two great planets is that they are almost as soft as water. They spin very fast and have a ten-hour day, and this flattens them out like a fat cushion instead of a sphere. The earth's crust is a bit plastic, so the spin makes it twenty-six miles wider at the Equator than along its axis, between the Poles, but Jupiter is much softer and six thousand miles wider around the middle than between its poles. Far beyond, Uranus, Neptune, and Pluto are out in the cold.

This leaves earth in sole possession of the miracle of vital balance.

After zooming away at a great enough speed to offset plunging back into the sun, the fiery blob reached a position of equilibrium. Then the elements that were destined to make living things and nourish them packed themselves into the earth the same way that the man in the supermarket packs your groceries—heavy things on the bottom, light things on top. One is heavier or lighter than another according to the number of particles in its atoms, and so our familiar gravity arranged things by causing the heavy elements, mostly nickel and iron, to sink to the center of the earth; the medium-weighted elements, such as silicon, ended up on top of this in the form of a crust of granite; while lighter elements, nitrogen and oxygen, took their places above the crust to become the air we breathe. Hydrogen, the chief ingredient of sun fire, is also the chief ingredient of our water. This lightest element would have escaped into space and been lost from the earth, except that it was captured in water by combining with oxygen. Fortunately, there is lots of oxygen in rocks of the earth's crust—granite is 50 per cent oxygen mixed in with the silicon. So water happened in large quantities when two atoms of hydrogen and one atom of oxygen were locked together and turned into H_2O. This chemical experiment turned out just fine, as it provided plenty of water to make life possible.

The next lightest element, helium, which is abundant in the sun's atmosphere, did escape from earth. Only a slight amount is left locked up in a few minerals and in natural gas. But fortunately helium is not needed for our vital balance. We use helium only for blimps and for getting deep divers and caisson workers back to normal air pressures after they have spent some time deep under water.

The air is just right for our vital balance without any other gases. We may complain that winters and summers are too cold or hot and say, "It isn't the temperature; it's the humidity," but the atmosphere makes us a good greenhouse to live in by insulating us from any touch of burning or freezing that would instantly destroy delicate life, such as 460 degrees below zero—the absolute zero of space—which is the temperature a few miles overhead.

Another lucky chance is that a trace of ozone was held in a high stratosphere layer. There is so little of this ozone that if it were all concentrated into a layer of pure ozone like a transparent bubble enclosing the earth, this ozone film would be only one tenth of an inch thick. Yet this trace of ozone is enough to absorb lethal rays from the sun, shorter and deadlier than the ultraviolet rays which cause sunburn, before they can reach us. If this small item had been omitted we would not be around to talk about it.

The density of the atmosphere is just right for doing us another good turn. Earth is a target for countless missiles from outer space. Because of our speed, we strike vast numbers of fragments of shattered planets or crumbs from comets' tails, just as raindrops pelt thicker against your windshield the faster you drive. The total number of meteors hitting our atmosphere every twenty-four hours is around 750,000,000,000,000,000, but it doesn't matter what the sum is because almost all this buckshot is burned up many miles high in the air by the friction of the atmosphere. This is lucky for us because these fragments travel at such terrific speed that they would perforate an animal's body like pistol bullets fired point-blank if they ever reached the ground.

Some of this small shot aimed at our planet is big enough to catch the eye as shooting stars. These are about the size of croquet balls. Although they are only a small part of the total, they number millions per day. These shooting stars come down through an increasingly dense atmosphere; they are usually burned up fifty miles overhead, often with a flash and a loud report that has startled drivers into a ditch, pilots to bank their planes, people to phone the police. But a few are not burned up by friction with the atmosphere. The biggest meteor in history hit the earth in eastern Siberia in 1947. It weighed one thousand tons and its detonation flattened trees across fifty miles—it could have been one of the fragments of the missing planet. These packages from the Solar System contain nothing new in the way of elements; but they do bring tangible evidence that the elements are universal. Moreover, meteors bring us a gift of around five tons of iron and nickel every day to add to our earth's crust.

So, on a ball splashed out of the sun, or thrown off as a spark from a super-nova, or condensed from an icy cloud of cosmic dust, here we are with a piece of universal real estate exactly the right size, at exactly the right place to have a vital balance. The stage is set. Yet something else is needed to bring animals and plants into being upon it. That something is a special kind of energy to become the power of life.

One kind of energy was on hand even before earth was born. That is the tug of gravity which is so familiar we pretend to know what it is. We use it in walking and flying, digging and playing baseball. Every plant and animal uses the force of gravity in every movement; muscles are designed to operate against it, and structures of wood and bone to resist it and grow up from the earth. Gravity is one kind of energy that doesn't have to be transported. We employ its ever-present power in hammering a nail or jumping on sticks to make kindling for a campfire. Gravity is indispensable. But this is not an energy that can make things come alive.

Another kind of energy that comes with the elements is the atom's electric energy. Man has put this to many uses, yet there is no evidence that it makes living chemical combinations. It is universal energy in all matter both living and dead. Nevertheless, electricity plays a big part in living bodies. For one thing, it relays impulses in nerves.

Atomic energy has been abundant on earth from the beginning. This giant is locked up in every atomic nucleus, and we nave a hint of its might when it blows its top. Such explosive power does not keep things growing, breathing, running, procreating. Everywhere we look among the suns and comets, meteors and planets, we see the devastation of the energy locked in atoms, which, when released by an explosion, leaves terrific heat or deep freeze and turns planets into glaring deserts where a living cell would be snuffed out in the tiniest fraction of a second.

It takes an energy different from all these to create structures as intricate and beautiful as a leaf, an iris of an eye, a slender leg of a fawn, the wing of a bird—and to animate them. Animation is not produced by a primeval wham and then stored in rocks to be used as a reservoir for life to draw on through the ages. Life energy is a gentle energy, constantly renewed in measured amounts, steadily applied along the flow of time. This is the energy of light delivered to earth across the vastness of cold, black space, fresh, regularly every day.

We can sense light energy by lying in the sun to feel its warmth, by seeing buds in the spring swing open and move forward at its touch, by watching salmon driven up from the sea to spawn, by the flash of fireflies and the pinwheeling of whirligig beetles. All of this seems so real and tangible and ever-present that we overlook the fact that this energy is transmitted at a definite speed (not instantaneously, for it takes eight minutes to cross over from the sun) utterly unfelt and invisible and, so far as we can sense it, nonexistent until it touches something.

If that something is our eyes, we see light; if it is dust or water vapor in the air, we see blue sky instead of blackness; if it is sand, garden humus, rock, water, whatever is touched by this energy is warmed up by making the molecules of the substance vibrate faster.

Some of this sunlight energy bounces off an object it touches and thence into our eyes so that we see it. This reflected energy, greatly reduced from the original, is comfortable. We live in a world of reflections where we see the faces of our friends, or an apple, a dog, the Golden Gate Bridge, the Empire State Building. After crossing ninety million miles of subzero blackness, and after filtering through a six-hundred-mile-thick blanket of atmosphere, the energy of light is still so intense that we cannot look directly into the sun without agony. One fanatic forced himself to look squarely into the face of the sun for eight minutes, the length of time that it takes the rays to reach his eyes, went blind, and destroyed himself.

Faced with trying to describe this state of being alive, science is humbled. The secret of life hides behind words like radiant energy, light, heat. Much is written about waves of energy or electrified particles recently discovered, called photons, that zip through space. It is hard to pin down light to laws of physics. Light energy acts like particles of material substance sometimes and like vibration waves at other times. It may alternate, taking the form of one or the other.

A photon of light is an electron without a nucleus to rotate around that would have turned it into an atom. It is possible to contemplate that this particle can travel with not the slightest reduction of velocity, as do the suns and planets; and that it can carry its tiny ray into our staring telescopes from the farthest star, coming 186 thousand miles closer to the telescope every second yet taking a million years for the trip. Why does a ray of light energy take any time at all to travel? Why the delay of eight minutes between the sun and the earth?

A constant speed over so long a course speaks of a tremendous mystery. Although distance never slows or quickens a ray of light, its speed at the end of a million years or eight minutes being exactly what it was when it started, yet its power to warm up what it hits decreases in proportion to the distance. This is why the planet Mercury is too close to the sun ever to stop blistering, and Pluto is too far away ever to thaw out. In fact, the earth would be much too close to the sun for comfort because the power to heat up things at our distance would turn everything on earth to cinders in no time were it not for the atmosphere. By the time the light energy reaches the ground it has lost much of its heat by agitating and heating up so many air molecules as it came through the atmosphere. What is left of this power when the light reaches the earth's surface is just the right amount of energy to put life into operation.

This light energy serves another great purpose for life in the way it makes weather.

A wind machine of great power is operating a short distance

overhead. Recently, high-altitude jet bombers have found this
wind machine six miles above the earth. Here are ribbons of air
in narrow jets as though poured from the nozzle of a hose.
They are westerlies, but their streams, thousands of miles long,
loop from the Pole to the Equator. Much of the immense energy needed to drive this air rises from tropical seas warmed
by the sun. A measure of this power generated in the atmosphere, yet always controlled in a definite pattern, can be real-
ized from the fact that the hurricanes which carried away
houses, flattened trees, brought floods across New England were
clocked around seventy-five miles per hour. The mightiest tropical hurricanes around Miami are ninety miles per hour, and
when that happens almost everything in the path flies away.
Yet the great wind machine overhead has jets ceaselessly streaming at one to three hundred miles per hour while we go about
our business on a beautiful clear day. It is these jet streams that
generate our weather, which, whether we like it or not, is indispensable to our well-being.

In this way, the energy of the calories delivered by sunlight powers not only living bodies but also the machinery of the
earth's crust to keep life going. The warming of oceans and
lakes puts velocity into the molecules of water, which lightens
them so that they fly up into the air as vapor, blow over the
land, and pour down again as rain or snow. This machinery,
powered by sunlight, lifts and deposits some three hundred and
forty cubic miles of water every day around the earth. It takes
power—the sheer weight totals sixteen million tons of rain per
second. Though winds are fitful and clouds are capricious in
any one locality, the world-wide result is dependable, and
water is in good supply where life needs it.

Plants tie in with this water-lifting operation by using their
own bodies as pipe lines and lifting their breathing apparatus
up into the air. Animals tie in with it after the power of the
sun lifts water from the ocean high upon the hills, from whence
it descends to rivers and lakes. In the immense circuit of this

tonnage of water the earth is endowed with a redolent freshness and essence of life, where lakes and streams, oceans and moist soil are summoned up and fitted together, supporting animals and plants in salt water and fresh water, on the land, in the air, and, marvelously, within the bodies of each other, always bathed in water.

At the temperatures of the earth where animals and plants live, water is fluid with a healthy ebb and flow, mixing and distributing the elements in streams and lakes and seas—and entering into all living bodies, where it carries on the same mixing, vital streaming. This movement of nonliving water has a kinship with the movement of life.

Water was the stepping stone which, after millions and millions of years of trial and error with chemical combinations, led to the elements' greatest invention—protoplasm.

Thus, the earth's crust, formed by gravity, powered by the soft warmth of sunlight, supplied with the eight chief elements of life—oxygen, nitrogen, hydrogen, iron, sulphur, magnesium, calcium, and carbon—selected from the whole list of ninety-two, was ready to take the first step toward populating the earth.

The River of Life

Lɪꜰᴇ ʙᴇɢᴀɴ ᴏɴ ᴇᴀʀᴛʜ when a few elements (principally carbon, oxygen, and hydrogen), cooked by sunlight in warm water, gelled to form a peculiar chemical we call protoplasm. Large batches of this must have accumulated in pools in the steaming mud. It quivered and flowed formlessly, like egg white.

The first week this jelly turned up in a sun-warmed low-tide pool, it may have pulled apart in the cool of night, separating the way a coat of paint reticulates and breaks up when it shrinks. These smaller units could move faster, eat faster, and multiply faster than the large mass. This established the first law of body building—that the most efficient, most aggressive size for protoplasm is that of a microscopic cell. Tiny monads expose the maximum surface for absorbing food dissolved in the water that bathes them. Unlimited food constantly entering a cell from all sides brings unlimited energy. Utmost vitality and creativeness are found in smallness.

Wherever the living cell is located, whether at the growing tip of a sequoia, in the breast of a robin, the brain of a bear, the tail of a fish, the eye of a snake, it is always microscopic and always bathed in salt water that brings it dissolved nourishment. Blood has about the same saltiness as the sea, and so does the fluid of the brain.

So perfect is the original one-cell form of life, and so potent both for body building, for activating nerves and muscles, and for procreation, that the cell has never altered its basic size or nature from the beginning of life even to this day when snails and whales move through the water, and ants and elephants troop out of sun-warmed swamps, and a man is kneeling on the shore to make notes, in awe and wonder.

If you feel as big as a god in contrast to the River of Life circulating inside a microscopic cell, glance at the Milky Way, which is 150 thousand light-years across. If you still consider those jelly specks insignificant, take heed that they are you. The body of an animal is one cell or a billion. The protoplasms arranged themselves in a fine way to build you and then loaned you their own senses, even to the electricity that brings ideas to your brain and action to your muscles.

Man, looking out from within his own share of protoplasm, can see life objectively and enjoy the illusion of looking at something other than himself. No other animal can look at the River of Life and call it fascinating. But we, peering through the transparent membranes of our own cells, can enjoy the way protoplasm flowing in a dog makes him wag his tail, and in a bee makes it dive into a willow tassel, or how, flowing in bodies, protoplasm makes them do whimsical things—a robin pulls an earthworm like a rubber band, a fox chases a rabbit, a lobster fans its babies, bees mate in mid-air, submerged porpoises squeal like children.

Every individual, starting as a single cell, repeats in its own little life the age-long ritual. This is true whether the body will be as sheer as a jellyfish, vibrant as a hummingbird, massive as a hippopotamus, or tall as a sequoia.

This single cell, the first-person singular of an animal or plant, is called by an old Norse word, egg. This egg cell takes the first step toward building an elaborate body in the same way that one-cellers build large populations by running a partition down the middle and dividing in half. Then the two daughters grow to full size, and thus one cell becomes two cells. From here on simple arithmetic works wonders. Two cells both divide, becoming four, then eight, sixteen, thirty-two, sixty-four, and so on, accumulating an animal or a tree as big as you please. Growing halts, but dividing continues for repairs and replacements when the creature is the size of its kind. A fly has about twenty million cells; a human being has one hundred billion; an elephant proportionately more.

The protoplasm of your one-celled egg divided until there were some one hundred billion of themselves that you might be full grown. The dividing system is astonishingly efficient. It takes only fifty successive cell divisions from your first one cell to build you big with the one hundred billion. Then you have your share of the River of Life, and, under sealed orders, your cells stop dividing, you grow no bigger. But replacements will be needed. During three score and ten years, a man's body needs ten times the one hundred billion cells that total an adult. This maintenance job calls for more cell dividing, so the descendants of your starting cell may have to produce a thousand billion for your life. It seems incredible that a huge crowd like you is only fifty to sixty generations from the original single egg cell that was your entire self to begin with. This is the wonderful arithmetic of the living cell.

By simply dividing in the middle the living cell multiplied primeval populations and it repeats this same simple act to make big animals grow. In fact, we can catch glimpses of both the primeval and the present-day life all mixed up together in the world around us. One-cellers are still coalescing to form many-cellers, even as they did seven hundred million years ago. Right beside them modern achievements such as mammals condense their whole being into the nucleus of the single egg cell, and then the personality and architecture of the giant animal rise out of that microscopic speck. This is the way it is with your dog, cat, cow, and you. Protoplasm, with its insuppressible creativeness, has tried out millions of ways of building big bodies.

THE BACTERIUM

Protoplasm also experimented with a living unit much smaller than the body-building cell and turned out an item which has terrific vitality and holds the world record for fast reproduction. The bacterium is a speck of sheer, hungry protoplasm which does not flow in a living cell. The bacterium has no personality because it has no nucleus. The nucleus is the control board of the living cell, curbing crazy tendencies and serving as a strongbox for genes that stamp the cell with individuality and pass this on from generation to generation.

The bacterium does not even represent a third kingdom with plants and animals. It is an entirely different kind of life. Some bacteria need no oxygen. The bacterium is sometimes called a plant because it can make its own food out of raw materials, sometimes called an animal because it can live on other animals and plants and creep around over a surface and act like a little animal. The bacterium often draws out threads of protoplasm as a spider draws out silk threads and whips these violently to propel itself on a line with its axis. This is pulling action like that of airplane propellers. Some bacteria have the whipping apparatus at one end, others at both ends, so that they have no bow or stern but move back and forth like a ferryboat. The bacterium is a law unto itself; it is neither plant nor animal but both at the same time. We can call it a pilot model of a living thing that never got anywhere beyond itself.

For the creation of big living bodies, the bacterium turned out to be a dead end. Bacteria, unlike body-building cells, have no capacity to organize a combination in which they co-ordinate and divide up the work. They perform countless important chemical experiments with skill, but often in an unexpected and capricious way. A bacterium with twenty minutes to live spends its time in riotous living.

This uncurbed vitality has a profound effect on the River of Life and all its works. The bacterium packs an immense power both for the well-being and the destruction of other kinds of life. It is closer to the elements than the River of Life. It can eat elements raw, while the River of Life must have them converted for nourishment. For example, the bacterium eats raw nitrogen in the soil and mixes this in its body in such a way that plants can then use the nitrogen to make the chlorophyll of their leaves. With supplies of elements for life on earth limited by the acreage of the earth's crust, the bacterium gives the elements turnover by eating them, so that the River of Life can use the same elements again and again.

When bacteria devour elements that have been locked up in animal and plant cells, they perform a vital service. These bacteria pounce on dead plant and animal materials, eat them, and digest them, separating the locked-up elements so that they can be used again for fresh animals and plants. These cell eaters cause decay. Without them, the Garden of Eden would have become an impenetrable clutter where nourishing mineral elements were locked up in dead bodies, and life of big animals and plants would have been choked and starved.

Moreover, without the weird, untamed bacterium, a link would be missing in the circuit of food. A menagerie of miniature creatures, which are single cells living as complete animals, depends on the bacterium for its food. The bacteria that eat cells are devoured by living one-cellers, and these in turn are eaten by creatures made out of a few cells, and the few-cellers are eaten by many-cellers, and this ladder of life reaches away on up to the blue whales, the biggest animals on earth. Ultimately, we who pride ourselves as being so far above the bacterium that it can't even see us are eaten by the bacterium, and the circuit is closed.

While bacteria are tied to the raw, nonliving elements and are closer to them than cells, still they are truly alive. This cannot be said with certainty about another key performer in the melody of life which is stirring up excitement today. Viruses are so much smaller than bacteria they are beyond the reach of the ordinary highest-powered microscope. Glimpses of them have recently been caught by the electron microscope. This shows only the reflections of their bodies in patterns of vibrating electrons. They appear as shadowy spooks with no body details.

The hue and cry about viruses is incited by their villainy. They are demons that penetrate body cells and fire them to uncontrolled activity. This causes polio; sparks flu and head colds; kills plants (tobacco mosaic, wheat smut, Dutch elm disease). No one has anything good to say about these ferocious particles.

PROTEIN

Viruses appear to be protein molecules on the loose. But when protein is not on the loose, it is a magic word for abundant living. The wonder of protein is that it can *produce itself* and then proceed to control and operate the cell which contains it! It possesses blueprints for a certain kind of animal and then dictates how and when that animal grows, eats, runs, hollers, procreates. Protein does all this with only five of the ninety-two elements (carbon, hydrogen, oxygen, nitrogen, and sulfur), with traces of other elements mysteriously inserted here and there. Protein holds life in its hands with its vital and delicate chemistry.

The control substances created by protein to keep a body in good running order are known as vitamins, enzymes, hormones. Protein not only installs the living machine but also thereafter orders its cells to do whatever is called for to meet events as they turn up. If you cut your finger, protein sum-

mons cells to fight infection and other cells to divide in such a
way as to heal the wound. This gives protein a sort of intelligence which drives the body as a pilot drives an airplane. High
in proteins means high in energy and good health.

For more than a century chemists have tried to analyze protein so as to reproduce its labyrinthine structure. This mysterious keystone of life is one of the most complicated substances known. After ten years of concentration on one
insulin molecule, which is one of the simplest proteins, it was
finally announced just how it is put together. This may be
the first step toward man's creating some creatures of his own
to serve his purposes. The solemnity of this announcement by
the Commonwealth Scientific and Industrial Organization of
Australia is revealed in the formula. In case you want to make
protein on a do-it-yourself plan at home, the recipe for one
molecule of protein is 254 atoms of carbon, 377 atoms of hydrogen, 65 atoms of nitrogen, 75 atoms of oxygen, and 6 atoms of
sulfur. In case you have any difficulty, consider how nature is
making protein easily and abundantly in your body as needed.

Protein is the genius of the living cell when it is locked
up in protoplasm or fixed in a nucleus. This tiny grain is a dangerous fiend when it is free to roam as a virus. Protein has no
protoplasm but it possesses dynamic power when combined
with the River of Life in a cell. Sometimes this molecule behaves like a hungry little animal that acts and grows, and sometimes like a rigid nonliving crystal.

Protein must have crystallized in the primeval mud or shallow pools of warm, still water at the same time that protoplasm
was gelling. Without protein, protoplasm would have been a
potency without guidance and presumably would have remained just a quivering blob of jelly vanishing when the pool
dried up. But with protein, the quivering blob was inspirited
to form cell walls, to divide, to assume certain shapes, and to
keep the River of Life flowing. But not all protein molecules
became incorporated with protoplasm to create the kingdoms

of animals and plants; some remained free and fierce and fatal as viruses.

These are echoes of the song of life that reach us from a stage being set on a ball of sun stuff a couple of billion years ago. It was a strange, raw earth with a crust that was cooling and becoming hospitable, where protoplasm, bacteria, and proteins were composing melodies at the source of the River of Life.

The First Zoo

THE VERY FIRST DAY that the River of Life started to circulate it must have been agitated by hunger. In twenty minutes something caused it to divide, and before the sun had set on its first day the pool was well populated with protoplasm. Some had pushed out fingers to wrap around food merely by pressing against the elastic film that enclosed the protoplasm. Others drew out long, slender threads of protoplasm which were waved around so that the cell, as buoyant as a tiny bubble, was propelled to conquer other drops of water. In some such manner earth's first population of one-celled animals began.

It was a long time before man knew there was such a vast population of these creatures occupying every cranny of our world, springing up by a sort of spontaneous combustion wherever there is moisture. Today we can watch them perform in a microscope as easily as we watch the actors of a movie on a screen. Nevertheless it takes an effort to think of an animal as complete in one single cell and to realize that these are the original models of the first living things, and, in a sense, the ancestors of all the big animals that troop around us today.

If, never having seen such a thing, you tried to draw a blueprint for a number of animals whose bodies consist of a single cell, the proposition would hardly seem valid or possible, and the designs would not have much variety or appear able to carry on life. On the other hand, the real life one-cellers are so successful that they far outnumber all flies, ants, and mosquitoes, plus all animals of the woods and fields, all birds and fishes, all people in traffic jams.

The hairs of their heads are numbered, and each hair is just the right length and flexibility to fulfill a particular purpose for its animal; each finger, dimple, and gene is just the right size or weight to work in co-ordination with every other part. In form they are animated balls, saucers, snakes, boats, strings of beads, triangles, stars, and so on. The River of Life is basically simple, acting and living by a few basic rules, but its sketchbook contains every pattern in sea, soil, and sky. What bizarre bodies the River of Life can make out of one cell passes comprehension. The book says there are twenty thousand kinds of *Protozoa,* a Greek word that suggests "First Zoo," but as we have only begun to search the immensity of their worlds, that is doubtless only a small fraction of their endless, weird forms.

THE AMOEBA

This menagerie of miniature creatures has some outstanding VIPs who in the days when they were the only kind of life on earth were destined to play leading roles in creation ahead. One such VIP is the famous *Amoeba.* Listen to yourself say that animal's name and you'll hear an echo of "automobile." Both the amoeba and automobile have an echo of mobility, moving around, changing.

It is the commonest of the one-cellers. Doubtless some millions are living in your house, many of them inside your alimentary canal. But don't be alarmed—amoeba is not a bacterium but a gentle, orderly creature no more alarming than the living cells in your body. It can be found in sediment from the bottom of a pond, or scum of stagnant water, or in water where fragments of dead leaves or grass have stayed overnight. It congregates in these places for the same reason that people congregate in fertile valleys where food is more abundant, as the amoeba's favorite food is bacteria. It averages one hundredth of an inch long, and a drop of water is to it a huge goldfish bowl in which to creep happily about.

The exciting fact concerning the amoeba is that this elemental blob without any accessories (it does not even have propelling hairs) can carry on all the basic life activities of higher animals. The amoeba has no bones or brain, no stomach or kidney, no face or feet, no front or back, but it stalks its prey, swallows and digests, expels the waste, flees from danger, and multiplies. As it is transparent, you can look it through and through, and what do you see inside that indicates how it can enact so much energetic living? You see a bit of translucent gelatin with a rhythmic movement, pliable, sensitive and ever ready to respond with a change of body shape, or move in a different direction.

The amoeba's motion is never impulsive or haphazard; it has an air of dignity as one who always makes the right decisions and has imperturbable self-possession. If, with a medicine dropper, you mingle grains of soot in the water surrounding the amoeba, you can see how its River of Life flows. The currents inside the amoeba and the water outside flow interchangeably. When it wants to step forward, the flexifilm of its cell wall is pressed in from the sides and pushed in from the rear, causing a "false foot" to be pushed out. This is the same kind of pressure that makes a tube of toothpaste work. The amoeba's body, encountering grains of soot, enfolds them, and they are sucked in, absorbed, to ride around inside in the streaming protoplasm. Inside the body they flow forward along the top side and down over the front end of the false foot and then move back along the lower side. If the amoeba, under water, is rolling along a hard surface, the grains of soot flowing inside it will stop when they touch this hard surface. Then the rest of its body rolls over the specks, and these are picked up when the rear end of the body leaves the surface. In this way the caterpillar tractor proceeds over rough ground, and the amoeba is so small that almost all ground is rough to it.

The amoeba's River of Life is not all clear fluid. Tiny specks of flotsam and jetsam circulate in it. Some are food, or bubbles of water, or protein crystals—many unsuspected structures and materials appear to our wondering gaze as the microscope plumbs deeper into the life stuff. The amoeba, which looks like a speck of albumin, is a complex organism, a blend of many substances dissolved in a fluid that never stops flowing. The outer stream just under the skin becomes the interior stream and then reverses. The rear becomes the front; the top, the bottom. The amoeba has no part and makes no motion that can be separated from any other part or motion. This melody of the River of Life in the amoeba is that of every living cell.

The world in which the amoeba is a leading citizen is shared with other one-cellers, some of which have discovered some new and revolutionary gadgets, such as a hair. For a hair to quiver or sway calls for less energy than for the whole body to squeeze and push. Even though squeezing and pushing is done smoothly and rhythmically by the amoeba, it is the muscular act of a contortionist. A hair vibrates easily, propelling the body through the water in search of food. Even more important, the hair whips up purling currents that bear bacteria and fluid food to the animal so that it doesn't have to move much, if at all. The River of Life with all its vitality and creativeness is ever ready for short cuts.

While the amoeba went flexing and flowing around, never needing a hair to help it, a vast number of fellow creatures in the First Zoo were making a wonderful success with hairs. Equipped with hairs that could both propel and feed, they didn't have to change shape constantly like the amoeba, and their bodies could be more rigid and stronger. This made it possible to add devices like mouths or stomachs. The invention of hairs revolutionized the lives of one-cellers as much as the invention of the wheel revolutionized men's lives.

THE PARAMECIUM

The most elegant of all one-cellers, the one possessing the most luxurious body accessories, the whopper of the First Zoo, who moves with the stateliness of a big ocean liner among little tugs, fishing boats, and dinghies, has a name that sounds like a Greek emperor, *Paramecium*—"long oval fellow." Its other name is the slipper animal, so called because its body has the outline of a footprint with a long, slender toe and a tapering heel.

When bits of decaying plants from a stagnant pool stand a few hours in a glass of rain water, the paramecium appears as if by magic. It is so big you can see it with the naked eye by holding the glass of water in which it lives up to the light.

The paramecium's graceful movement is produced by its use of hairs, showing how the River of Life first started to add to a body an apparatus synchronized with its flowing protoplasm. This genius of protoplasm for making accessories eventually produced fin and feather, antenna and proboscis, tooth and claw—in fact, most of what we see meowing, mooing, chattering, and crawling around us.

Most hair-users of the First Zoo usually have only a few of them fore or aft, often only one or two. But the paramecium has thousands of short hairs all over its oval. Each hair emerges through a hole in the skin, with room to bend and quiver. It is short and stiff so that it responds quickly to an impulse and is always kept under the control of the paramecium's emotions. Lines of hairs are connected to a network of fibers like wires just below the skin, so that a jerk or an impulse on the system will make a row of hairs vibrate in unison. The animal has many of these hook-ups and moves them in series, so that the hairs spiraling around its body bend in waves, like wheat before a strong wind.

A groove at the forward end of the paramecium spirals back toward the middle of its body, making a deep, funnel-shaped depression. Long, strong, vibrating hairs lining the rim of this groove send swirling currents of food into its spiral funnel. This early model of a mouth designed by the living cell has worked with great efficiency, supplying the paramecium with lots of food for millions of years.

The strong beat of these groove hairs, always in the same direction, drives the bow of the paramecium to the left, just as pulling more strongly on one oar turns a rowboat's bow. The animal would go around in circles until dizzy except that the hairs on his body are in a spiraling row from head to foot. This makes him revolve as he moves forward through the water. Therefore, the turn left when the groove is on top becomes an equal turn right when the groove is on the underside. This keeps the paramecium on a zigzag course without the necessity of reversing propelling hairs.

THE STENTOR

The paramecium's lordly success is matched by the *Stentor*, another elder statesman of the First Zoo. The stentor is named after the Greek herald who had such a big voice he could yell as loud as fifty men. Remarkable as the stentor is, it has no big voice to our way of hearing, but the big voice is suggested by the shape of its body, which is that of a long, heavy trumpet designed to resound with the roar of fifty men.

This trumpet body is sky blue and usually attached to a bit of weed or stick by a speck of glue on its foot. It sways rhythmically back and forth, around and around. A spiral of hairs mounted in a single row like eyelashes on the rim of the trumpet vibrates swiftly in series while the animal sways. This creates currents that follow the spiral path of the rim around and down into the center of the trumpet. The whole hungry vortex travels back and forth as it searches the water within the reach of its long, elastic body. The predicament of small one-cellers caught in this situation is that of people drawn into Niagara's whirlpool. Thus the stentor solves its problem of getting food without running around.

Although the trumpet with its vortex is great for getting food, the stentor may assume many shapes. This one-celler is the original rubber face. When very hungry, it can extend and stretch far, opening its bell wide. When well fed, it relaxes, slows the swaying to a halt, and shrinks to a formless pile of meat dropped on the floor.

The stentor is also quick to wrath. One-cellers are not mere automatons or puppets. If a mean man beyond the stentor's ken causes him to collide with the point of a needle, he recoils angrily, shrinks to the heap, and then suddenly stretches up again, evidently trying to scare you. Repeat the annoyance, and the stentor's reaction is less violent. Repeat it again, and the stentor shrugs it off. At last it does not bother to shrink to the heap at all but accepts the situation and turns a little to one side. Stentor, with only a single portion of protoplasm constituting its entire person, has been brain-washed.

If the stentor's digestion is disturbed, it must meet the problem in a different way. This is a matter of life or death. See what happens if you spray India ink into its vortex. When this, caught up in the swirl, touches its gullet, the stentor suddenly reverses the beat of its hairs, causing the current to whirl up and out and expel the ink—the first example on earth of an animal practicing the useful art of vomiting.

If the ink annoyance is repeated until the reversal of currents appears fruitless, the stentor falls in the heap from which it suddenly extends. If the lethal shower of ink particles continues, the animal falls in the heap and shoots up its body so vigorously that it tears its foot loose and goes swimming off on a spiraling, revolving path, like the paramecium. When it finds

5

a suitable place in water abundant with good food—and no ink particles—it fastens itself again and proceeds with business as usual. The stentor has a lot of sense in that cell of his.

THE COLLAR MAN

Although a certain flagellate with a collar is not aristocratic, like the paramecium and the stentor, it is one of the VIPs of the First Zoo because of a peculiar invention. The body of the collar man is fat, like the toy clowns with bottoms that won't tip over. A long, flexible hair, much longer than the vibrating hairs of the paramecium and the stentor, is attached to its top. This hair is called a *flagellum,* "little whip," or "little flag." It moves slowly like a flapping flag. Many kinds of First Zooers with similar hairs that flap slowly instead of vibrating are called *flagellates,* "those-with-little-flags," the flagmen.

The collar man has a large nucleus in his broad bottom and, as if to balance this, a tall, wide tube on top surrounds half the length of the long hair. The animal resembles a flask with a hair sticking up through the middle of its neck. Both tube and hair are transparent protoplasm, projections of the animal's River of Life. When the hair whips back and forth through the water it drives a nourishing stream down into the collar which funnels in nourishment from passing currents. This trivial animal doubles its food-getting capacity with its collars, a discovery that is going to prove very useful—the first giant animal ever created will have no stomach and will get its food in the same way.

GLASS NEEDLES

Glass needles invented by First Zooers are almost as important as hairs. Although a glass needle drawn out to fanciful fineness has the form of a hair, it is entirely different. Hairs of the one-cellers are animated projections of their protoplasm, but glass is hard and lifeless material. This is a forerunner of much body structure yet to be invented, such as bones, shells, claws.

The needles are made by certain one-cellers who have the skill to separate out the element silicon dissolved in water. They drink this solution and combine the silicon with oxygen in their bodies—exactly the chemical process for making glass. The point of the glass needle is poked through their skin until it sticks way out from the body. At first the new needle is coated with protoplasm, which adds more glass to the tip and widens the diameter. When the needle is too far out from the body to add protoplasm at the tip, protoplasm is pushed up from the base to keep the coating intact.

Glass needles made by ocean creatures, called the *Radiolaria,* are fastened together making glittering skeletons as fancy as snowflakes. The light, fairy-lace extensions of the radio animals are so finely spun and buoyant that they keep the creature from sinking. In this way the one-celled radio animals can spend all their lives near the surface, where sunlight penetrates their bodies, to touch a cell of seaweed that the radio animal has swallowed. Even in the First Zoo, chlorophyll was needed, so the radio animals carried green leaves in their stomachs.

THE DIATOM

Diatoms were the most important plants in the landscape of that strange other earth of a billion years ago when the entire population consisted of one-cellers, and, after hundreds of millions of years, *diatoms are still the most important plants for life on earth.* A diatom matches the ingenuity of the radio animals in the art of glass making. Come June, these single-celled plants may double their population in a day, so swiftly do they build their beautiful glass and then divide. They would soon choke the seas except that silicon needed for glass boxes

is in limited supply. Oxygen, which must be combined with
silicon to make glass, is inexhaustible, but silicon locked up in
rock must be dissolved in water for diatoms to use it. A diatom can only divide as fast as it can make glass boxes.

Yet the small amount of silicon dissolved from granite and
diffused through the oceans supplies enough glass for a diatom
in every drop of the wide sea waters touched by sunlight!
These green leaves enclosed in jewel boxes are pastures for
nine tenths of the food of everything that lives in the seas.
This is an arresting example of vital balance, in which the key
is a trace of silicon. Without a few molecules of glass in every
drop of water, there would be no pastures in the surfaces of
the sea water everywhere, no fish in the sea, no animals on land.

Diatoms also make glass needles for buoyancy the way the
radio animals do. But diatom needles are sharp and long, not
supported in lacy scaffoldings. They are so delicate that they
easily break off and vanish. To find another trick for buoyancy,
diatoms make oil as well as glass. With specks of oil in its River
of Life a diatom can bob buoyantly near the surface, where
sunlight will operate its food-making machinery. This diatom
oil is a large part of its food value, like starch in potatoes, sugar
in beets.

There is startling evidence that during millions of years those
specks of diatom oil, accumulating in tonnage of microscopic
diatom populations, have given us oil reservoirs we are tapping
today. In that case, until atom power takes its place, we have
the oil of diatoms stored through the ages. We have these orig-
inators of petroleum to thank for our cars and airplanes and
oil burners.

The glass box comes in a bewildering variety of shapes—
circles, squares, shields, triangles, ovals, rectangles—always exquisitely ornamented with geometric etchings. These are filigreed in pure glass with such fine skill that a human hair would
have to be sliced lengthwise into four hundred slices to fit between the marks. These etchings are lenses by which a ray of

sunlight is split and filtered into wave lengths of power when delivered to the chlorophyll food machinery.

You might suppose that a glass box buoyant in the sea would move as capriciously as a leaf in the wind. But in the world of the First Zoo, where this marvelous plant was designed, plants move around like animals. It has its own way of going places. A glass box moving through still water without any moving part looks uncanny. A diatom has no hairs, no feet, no fins; the box is rigid, and the glass needles are tightly fixed projections of the box. What is more, a diatom without glass needles moves more easily than one which has them.

The trick lies in minute holes in the glass box. Threads of protoplasm flow out of some holes and into other holes. The slight friction of these threads against the water is enough to move this airy-fairy, one-cell submarine in a direction opposite to the direction the threads flow, so the holes from which they emerge must be forward; the holes into which the threads flow must be aft. This kind of locomotion using the friction of moving living threads of protoplasm is unique in all life.

Another puzzle is the way a diatom can divide and multiply so fast inside a brittle glass box filigreed with geometric designs. Its structure and etchings are on a radial plan with no central axis. How can two halves be duplicates?

Diatoms solve this in the only possible way. The box is made with two loose parts, a lid and a bottom—a feature which gives a diatom its name, "clean-cut-in-two." The lid overlaps the bottom like suit boxes and candy boxes. When a diatom divides, it simply lifts the lid, and the top and the bottom each carries off a half share of the River of Life and chlorophyll, and half of the nucleus. This leaves two boxes without lids in which protoplasm is exposed. Then each portion of protoplasm energetically makes another half box that is shaped, fitted, and etched with precisely the same design as before.

The First Zooers are now well practiced in a variety of the ways of life. They have tested their powers by creating pieces of equipment like hairs for moving and food-getting, fans for swimming, suggestions for fingers and feet, needles, scaffoldings, and glass for skeletons.

The paramecium and the stentor carried pilot modeling farther by showing what mouths can be like and by setting up networks of nerves to co-ordinate moving parts inside and outside the body. They have gone as far as they can go in building up a whole complicated animal out of a single cell. The single-celled diatoms established for all time the efficiency of chlorophyll in making food out of water and light.

The one-cellers, after having been the sole inhabitants of the earth for untold ages, are now ready for a revolutionary experiment.

The First Zooers turn to the amoeba and the collar animals to execute a tremendous project. Both of these have bodies so simple, so flexible, that they can press together and merge easily. Also, as we shall see in the next chapter, they have peculiar equipment that can be used for making a sponge, the world's first many-celled animal.

vi. *The amoeba, an elemental blob that carries on all the basic life activities of higher animals.*

vii. *Radiolaria: microscopic ocean life that spins glass needles into glittering skeletons as fancy as snowflakes.* [OVERLEAF]

viii. *Diatoms: ocean plants that make glass boxes, filigreed with geometric designs, to live in.* [OVERLEAF]

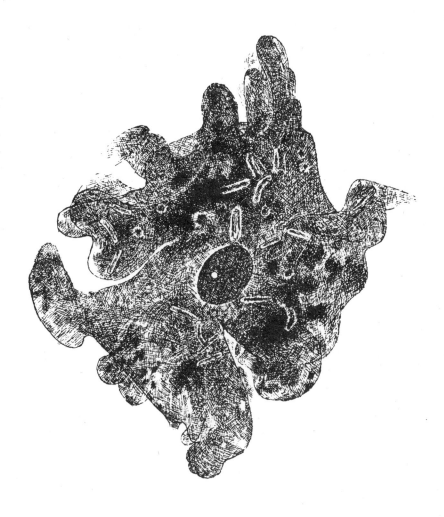

PLATE VI

BERNARDA
BRYSON

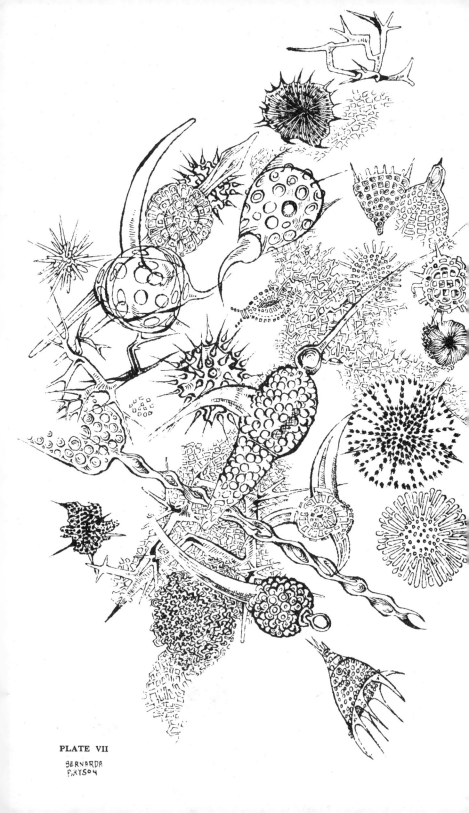

PLATE VII

BERNARDA
BRYSON

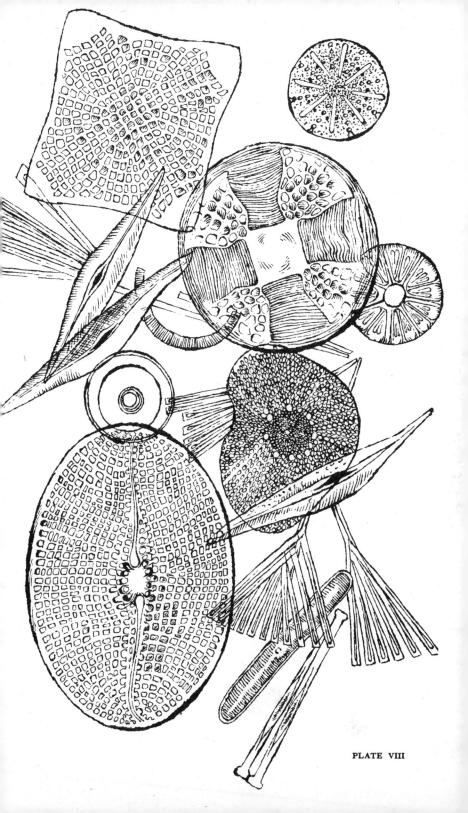

PLATE VIII

The First Giants

SPONGE IS A PROSAIC WORD suggesting a big man washing a car with something that looks like a hunk of moss. Even some people who go out in sponge boats at Tarpon Springs, Florida, to cut off sponges with long-handled pruning shears think they are a peculiar kind of seaweed. A sponge has been considered to be crystallized sea foam, submarine nests of sea worms, or something on the order of a wasp's nest or honeycomb made by a marine creature. But the truth is that a sponge was the first giant animal to be built in the First Zoo, a forerunner of the animal populations that swim and fly and run on earth today. The sponge was made so well that it has survived all the changes and excitement of a billion years by serenely eating, growing, and procreating to live in the menagerie of today's world.

Sometimes our minds roam through awe-inspiring spaces of the sky to imagine what sort of beings live on other planets. If we merely look at a sponge, we can actually see, not the monster of an amateurish imagination, but a real animal so weird it has no head or expression, no tentacles or way of gesticulating, no legs or way of moving a fraction of an inch, no stomach, no heart, no nerves or way of feeling; and its body branches, with no fixed shape. This is the masterpiece which the amoeba and the collar animal of the First Zoo were called upon to make.

In order to appreciate the grandeur and daring of one-celled beings undertaking to make a sponge, it is necessary to put yourself into a micro-viewpoint. In this perspective a sponge surmounts the horizons of the visible world and disappears high up beyond the reach of the senses. In proportion to man's size countless Everests would have to be piled on top of one another to reach as far as the top of this enormous animal's body. Instead of arithmetic based on ten fingers, we are confronted with astronomical numbers which can't be counted but can only be measured by bulk, the volume of one-celled bodies. It matters not how many billions of cells plans call for; the one-celled beings can multiply themselves easily to achieve any mass, pouring themselves into the structure with no more tally of their numbers than the grains of sand on a beach.

The building of the sponge begins when a few amoebas and collar animals assemble in response to a mysterious summons. The amoebas extend their lobes toward the mobilization place, and their protoplasm flows a bit more strongly as they creep together under a magnetic spell. They hug and flow around one another and gently merge.

Any number of amoebas can start this action, which proceeds steadily on a definite course. If only two or three amoebas are gathered together, presently there are countless more. As the mass increases, it flattens out exceedingly thin. The amoebas are stretching outward on one plane like spreading fluid. This dynamic action appears to be independent of the law of gravity; the plane may extend in any direction as it clothes a new kind of animal with a skin. The skin has folds, although to a single amoeba it would seem flat for the same reason the earth's surface looks flat to us. By folding, the sponge is forming colossal tubes.

The thin, strong, elastic skin has inner and outer layers. The amoebas fill the space between these layers with jelly, which gives bulk but which serves primarily as an internal transportation system. The amoebas are confronted with serious problems of logistics because of the immense distances inside the sponge. So those which have not merged into the skin are free to travel far and wide through the jelly layer. These traveling amoebas help with many odd jobs such as making pores in the skin, or throwing themselves in to make extra tubes where needed, or by producing glass needles to shore up the structure if it is located under pressure deep in the sea.

While this goes on, the collar animals are also gathering together, excited by so huge a project, and they also multiply rapidly. Their myriads stand together, shoulder to shoulder, lining cavities of the body. In this way this animal, lacking a heart, uses a million funnels with a million pumps of little waving flags to stir up currents which add up to a full, strong circulation. Moreover, this animal, lacking a stomach, uses a million stomachs with the bodies of its skin amoebas, which catch and digest food from the currents that bathe them. The amoebas share the energy of this food with the collar animals. If they stopped waving their flags for an instant, the animal would die of heart failure. Finally the masterpiece is complete —a giant animal without blood whose circulation consists of the salt sea water.

The body of a sponge is, therefore, a living jelly sandwich fashioned into a system of catacombs and caverns. Its outside surface is perforated with pores called *ostia,* "doors," through which threads of water are sucked by the flapping of flags underneath them. These threads run into larger and larger channels until they swell into streams that fill big chambers and canals, bringing soup of dissolved diatoms and bacteria, and all the time-honored food of the sea to the whole interior of this prodigious creature. People who explore the eerie tunnels and chambers of Carlsbad Caverns or Mammoth Cave see a system of galleries no more wondrous or intricate than those of the sponge animal.

This great production depends on co-ordination all the way through. Myriads of flagmen must line up at the right places to wave along the threads of currents entering the doors through large sluices and must then expel them through craters called *oscula*, "little mouths." This system of doors, canals, and little mouths serves the sponge as efficiently as veins and arteries serve later animals who don't look like sponges but whose bodies operate in a similar way.

Something else important is needed. Such an enormous jelly-like structure would collapse into a hopeless heap unless it had rigidity and strength on a scale never known before in the world of the First Zoo. Tiny things supported by water could have a delicate membrane for a skin and be squashy and tenu-ous. But now a start had to be made in heavy construction. Over distant horizons there were living worlds to be built call-ing for bone and wood and porcelain. The sponge posed this challenge; its master carpenters, the amoebas, tackled it.

A sponge's skeleton does not have to be as strong as the bones in an elephant's leg; but neither can it respond by undulating with the currents like a jellyfish. It is fixed in place and subject to changes of pressure and much buffeting. This problem was solved when some of the amoebas discovered a chemical for-mula for toughening threads of their protoplasm, then fusing them to make a horny fiber, and weaving this into a flexible, springy fabric. This unique material, called spongin, gives the elastic rigidity that makes a sponge spring back into shape after squeezing. Perfected and tested in restless sea water for millions of years, spongin is so enduring that it will wash any number of cars and windows without wearing out.

However, the sponge builders found spongin unsatisfact

for bigger and better sponges that could live under deep water pressure half a mile down. So some amoebas borrowed the glass needle formula from the radio animals and diatoms of the First Zoo.

Theirs is a marvelous act of precision and co-operation. Three amoebas move toward each other from nearby places in the skin jelly. They creep together until the front tips of their bodies meet in a cloverleaf pattern. Then each divides, producing two cloverleaf patterns one exactly above the other. Each upper and lower pair fuses and three glass needles start to grow between them where their surfaces touch. At first each glass needle is embedded between its two amoebas. As a needle grows longer, the upper amoeba follows it out and keeps it growing longer, while the lower one stays at the base and makes it thicker and stronger, and pushes it out. Ultimately, the outer amoeba working on the top uses itself all up in making glass and vanishes, while the lower one at that instant moves slowly toward the tip, building up the strength of the glass as it goes. In this way the glass tripod made by a double cloverleaf of six amoebas is drawn out to a precise length and thickness and set at the best angle to give maximum support.

Earth's first giant animal is showing what one-cellers working together under direction can do. Delicate precision in the tools of life, combined with sufficient strength to serve a need, is also the art of stamens and pistils, the perfection of the retina of an eye, the antennae of an ant, the proboscis of a bee, the crystal lenses that cover a butterfly's wing, the firefly's lantern, and the halteres of a housefly.

The glass tripod of a sponge uses the simplest principle of structural support. Everywhere the living cell builds with triangles and tripods—the form of a tree tapering toward the top; triangular pods and seeds; lilies in multiples of three in every part; the body of a man with feet together and arms outstretched horizontally in an equilateral triangle running between fingertips and toes to fingers. This keystone of a firm form was used from the beginning with exquisite perfection and accurate mathematical calculation, hidden inside the uncouth, rough-hewn sponge animal.

Some sponges have great numbers of these glass tripods. Some have double tripods. It depends on the water pressure and the amount of beating a sponge gets in its location. Always the glass is made by the amoebas in just the right places and set at just the right angles to serve most efficiently at a given point.

When and why some of the more energetic members of the First Zoo were called to sacrifice their individualities to big-animal making is a top secret, but strangely the cells of a sponge have never completely lost their personalities as separate animals, even after the age-long time that has flowed through their ancestors.

Pulverize a living sponge to finest powder and separate the amoebas and the collar animals of its body into one-cellers. (A sponge sold in a drugstore will not do because it is but the dried spongin skeleton of the animal.) Rub this live dust through cloth to make certain the cells are single, then gently mix and stir them and place a dab of this mush in a spot where a sponge can grow.

You do not have to worry that this is cruel treatment which has snuffed out the life of an animal. Before your eyes events are re-enacted as they must have occurred in that primeval world of life when the first sponges were assembled. The disorganized cells behave and look like amoebas possessed with an irresistible urge to club together; the collar animals energetically seek to join the crowd, using their waving flags for propellers to get there faster.

Compared to this a scrambled egg is hopeless anarchy. It cannot sort itself out, rearrange its parts, and live again as a chicken. But that does happen with the sponge. Presently, the animal just ground to dust is rearing itself again, rebuilding its labyrinth of canals, restoring its circulation!

THE DICTYO

Another exciting example of original life creation is seen in a queer live thing called the *Dictyo*. The dictyo is one of the slime molds, neither animal nor plant. Slime molds act as plants in the way they reproduce by means of dry spores blowing around in the wind like mushroom spores or bread mold spores. But if slime mold is a mushroom, it has a startling way of its own, for it also acts like an animal by going on the prowl for food.

The name slime mold does not do justice to the weird action and strange beauty of this form of life. A slime mold is a spoonful of protoplasm that has survived en masse. This was the state of protoplasm as it quivered in lukewarm water before it was partitioned into cells.

Such a spectacle may sound rare, only to be seen in an exotic Madagascar canyon or a jungle of the Cameroons. On the contrary, slime molds are common in damp woods, everywhere in our country. You don't often see them for the same reason you don't see a mouse every day; they hide in dark corners and shun the sunlight. Their bodies look like uncooked white of egg lurking in shadowy places under damp, rotting logs and leaves.

Pushed out of hiding by hunger, the glistening mass creeps over the woodland floor, flows up wet black stumps and across the stippling where the stump was sawed on top, devouring food as it goes. If a squirrel has hollowed out a hole in the rot for a cache of nuts, the slime mold will flow across it, dropping plasmic fingers down to suck up bacteria. When light strikes this weird ghost, it flashes with spectral colors.

We come upon the dictyolets as a mob of undisciplined single cells hurrying around in all directions in a brutal struggle to get food before somebody else gets it. Whether in a one-celler or in a whale, hunger is the dominant passion.

The dictyo's fast and free cells are chasing only bacteria of decay; they do not chase other kinds of food because they have

a particular desire for bacterial beef. When well fed, the dictyos divide and multiply, quickly producing a big population
of single-celled individuals, independent, ignoring their fellows, ferocious, voracious—just a mob scene.

When their numbers have increased to a certain volume and
their bodies are turgid with energy, the dictyolets suddenly
suspend their fight for food. They stop zigzagging, knocking
each other about, gorging themselves. They stand for a moment in a haphazard throng, like people on a football field after
the game, with denser clumps here and there. Then something
happens to set them in motion again; the crowd acts as though
an air raid siren were blowing. They turn with one accord and
stream toward points of attraction where the denser groups
are standing. Mysteriously, the crowds form the pattern of a
magnetic field.

We are watching the mobilization of life on a vast scale. In
proportion to the size of the dictyolets, it is as though people
scattered over the state of Texas, at the sound of a whistle,
were to stop acting like cowpunchers and form lines of march
toward spots where without hesitation and with great engineering skill they proceed to build a new and wonderful city
towering out of sight into the sky.

The dictyolets all face in one direction, bumper to bumper,
forming an order of march that bobs and flexes like a bit of
animated ribbon as it moves over an uneven surface. Travel
over rough ground is made easier by those in front who lay
a carpet of slime over which the crowd squeezes and slides
along.

Some are so eager to get on the bandwagon that they climb
on top of others until they resemble a fat caterpillar bobbing
along rather than a ribbon. The dictyolets who have been fierce
individualists in wet, shadowy places are now with one accord
looking for a sun-warmed spot.

When the warm, dry place is found, some dictyolets fuse
their bodies to form a tough, flat disk anchored firmly to the

surface, while others crowd around waiting to jump in. When the disk is finished, more dictyolets crowd over it, climbing on top of one another by the thousands. Their rivers of life stop flowing; they die, toughen, and transform into a rigid column which mounts higher and higher, far beyond the perception of the dictyolets waiting at the base for their turn to come. When the column has reached a certain height, more waiting dictyolets swarm in to mount to the top. There they divide vigorously, rolling themselves together to make a huge ball. The complete and beautiful dictyo now looks like a corsage pin stuck into a poker chip.

All dictyolets in the ball on top are alive, but asleep. Their rivers are sluggish; their skin is dried and hardened by sunlight. They have become a resting capsule of life, slowly changing back again to a mob of rabid individualists. They are like a ripening seed.

When dry and ripe, the ball at the top of the dictyo's column explodes and its dictyolets ride the winds. If one lands in a shadowy, wet place, it will burst its crust and divide, and soon dictyolets by the thousands will again be rushing around, looking for beef. Thus, the dictyo cycle begins again—scrambling for food, building its tower, bursting its ball—over and over as it rolls down the corridors of time.

Who blew the whistle to collect dictyolets when they were dispersed? How did they know where the assembly place was? What made them turn with one accord toward it? *Acrasin* is the secret. This word comes from Dr. Bonner of the Biology Department at Princeton, dictyo's leading exponent. He borrowed a copy of Edmund Spenser's *Faerie Queene* from the English Department and found a witch in the book named Acrasia who attracted her lovers from afar and transformed them into beasts. Dr. Bonner then named the strong drug used up by the dictyolets acrasin, "witch's magic."

This drug is potent only in the life of dictyolets; it has not yet been separated from them or used for people. Witch's magic quickly evaporates, and it is not stored up in dictyan bodies. This weird chemical is produced only by dictyos and cannot be made in the laboratory. When well fed, dictyolets sweat acrasin, and its odor spreads so that others smell it and are instantly attracted to wade in it. It is most concentrated and has the strongest pull where the most dictyolets are close together. The more scattered ones turn toward these points of concentration, and the mob gathers.

The discovery that acrasin is the magic ingredient seems to reassure us that the dictyo is not supernatural—at least, not any more so than the rest of life. But finding a word for it explains nothing. Nature performs supernatural feats in a natural way regardless of what we call it.

When separate dictyolets rush to their stations to build the dictyo they are behaving much like the living cells of every animal body. Arriving at their stations, they summon up just the right amounts and kinds of materials for making structures that belong in the particular place where they find themselves. This the dictyolets do by dividing vigorously the moment the band wagon arrives at a good site. After the column has reached a certain height, those which have mounted to its top may find themselves without enough volume for the ball. In this event they proceed to divide vigorously to fill the volume of the ball, building it always to the same size through the millions of years.

The dictyolets were not seeking security; they were foreordained to rush together, surrender their bodies, and make a big dictyo. But elsewhere in the First Zoo one-celled animals were initiating social security.

THE VOLVOX

It is fruitless to argue whether a *Volvox* (from Latin *volvere*, "to roll") is a colony of little animals stuck together, working in unison, or whether the First Zooers were trying their hand at assembling a giant animal. Either way the volvox is a great success. It rolls through its world in a fresh-water pond looking like a huge golf ball, revolving for a while serenely in one direction. Then just as you are reminded of the earth turning on its axis, it stops, reverses, and revolves in the opposite direction. This superb living sphere consists of thousands of one-cellers with waving long hairs like the sponge's collar animals—but minus the collars.

Those in the First Zoo who had tall collars to funnel in food prospered and increased on their own and could even detail some of their surplus population to making sponges. But a simple oval body with only two hairs to wave and no collar cannot always get enough to eat, so these cling together in a beautiful hollow ball.

If you pulverize a volvox, setting free its members, they will flag themselves around, seemingly happy and alive all by themselves. But when they bump into each other, they cling together, start a jelly ball, and build another volvox animal. If kept apart, they live out their single lives and die. Doubtless they have formed the habit of living as a volvox ball, have lost all desire to be alone, and need the ball form to reproduce.

The volvox revolves by beating its hairs in unison. If each one whipped independently, it would make a stir, but the ball would not turn, and the individual volvoxes would be in the fix of stationary animals—buried up to their noses and unable to prowl for more food.

The River of Life always comes up witn the right answer. Strands of protoplasm connecting the thousands of pairs of hairs are run through the jelly. Thus the volvox animalcules operate as a connected system, so that tne flags will wave in unison like flags in a steady breeze. Then, as though changing their minds about a good direction, they stop waving and start again in the opposite direction. The result sends the volvox rolling this way and that, allowing it constantly to explore for fresh supplies of food.

The volvox always turns on its axis with the north pole up

and the south pole down. It is attracted by light, rising toward the surface of the pond by day, sinking, sleeping, and barely stirring by night. The inhabitants of the volvox's northern hemisphere have green chlorophyll, which is kept turned toward the sunlight as it rises.

The inhabitants of the southern hemisphere of the volvox are not green. They are engaged in reproducing the volvox ball in a curious way. A dimple is pushed in, forming a round projection on the inside which soon rounds out to become a young volvox suspended in the jelly in the hollow of the mother ball. At this point a serious problem arises. A poked-in dimple puts the outside of the mother's body with its waving hairs on the inside of the baby's body. Waving hairs inside a volvox are no more use than a propeller inside a cabin.

The baby ball has a small hole. When it is getting ready to leave, its walls suddenly collapse and wrinkle; then it strains with a great effort, turning inside out while it squeezes through its hole. With the flag ends of its cells now pointing outward, it sprouts a vigorous crop of fresh flags. It can at last revolve and begin swimming lessons inside the mother ball, until it is ready to escape through a hole that is provided for the purpose and be on its own.

The sponge was an attempt to make a giant animal with an open system. This was an outstanding success from the viewpoint of the amoebas and collar animals, and, true, the sponge has lived on earth probably longer than any other many-celled animal just by being an arm of the sea and running like a water clock.

Nevertheless, the sponge has limitations that prevent it from digging in the soil, running in the grass, alighting on a treetop, or eating at the Yale Club. Revolutionary changes in the structure of animal bodies are needed if animals will ever be able to do these things.

Protoplasm flows best and keeps its creativeness when it is

enclosed in a microscopic droplet, as we have seen. Even the ingenious River of Life cannot fill the skin of a dog with a heaving mass of protoplasm and have it run, bark, and wag its tail. Bodies which can do that must be sealed off from their surroundings to a degree where food, instead of being soaked up constantly, can be eaten occasionally and energy stored. This calls for fitting animals with personal control of impulses and body warmth, much warehouse space for food storage, thermostats, pumps, valves, control boards. All this must be assembled in parts of the body where they feel comfortable and installed in a system of supply and disposal in constant touch with the outside world. Such an animal, ready to eat, go places, or multiply according to the stress of its protoplasm, must be made with a closed system.

THE HYDRA

When we search among the inhabitants of the First Zoo to find the earliest model of a closed system, we come upon the *Hydra*, which has a little stomach and a little mouth. It has not yet packed in a heart or other organs, and the one opening serves for an entrance and an exit.

This astonishing creature, resembling a bit of string attached at one end to a submerged twig and frayed at the other end, has some characteristics of the nine-headed monster that frustrated Hercules by growing two heads if one was cut off. If a hydra is cut in two, it will grow a new head on the part with a foot, and a new foot on the part with a head, and there are two hydras. Or a hydra can be given two or more heads by grafting them on from other hydras. But these tricks are not unusual in the First Zoo. The hydra's chief claim to fame is a stomach and a mouth.

The creature is practically all stomach, in the form of a long slender tube. We have spoken of its head as merely the end where its mouth is. The frayed part is a fringe of tentacles attached to the lips. These are not merely hairs of protoplasm poked out, but living cells that respond to the animal's nervous system, embedded in the skin of its body like a wire mesh. With this mesh of nerves the hydra can operate its whole body as a stomach and at the same time wave tentacles to catch food.

The tentacles dragnet the water by extending far out, a distance four or five times the length of the body, and then sweeping back and forth slowly. When a tentacle touches prey, it sends back a signal to its lip, where special cells have little wires coiled up inside, under tension. Some of these wire springs are released and shoot themselves out as poison arrows, piercing the body of the target. Then the end of the tentacle coils around the victim, squeezes it, brandishes it, and, fluidly bending like the arm of a ghost, puts the meat in the hydra's mouth.

The hydra has a particular taste for a little shrimp. Evidently, the microscopist who first studied the hydra was a student of Greek mythology because he named the hydra's favorite meat cyclops. Its resemblance to the monsters of Sicily consists of one unblinking eye at the big end of an egg-shaped body. The rear end of the cyclops has two pipes from which long, delicate, smoky feathers wave, but these do not move it fast enough to dodge the hydra's poison arrow. The eerie end of a cyclops spells for us the beginning of swallowed food and digestion.

The hydra has some tricks for moving around that are worth seeing. If he wants to shift a short distance to reach a near-by fishing area, he can shuffle along. It's as though you were fishing from a dock and, without bothering to gather in your line and stand up, you just bumped along on your buttocks. The hydra's version is to loosen the attachment of its foot and then make the foot move like an amoeba. It puts out lobes, flows, flexes, and creeps, carrying itself along.

If hunger tension drives it to find an entirely new place, it shortens its tentacles, bends double, placing them like a tripod beyond its foot, lets go its foot, carries this up and over in a great swing, and proceeds in the manner of a tumbler crossing the stage. However, a tumbler revolves fast because he needs the momentum and he can't rest long upside down. The hydra, on the other hand, has no upside down; its movement is deliberate and self-possessed. It may poise with a fine handstand and then continue in slow motion its tentacle-over-foot somersault.

The hydra, with no up or down, may attach itself to a vertical surface and hold itself out horizontal. From this position it tries a third way of moving to better cyclops grounds, which shows the unimaginable imagination of protoplasm. The hydra distills from the water a gas bubble, and with this attached to its foot it lets go; the bubble shoots up toward the surface, carrying its foot up with mouth down. It hangs from the floating bubble, with plenty of water beneath for its downturned tentacles to drag. This closed system invented by the First Zoo is a masterpiece.

We have witnessed what life was like when it began on earth. We did not have to go back a billion years in imagination or discern an obliterated trail of evolution through fragments of rock. The astonishing fact is that time vanishes in protoplasm. It lives in the forever present. The First Zoo flourishes today in the low-tide pools of our Atlantic and Pacific coasts. The little one-cellers are still the most abundant inhabitants of the earth. A pool of water beside your house teems with First Zooers. We have picked out only a few of the thousands of fanciful varieties to reveal the genius of life stuff which equips droplets of jelly with flexing lobes and with banks of hairs beating in unison, causes them to multiply swiftly and silently create their numbers out of air and water, drives them to merge so as to raise up an animal millions of times bigger than themselves. To keep that animal from collapsing, it summons up inside the creature's body a strong, perfectly engineered scaffolding of glass needles.

The River of Life is flowing deeper and stronger.

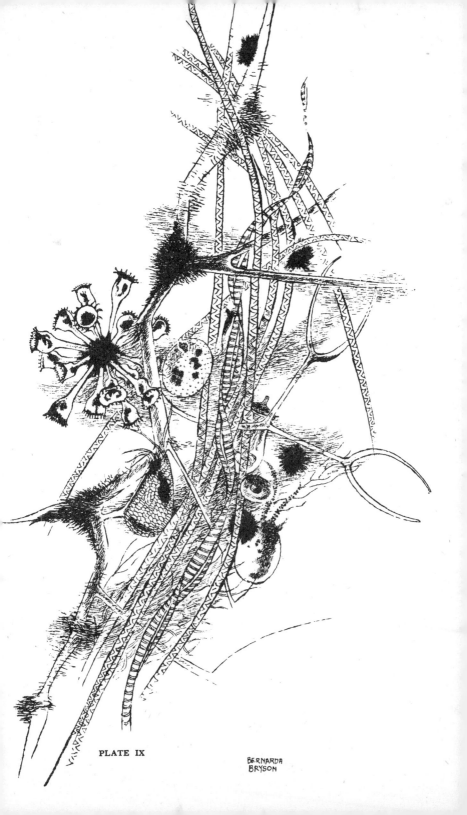

PLATE IX

BERNARDA
BRYSON

Part Three

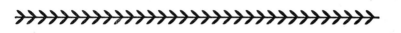

ANIMATED
TOOLS AND EQUIPMENT

Electric Animals

HAVE YOU EVER STOOD STILL in the darkness of night with all senses alert to hear and see and smell the wonderful natural world which lies just beyond headlights and street lights and house lights? Once when I tuned into that country world something big and violent struck me and knocked me down. Against the sky I caught a split-second glimpse of a deer leaping away, probably as terror-stricken as I was.

We consider ourselves individualists but if anything fills us with dread it is being marooned in silence and darkness. We love a crowd. We have become so conditioned to noise and lights that we wrap these around us for comfort and security with the same fervor that we wear clothes, though we come into the world as naked as a shelled almond.

One dark evening just before starting for the country, I looked from a tenth-floor window at swarms of people milling around the corner of Lexington and Forty-second Street. I was struck by their likeness to insects and even felt a little disdain for their intensity and the way they were rushing about. The swarms headed for trains or theaters were made all the

more eerie and ridiculous by being caught in the orange flashes
of neon signs, while buses moved in their midst like giant,
luminous-eyed beetles.

Three hours after I saw the people-insects at Lexington and
Forty-second, I saw some other night insects that didn't resemble people at all. I turned into a dirt road, passed a bank
of hemlocks that looked like a deep forest in the glow from the
headlights, crossed a stone bridge over a brook, and stopped
at a clearing among tall oaks and lindens. When I switched off
the engine and lights, at first it was blinding black, scary quiet,
and lonely. It takes about twenty minutes for the eyes to become dark-conditioned and for the feelings to get used to not
wearing the protective clothing of noises and lights. So you have
to wait a little for the other world to come through.

When it does, the night is filled with magic. Small sounds
filter through the stillness—the tinkle of the brook, the distant
bark of a dog, the musical notes of a restless wren, the whir of
a June bug, the strident scrape of a cricket. Eyes begin to see
the unseen. Stars pierce the sky; then suddenly over the garden, you see the black air traced with living sparks!

These are not yellow and red and swirling like sparks from
a fire; these are separate white sparks moving deliberately,
independent of each other, flashing on and off. Some are close
to the ground, some thirty or forty feet up, but most are around
ten feet above the ground. Their tiny white flashes do not dis-
pel the darkness but they fill it. You can count a hundred in
a minute. They catch your attention, ease your feeling of
loneliness; they are reassuring. They are not violent and noisy
like riveting and honking; they are gay and free and gentle.

When I saw so many fireflies over my garden I thought if
fireflies existed only at this one place on earth, how they would
excite and mystify the world and make sensational headlines
like "AIR FILLED WITH LIVING SPARKS! *Report they were tossed
out of a flying saucer.*"

I counted the seconds between flashes over and over again

and followed individual sparks as far as I could see them, trying to discover a pattern. I also tried to hypnotize myself by staring at the flashes to tune in on their world and understand what they were saying.

A flashing firefly is thinking out loud, and since this is a matter of personal feelings the flashes are very irregular. Many give a single flash at four- or five-second intervals indefinitely repeated and then go dark. They glide slowly and smoothly, buoyantly up, down, and around. Occasionally an ardent lover makes a horizontal run, letting go with extra-bright triple flashes at faster intervals.

The book says that a female firefly living closer to the ground answers the call light of the male with a regular two-second flash. This is probably true of the English female fireflies called glowworms, which have no wings, but the American fireflies have not yet caught on to the advantages of the Morse code. Either this is imagining a nice romance, as though a firefly, unable to tell a female by smell, must depend on a code as you identify a lighthouse at sea, or else the firefly flashes I have observed are all stag affairs. I have never detected the regular two-second answering signals.

A firefly keeps on sparking when it drops down to rest; then, when you walk over to it and disturb the air near it, the lamp glows dimly but visibly and you can easily catch it in the beam of your flashlight. Stay dark while you close in and get your face within three feet of the white glow in the grass or bushes. Then switch on your flashlight and pick up a slender little beetle. It's perfectly harmless and doesn't struggle much, so you can examine the creature at leisure.

Tough wing covers have a gun-metal finish with yellow edging, exquisitely fashioned with parallel edges. A funny little round head with popeyes is completely hidden from above under a shield. When you have seen this fine shield protecting the head from a blow from above you will never forget it. When the firefly flies it first makes a fuss rotating the tough wing

6

covers to one side and then unfurling filmy, translucent airy-fairy wings.

The lantern looks like a patch of ivory near the tail end of the abdomen. If the firefly is nervous and agitated this bit of ivory pulses with waves of light—the tiny teacup contains a tempest of luminous fluid. Hold it loosely in your hand, breathe on it, and it will glow with a greenish-yellow light.

This lantern equipment is one of those efficient, matter-of-fact inventions of life that science can't precisely figure out. Protoplasm in the cells of the last two or three segments of the firefly's body is largely replaced by a butter of carbon, hydrogen, and oxygen. This butter is permeated by a mesh of air tubes and nerves. When the firefly gets excited it draws in oxygen which unites with the fat, producing a slow combustion that is instantly luminous. The glow of this lantern is intense but not hot—not even slightly warm to our touch. The butter does not seem to burn or to be consumed as in ordinary combustion, or else it is replaced instantly by more of the illuminating stuff as easily as skin glands make perspiration.

The butter of the firefly lantern is a peculiar chemical called *luciferin*, Latin for "light-bearing." This will not light by itself at the touch of oxygen. There must be some *luciferase* mixed up in it. These miracle drugs can be separated from the firefly. Catch a lot of them, and if you have no sense of cruelty but a lively sense of curiosity, crush their lanterns and the luciferin will still glow at a breath of oxygen. The experiment can be carried a step farther by pouring hot water on the yellow lantern material, which destroys the delicate luciferase. Then you can get no glow out of the luciferin, which is not destroyed by the hot water, until you add some fresh lantern stuff, which makes the old heap glow again.

The exciting point is that the protoplasm of the firefly has conjured up for its special use a unique light-bearing chemical and mixed in with it a light-causer as a fuse. It then puts all this into a system of oxygen pipes under the control of nerves that will call for light, turning it off and on, making it brighter or dimmer. In addition, the device is placed at the best position to be seen from below as its owner flies overhead. It is contained behind a clear, transparent skin curved to act as a plastic lens, and a reflector layer of white crystals is arranged behind it to increase the light. The only perfection and sensitivity comparable to this lantern of the humble firefly is that of the eye —yours or a firefly's—which detects the flashes.

Why all these pyrotechnics over the garden? The answer came to me as I lay in bed thinking about the people on Forty-second Street and the fireflies. Something tremendous had happened to my garden. This is an area of five hundred square feet which some years ago I fenced with heavy wire on red cedar fence posts to keep deer and rabbits out of the vegetables. For six years loads of fragrant manure were dumped in and the soil was deeply turned. Fat asparagus spears were thrust up, string beans dangled in heavy clusters, tomatoes burgeoned, cucumbers scrambled around. Three years ago there was no time to tend it, and last year the garden was forgotten when I was away around the North Pole. In the third year of going undisturbed the place produced the lustiest, finest weeds on the face of the earth, far beyond my feeble efforts by the time I turned up with a spading fork weeks too late. I shifted to a scythe and after sweeping about on the fringes of the area I surrendered, plumb tuckered.

This neglected place weighed heavily on my conscience. I tried not to think about it and hoped that people would not catch sight of it. The fence was slowly but surely disappearing among the brambles, and the victorious weeds stood shoulder high. It was a disgrace, a blot on respectability.

A thousand sparks of fireflies finally sparked an idea and I rushed out in the morning air to see what I had not seen before. Now, instead of a disgraceful weed lot, there had been bestowed on me a gorgeous, lush jungle filled with a fanciful menagerie. The garden had turned into a frisky free-for-all for the great joust of living. The enriched soil for three years had been pulling like a magnet and the countryside had showered it with seminules.

This was no longer my property. As I parted fresh green goldenrod, giant black-eyed Susans, tall hawkweeds, and grasses, I felt like a trespasser in a vast world inhabited by multitudes of curious nations. From this the fireflies had risen. Now every cubic inch from the living soil to the height of the jungle some five feet above the ground was the scene of the fierce drive to live. The Festival of the Summer Solstice, the longest day of the year, when more kinds of wild flowers are blooming than on any other day, was only four days away. The fireflies were the nighttime breath of this spot teeming with an invisible wealth of life. In the sunlight it was a totally different awakening. The fireflies, thousands of them, had vanished into the jungle. How many and what kinds of other creatures lived there invisibly can never be known.

THE WEED JUNGLE

Have you ever peered into a place where everything is light green, the sap fresh, the sun warm, and encountered its magic life? The spittle palaces of the froghoppers glitter on every hand. Froghoppers know that herbs grow tall and juicy so that they can stab them and blow bubbles—bubbles of sap, for froghoppers, are just as weatherproof and sunlight-collecting as our glass windows. In fact, the curves of the bubbles act as lenses that focus the sunlight and give the froghopper eggs a warm and hospitable womb.

Tiny spiders travel up and down long, invisible threads beneath the upper leaves. They know that the weeds grow tall just for them to have more scope and play for their silk. Regiments of aphids in rich magenta coats stand on their heads and kick their heels in the air as aphids do. They know that the extra juiciness is for them, and they swell up like Chianti bottles. Tiny flies land on the sunny side of leaves like sparkling gold nuggets, a sort of sunlight version of the firefly sparks. Their glitter is iridescent. When you catch one and turn it this way and that the gold becomes bright blue.

I wonder why they are made to look so metallic. It must be because birds are not hungry for gold. I call them gold flies, a good name that you will not find in any book. The official name of these lively nuggets sounds like baby talk: *Dolichopodidae* (Doly-ko-podidy).

Deep in the jungle I hear a low-pitched, powerful hum. The honeybees have been summoned by a super-energetic dance and they are licking up the sap coating of the green young raspberries which the bees know were put there for them. The bees ignore all flowers and pollen round about. For so fragrant sweet and moist are the stubs of fruit that they are in a frenzy.

This tall jungle, which has risen out of earthworm territory in two months, is in no sense a tangle or pathless waste. It is organized and balanced in every detail to bear and promote the utmost life. Trails and roads run through it. One little path runs to a rabbit's nest, but baby rabbits are already raised and off to wider horizons, or maybe chased away. Twilight Drive is a boulevard made by a heavy body going back and forth over the ground and leads fairly straight through the jungle. This plunges into a dark, deep woodchuck hole, the biggest I have seen. The other opening of this great tunnel is about thirty feet outside the fence under a cranberry tree. Undoubtedly the woodchuck is sleeping far underground.

He has two purposeful roads through the weed jungle. Twilight Drive leads to a sunny spot. And for a hot day the woodchuck also built a hidden parkway into the darkest, shadiest area. This was constructed with dirt from his excavation piled in a long, straight course and smoothed off on top.

I would say that the woodchuck at this place is the most satisfied animal in the world, without one problem. He has a home, a family raised and gone, all his work completed, conveniences, plenty of good food; his ancestral enemies the bear, wolf, lynx, panther, fox are no longer around. He owns his place, tax free, for a woodchuck knows that the soil was put there for him to dig in, and he knows that all the vegetation enriched with so much live seasoning is assembled so that woodchucks, who really own the earth, may lead delightful lives.

All this was no concern of the firefly's, who owned the place at night.

THE RAILROAD WORM

The firefly's superb lantern is not quite unique among animals that live out of the water. A notorious relative lives in South America bearing the scientific name meaning "the one with hair standing on end" and the common name of railroad worm. This caterpillar of a beetle has two rows of bright white lights down its body, plus a big red light on its head. The white lights are turned on and off in pairs, or sometimes they may all be turned on together, as with a single switch. The red light is independent and may be shining at the same time as the others or by itself like a night light when the others are turned out. This animal has the same secret for producing light that the firefly has, at least for its white lights (or yellow-green when they are dimmed). But the red light is different. This is not made by a filter over white light, but it burns with a rich red color, and it constitutes one of those engaging little puzzles of science because no one has been able to figure out how the trick is done. Reports are unanimous that when the animal turns out its rows of white lights and leaves on the huge red light in its head it looks like a lighted cigarette.

THE NEW ZEALAND GLOWWORM

We who are always trying to find a purpose behind nature's fascinating ways like to believe that the firefly finds its mate with its flashlight and that the railroad worm lights up to find its food. But what shall we say about another rare example of animal light? This is a caterpillar discovered in a tunnel near Auckland, New Zealand, and which has made the Waitomo Caves, two hundred miles north of Wellington, famous, as people travel far to behold its lights.

This animal has no cozy name, but if you must call it by name this is *Bolitophila luminosa*, "the lighted dung lover." As there is no dung in the caves which it illuminates we can suppose that this caterpillar is the child of winged parents who feasted on dung and then laid the egg in the cave, from which this astonishing progeny was hatched. It hangs itself up by fixing a silk thread to the roof of the cave and then spinning enough length to dangle from this thread at a different height than its neighbors, from six inches to two feet. The top end of its body, where the thread is attached, has a shiny knob, suggesting the reindeer Rudolph's bulbous nose. This glows with an intense blue-green light. Here are the words of a British biologist, F. W. Edwards, after a visit to the bolitophilas in Waitomo Cave.

Our wanderings deep underground brought us to the edge of a pool. The guide made a speech about the glowworms which adorned the roof over the water, pointing out the long, glistening cobweb threads let down singly by each worm that dangled from it. Vibrations of air carried by talking or sound of shuffling paper affected the worms, which thereupon put out their lights. After due admonition to keep quiet and to leave all maps behind so they wouldn't rustle, we tiptoed in single file down to a lower level. . . . Then, putting out all our lights, we gradually became aware that a vision was silently breaking on us. . . . A radiance became manifest which absorbed the whole faculty of observation—the radiance of a massed body of glowworms as cannot be found anywhere else in the world, utterly incalculable as to numbers and merging their individual lights in a nirvana of pure sheen.

Seeing is not always believing when it comes to animal light. A cat's eyes do not glow in the dark with interior light. They have reflectors of silvery crystals at the back of the eyeballs that can collect the dimmest rays of light and make them shine at you. Frogs do not glow, despite many reports. When a luminous frog is seen it has probably swallowed a good meal of fireflies, which it likes as well as any other beetles. Those who go to the seashore turn up with stories about sand fleas aglow on the beach hopping around near a pile of dead seaweed. The fleas are aglow all right, but this is no fault of theirs. Many bacteria, especially those generated in dead seaweed, have learned the mysterious art of making their single speck of protoplasm light up. As they are only one cell big, their whole bodies are aglow. These particular bacteria have a passion for sand fleas. They seek them out and get swallowed. Then for a while the sand flea hops around with bright bacteria permeating its body and shining through its skin, turning it into a gay little ghost in its last hours of life.

The light of the bacterium is not tied into a nervous system as are those of the firefly and the railroad worm, so it does not flash on and off but glows steadily. Bright bacteria do not always live on the beach and turn sand fleas into specters. They may get into the kitchen if there is any meat or fish lying around outside the refrigerator. In that case you may come upon tomorrow's dinner beautifully bright and outlined with luminous art work as you see it in the dark.

Some of these light bacteria have been put to good use by deep-sea fish. In one fish, they get packed into pockets under its eyes, where they shine like the headlights of a car. Because the bacteria shine steadily, the fish has arranged black shades which it pulls up and down to flash its headlights on and off.

It is a wonderful idea for a fish to pack light-shining bacteria in pockets around its head for headlights. Almost always one kind of life is eating another kind. On the other hand, here is a case where two kinds depend on each other and both prosper and are happy. The glands of the fish supply food for the bacteria that it cultures in its pockets, while at the same time the bacteria are well isolated so that they do not proceed to eat up the whole fish. Thus the fish moves around in the dark water illuminated with an arrangement of lights like a truck on a dark road.

Those are fish of the dim twilight zone to a depth of around two thousand feet. Beneath them are abysmal black depths from which today's deep-sea explorations are bringing up fresh and unbelievable marvels every year. One of the greatest of these is the discovery of a population that makes its own bright lights.

This is a triumph of insuppressible protoplasm. Where no sunlight ever penetrates, where the water is only a few degrees above freezing, the place teems with life. These creatures are like all other beings on earth in that they are incessantly on the go to eat and to procreate. But as the sun never rises on them, their own bodies must supply the light for them to live by, and this is done with an astonishing art and efficiency.

The fish are comparatively small—around four to ten inches —with big telescopic eyes that enable them to magnify the dimmest pinpoint of light. The fish have arranged their lights in long rows from head to stern. Each kind of fish wears the same number of these lights. One, for instance, has thirty-two lights in two strings along its stomach, plus twelve lights around its face and six around its tail. Males and females have different arrangements of head and tail lights. We may assume that the fish can count so as to find their fellows in the dark, as well as recognize the light signals of male and female.

The light-making stuff is a greenish-yellow oily substance that acts like the glowing butter of the firefly. It is not automatic but under the control of the fish, which may coyly light one or two portholes, or blaze with a full blast of its batteries. Usually the lights are played like a color organ, a few notes at a time. In addition to helping two fish to find each other in the dark, the lights are used to lure prey. When the stomach lights are turned on full they cast a solid sheet of light downward, so brilliant that you do not see the individual lights. When some of the numerous little creatures that haunt the depths come into the range of this light they are attracted like moths to a flame. As they come nearer and nearer, the fish fixes them with its telescopic eyes. At a certain point it gives a twist, and that's that.

THE SPARKLE IN SEA WATER

Far above the lights of these fantastic fish we often see the sea water glitter when it is disturbed. This is the "phosphoros" that moved a Roman poet in 100 A.D. to extol "the sparkling skin of women bathers," and Lord Byron to speak of a pirate who "to his boat with haughty gesture sprung. Flashed the dipt oars and sparkling with the stroke, around the waves phosphoric brightness broke."

Sea water must be warm and it must be disturbed to glow. Around the prow of a boat where the little bubbling ripples run, or on a sandy beach on a moonless summer night where the surf boils with tiny waves just before the final glide, you see the wonderful sight of the burning of the sea. This was considered a supernatural spirit of salt water for centuries, since no one suspected that it was caused by myriads of tiny animals that light up when they are hit by oxygen, the way glowing embers brighten when you blow on them.

The phosphorus animal is a most peculiar member of the First Zoo. Although its entire body consists of only one cell, this is puffed out into a round ball so that its protoplasm is spread as a thin coating around the inside of the balloon's skin. Most of the body is filled with a fluid that is not protoplasm but a lightweight juice that has no function except to distend the ball and make it float. If you prick the animal this fluid spurts out and the whole body collapses. Since this is an animal and not merely a rubber ball it has to have some operating parts and a way of eating. There is a deep crease in the ball, with a nucleus at its inner edge that is the living mechanism of this animal cell. Out of the crease comes a hair which waves around like that of the flag animals—but very slowly, making only two or three passes per minute. This ball, which is big enough to see with the naked eye though nevertheless smaller than a grain of sand, would be a giant among the First Zooers, and as it waves its flag in a stately manner it collects really small animalcules. Somehow these are rolled into sticky balls and pushed down into the crease.

Apparently the thing is complete without lights. It can bob around, buoyant and free, to go places with the winds and tides; it can collect all the food it needs and get this into its crease in an edible condition; it does not have to find a mate to continue existence on earth because it can multiply its population with fabulous success, like the amoeba and the bacterium, by simply dividing into two parts, each of which becomes a whole animal. Why then does it have lights?

These are arranged like beads on strings which radiate from the nucleus through the buoyant fluid to points all over the ball. When the animal is tossed among bubbles it gets a smack of oxygen that makes these strings of pearls glow. They do not shine evenly and all through the body at the same time but in groups, like a starry sky.

If there is any other purpose than to lend wings to poets' words, than to add to the magic of the sea, it is a secret of life that has not yet been told. Science calls the phosphorus glow a vital act connected with muscle action—but where are the muscles? The light glows brightly at the first touch of an electrical stimulus, but then it tires quickly and goes out. This eternal carnival of the phosphorus animal with its little strings of lights is exciting and beautiful whether or not we know what it is all about.

It has the fascination of magic only because the electric impulses are on an infinitely tiny scale and directed in complicated ways which man can't copy or apprehend. Only the

River of Life can do it. We do not know how or why nerves and muscles release electricity. But with today's new precision instruments we are discovering that they do. Also we have discovered that the brain discharges electricity when it thinks.

A feeling throws a switch that releases circuits which operate muscles. Every contraction of a muscle generates electricity so that wings beat, legs run, fins wave, fists clench, hairs stand on end, cocks crow, snakes rattle, or fireflies flash. The parts of a body—eyes, vocal cords, and living light bulbs such as the firefly's—are not hitched up to a central dynamo. There is a speck of electricity in every cell of the body. When action is called for, millions of cells combine their electricity to send an impulse through the nerves to the right muscle. Such an impulse may originate anywhere in the body—from a thought in the mind to a touch on the skin. Only in recent years has this wonderful bioelectric field which permeates every living thing been detected.

A nonliving machine with electronic control behaves astonishingly like an animal. Norbert Wiener at Massachusetts Institute of Technology has made a machine that can run around the room, dodge the furniture, find the door, pass through, turn and go down the hall. This is a creature of the new and exciting science of electric communication and control called cybernetics, from the Greek word for steersman.

Thousands of radio tubes can solve complicated mathematical problems and even store information for later use, which endows it with memory. However, Dr. Edmund W. Sinnott of Yale in his fascinating book *Cell and Psyche* admits that while the electronic calculator is an accomplished robot he doubts that it can have an original idea or write a beautiful sonnet, as protoplasm can.

Perhaps the impulse of the firefly to shine its light comes close to bridging the age-long gap between mind and matter. The firefly's sense that releases electricity causes substance to light

x. *The glow of the firefly's lantern is intense but not hot—not even slightly warm to our touch.*

PLATE X

up. This suggests that the physical activity and psychic behavior leading to mind are fundamentally the same thing.

The origin of consciousness appears to be in protoplasm itself. The amoeba dodges around and engulfs its food, guided and driven by its protoplasm to survive in its particular environment. The firefly in the dark is also guided and driven to survive, while it evolves the reality of a light.

We have spoken of the lush jungle of creatures which is the world into which the firefly fits and thrives, where mates must have light to find each other, and where the light must be turned off for the protection of darkness because there are birds and countless creepers and flyers hungry for fireflies.

The firefly itself is not mysterious and uncanny. The astonishment is found in how rational this creature is. The inspiration lies in the River of Life which causes the firefly to act just the way it does.

PLANT ELECTRICITY

Nerve fibers are not required for sending electricity to different parts of a body. They are only needed to give the giants of the animal kingdom quicker communication to muscles. Without them animals could not run, fly, grab, embrace, chew, dig, moo, or whatever animals do. They would have no eyes, ears, antennae, fingers. Such animals would look different, act differently, and get their food differently—in fact, they would not be animals at all, but plants!

Plants don't need nerve fibers to be in harmony in their kind of time and space. They can get along splendidly on the electricity of their protoplasm without tying these into nerve systems for rapid communication between leaves and roots. If you, without nerves, were to wiggle your toes, the idea would originate in the subconscious quality of protoplasm, and then the electricity could be gathered together from many cells and would flow across cell walls instead of through nerve fibers down to your toes. This slow communication would take a few minutes, and meanwhile your toes, instead of wiggling, would droop and after an hour or so they would lift up.

This happens in a few plants that move their parts visibly without muscles and nerves. The Venus flytrap's leaves are in two halves hinged down the center. An insect attracted by the red surface stumbles over a couple of live cells that stick up like spines in which protoplasm is flowing actively, and this sends an electric impulse into the hinge, which closes the leaf like a book. The action is not instantaneous but it is fast for a plant; it takes a few seconds to go into action, although the distance traveled is but a fraction of an inch.

The Venus flytrap plant works by water power, without muscles. The cells of the hinge are distended with water under pressure, and when the signal comes the water is expelled into spaces between the cells, and the book which has been pressed open now deliberately closes as its hinge cells collapse. After the leaf closes, long spines on the edges revolve and interlace like fingers, forming a cage for the prey. These take a half hour to revolve.

The ingenuity of the River of Life knows no bounds. It seems to be testing its powers with the Venus flytrap to see if it can make a plant act like an animal. This Venus flytrap is a great curiosity in a plant but it has none of the dash and vigor of an insect or any animal catching live food. The fang of a rattlesnake shoots faster than the eye can see; so does the tongue of a chameleon; and the forelegs of a praying mantis are a lightning action. Yet note that protoplasm has called on electricity to supply the energy in the Venus flytrap. This has been detected and measured. It's a whisper of a fraction of a volt, like the charges which boost along ideas or contract muscles.

Mimosa, the sensitive plant, is the plaything of the tropics. A visitor is invited to walk along a path where lovely mimosas spread their leaves tinted delicate blue-green. Stretch out your hand to pick one to admire, or just jostle one as you brush by, and leaves on that side of the tree will fold up and almost vanish. Not all at once, but with waves of impulses, as when the wind sweeps across a wheat field. It is a still day and the waves are those of electric impulses, conveyed in regular order from leaf to leaf, stem to stem. Electricity has been turned on in the tree, and as it has neither wires nor nerves it sweeps in waves through the foliage, slowly through the protoplasm of its regular cells.

This is fast enough to be spectacular. The action is marvelously precise. A mimosa leaf consists of four fernlike leaflets spread wide from the tip of its stem. When the news comes that it's time to fold, each smallest leaflet creases itself lengthwise. Then they move toward each other as if closing extended fingers and finally the stem bends down to an abject droop.

Raindrops make it perform, or grazing animals. So the people who try to figure out a purpose point to the protection the tree gets from a violent tropical downpour, and from a grazing animal which turns aside when the nice green leaf disappears before its nose.

Men were greatly puzzled about the mimosa and said that the tree was afraid of them, until it was discovered that it operated by an electrical discharge. That seemed to explain matters and make it less mysterious. Personally I think it makes it no less mysterious, although extremely interesting.

There are many examples of protoplasm's going to extraordinary lengths. It always keeps on trying, building this or that which works for a while, until it loses balance with its time and place and then the whole organism is doomed. This can happen by getting too big, like the giants of the Age of Reptiles, or like the three-hundred-foot sequoias, of which only relics survive in California after having dominated large areas of the earth.

THE ELECTRIC EEL

The electric eel shows the exciting lengths that protoplasm can go to in building up body electricity, not merely in tiny volt fractions exciting ideas in brains and operating muscles, but as a means for getting lots of food fast and at the same time scaring away enemies. A bang with an average force of 350 volts (maximum discharge recorded at the New York Zoo, 650 volts) is packed into this monster that dominates fresh-water pools and coves far up the Amazon.

No reports of this creature reached the outside world until around 1800, when Alexander von Humboldt spent years exploring South America. Von Humboldt, a Berliner, met a Parisian named Aimé Bonpland, who also burned with curiosity, and these two became fruitful and thrilling explorers, working with the electricity of their ideas and imagination, which their compatibility welded into a mighty power for delving into the secrets of life. Von Humboldt saw the relations of things; he fitted life together and became a great ecologist while also studying life's background of astronomy and electricity.

In this day of specializing and in the face of such a mass of information beyond one man's grasp in a lifetime, there are few explorers with such an opportunity or such scope. I believe Donald B. MacMillan is one such who shares the tradition of Von Humboldt in our day. He has gone repeatedly through forty-five years to the north polar regions "to learn something," as he says. His observations add up to the greatest personal and first-hand collection of data on life from his chosen field. Polar bear, seal, walrus, narwhal, musk ox, plants that grow on the shore of the Arctic Ocean, the polar Eskimos, and the behavior of icebergs and sea ice.

Von Humboldt first heard about electric eels from Amazon Indians, who were terrified by them. They pointed them out from a safe distance on the bank and then ran away without giving any help in catching the eels, even refusing to lend a boat. So Alexander and Aimé sent horses into the pools, thinking that they might step on some eels and the eels could be captured in that way. Presently all was anarchy. The horses went mad, reared, kicked, and whinnied shrilly. In the seething tumult of mud and foam a few eels were stepped on and captured, and one horse was knocked down and drowned, a truly shocking exhibition.

The six-foot eel is four fifths storage battery, with all its vital parts—heart, gills, reproductive and elimination organs—crowded up forward just back of its flattened head. Through its length, trailing out behind, are two storage batteries resembling sinuous stacks of seven thousand pennies laid on their sides. Although contained within the body of the eel, this is as distinctive a piece of equipment as the trunk of an elephant. The River of Life has created these living storage batteries by converting muscles into plates with acid storage-battery jelly between. Because its big muscles are converted into storage batteries the fabulous electric eel is not a fast mover but can only ripple along slowly, using tiny muscles for swimming.

The head is the positive pole and the tail the negative. The discharge is a rapid-fire repeat, like a burst of machine-gun fire. As water is a good conductor, the electric field that sprays out of its head and curves around into its tail surrounds the eel with an utterly safe territory. In fact, little suckers have found this out and seek to share in the security; an electric eel is often loaded with these uninvited hangers-on. But the eel seldom gives full throttle, because it takes less energy just to stun little fish and eat them alive. However, in an emergency—such as the incident with the horses—when it lets go a volley with everything it has, the eel delivers a terrible wallop by curling around to bring its head closer to its tail for thunderbolt power.

Protoplasm has tried out electricity as a weapon in other kinds of creatures, but none achieves the voltage of the electric eel. The electric ray, called a torpedo, can produce two hundred volts as against the electric eel's three hundred. Its poles are on each side of the body and you have to press your hands against its side to feel the shock. Other rays have one volt of electricity. An Atlantic fish called stargazer has converted the muscles that move its eyes into little storage batteries. This does not make the true eyes sparkle, as its name implies, but gives it electric eyes to surprise tiny fish. When it looks at them the tiny fish are shocked and swallowed.

After a hectic hot day in the city you feel relief in leaning on the garden gate where all is quiet and harmonious, watching the fireflies in the dark, sharing this comparatively simple environment. But this is temporary; we are not made for this simplified environment; we have to go into the house to go to sleep or get something to eat. The firefly can stay where it is. Wonderful as that flashing is, the firefly has few other cards to play. It cannot direct its electric currents toward a variety of ideas; it can only flash and flash. But that serves. It has its harmony in time and space. The more harmony, the less change.

To maintain harmony a lantern generated electrically was installed in the firefly's nervous system, and a brain that could generate electrically conscious ideas and raise these to superb heights of imagination was installed in man's nervous system. The important difference is the capacity for enjoyment which imagination brings. I suspect this is unique in the animal kingdom, although you can't be sure when you see a dog wag its tail, hear a pussy cat purr, see a gliding gull tick the top of a wave with a little splash, or consider a blue-behinded ape sliding down a sandbank. It is in enjoyment that we find our harmony in time and space, and we derive vitality from the sensation which rises out of a combination of imagination and enjoyment that we call spirit.

Deliberate direction in protoplasm is not accidental. It is too universal—functioning in the living soil, in the seas, in lakes and rivers, on mountains and deserts, in the air all around the earth. Everywhere the common denominator is protoplasm, and what it supplies life in the way of organs, skin, skeletons, antennae, trunks, tails, eyes, tusks, claws, shows it has resources far beyond human imagination.

The discharge of an idea from your brain releases enough electricity to be measured by an ultra-sensitive meter. Even so it is very slight as we think of electricity. One tenth of a volt is produced by a very big and sudden idea. Electricity is used with such infinite precision by protoplasm that we can't talk the same language, electrically, as the living cell. Most animal electric activity is gentle and subconscious. All the automatic instinctive communications about eating, breathing, walking, are a permanent memory and repeated ad infinitum.

We have a wonderful opportunity for living because we can recollect happy ideas and get them out of storage, build them up ever more interestingly, and hitch them up together to make a poem. "That reminds me" is simply one stored-up idea being touched by a circuit from another stored-up idea. The capacity of the brain for building ever bigger and better idea circuits has no limit. A few people like Leonardo da Vinci, Goethe, or Shakespeare show what the human brain can gather together in the way of brain circuits. This is godlike compared to the firefly, whose little circuit is too tiny even to detect. But the firefly has enough to signal its light.

Chapter 13

The Antenna

WE ARE PROUD of our imagination and creativeness, but when it comes to thinking up anything original or different in the way of animals and plants in painting and sculpture, the human artist is without an original concept. All he does is make different combinations and proportions of existing parts which have already been seen. This applies to the most horrendous Oriental dragons and genii, the most satirical cartoons, the most fanciful Disney characters.

On the other hand, protoplasm holds the one and only basic patent for inventing new kinds of living things. It can organize its inner emotional crosscurrents to make practical living creations that are quite happy and healthy. The spectacle of life reveals this infinite creativeness to our eyes.

This begins in the one-cellers, where the River of Life organizes itself inside the cell wall as a complete creature fashioned with an oval body like that of a little seed. The first projections were hairs, and this kind of projection outside the body proper has proved so successful that the hair idea is one of the universal implements of animal life.

Hairs greatly enlarge the scope of life. They keep tender, air-breathing skin of insects, birds, and diving animals from being wetted so that they can seek food under water without drowning. They protect skin from burning in hot sun and control the rate of evaporation. Single hairs, like the few beautiful ones of the cat's whiskers, agitate nerves to which they are attached so that a cat feels its way around in the dark with them. A porcupine turns hairs into daggers for protection. There is something about animalistic hair that makes men wear mustaches to look dominating and important. (I always wear a mustache with great satisfaction on polar expeditions.)

Protoplasm doesn't stop to live off the proceeds of a registered patent. The success of the hair projection has led to other projections of many shapes and sizes. The array of projections constitutes the chief features of living things, gives them their personalities and dramatic opportunities for going places and reproducing, while composing the fairy story of reality. Otherwise, we might imagine that the inhabitants of the earth would be blobs, with the aspect of simple jellyfish or slugs, or slime molds. But we have seen what protoplasm can do without projections by installing equipment such as flashing lights in the bodies of fireflies and fishes and high-voltage batteries in the bodies of electric eels.

Because the compact, oval body is efficient for containing vital organs, it is basic for all animal forms, although it may sometimes be drawn out long and thin for the walking stick or strung like three beads on a wire as in the ant, o-o-o. Nevertheless it is the projections that give the most vivid variety and make the body exciting. These are legs, fins, wings, tails, and the parts of a face that turn into noses and tusks.

I do not know whether protoplasm enjoys these accomplishments. I am sure that they do not look funny to the characters that wear them. But was there ever a cartoon drawn by man more satirical than the trunk of an elephant, more horrendous than the tusks of a wart hog, more incredible than the projections of a lobster, more ridiculous than the legs of a daddy longlegs which raise aloft a body the size of a grain of wheat, or more fanciful than the locust antennae that come out from its forehead, curve backward, and sweep out behind seven times the length of its body, like a comet's tail?

The antenna projection proved to be a revolutionary success. Once protoplasm invented the antenna it let itself go and proceeded to conjure up the biggest population of land animals on earth, operating them with the dynamic antenna.

Insects are towering giants in relation to one-cellers and they are complicated, marvelous living mechanisms put together with millions of cells. But in our order of magnitude they are little. They range from the microscopic springtail to the giant New Zealand hoo-hoo flea.

The body of a hoo-hoo sent to me by a friend in New Zealand is like beautiful polished mahogany lying on the desk in front of me, and the insect extends five inches from tip to toe.

The small size of these antennae-users compared to our size seems to endow them with a certain strategic advantage, a kind of metaphysical power for attack, in the war between men and insects. We have brought into play flame throwers and heavy tractor equipment, but with all this we hold only temporary beachheads against these remarkable hordes traveling with us through space. You will find them fascinating if you stop to look. Like the bees, they are following their antennae and minding their own business. But I shall join you in slapping a mosquito whose business it is to suck our blood. And I have been expelled by superior force from a gorgeous hillside in southern Greenland and prevented from taking pictures of flowers that grew on the granite, retreating with unprintable sounds when "interesting insects" got in my nostrils, eyes, ears, and mouth, where they crunched.

The odd thing about the antenna, which makes it different from all other projections of animal bodies, is that it is not structural material of bone or muscle, such as limbs, wings, or projections that seize, nor is it a vital organ for eating, breathing, or reproducing. It is a projection of the brain.

It consists of a cable with hundreds of nerve fibers that come out of the front of the head, and these lead to sensitive plates and pits and points which extend far out beyond the body. These terminals contain a fluid similar to brain fluid. Each group of these nerve-end receptors is rigid, but to make the whole contraption flexible in the wind and to change its direction to pick up the mysterious messages that come from all directions through the air, the antenna is segmented. There is no muscle in the antenna, but it is set in a ball and bearing socket which is operated by a powerful muscle at the base.

Protoplasm uses a simple mechanical principle for holding together the segments of an antenna that can easily be demonstrated. I have tried it out by piling tin cans on top of one another and running a cord (tendon) down the center of the column. When this is drawn taut it keeps the tall, slender tower from collapsing, and it can be held erect by a firm grip at one end while it waves and bends with the jerking and flexing motion of an antenna.

Ingenious protoplasm gave the insect this special device for perceiving a much bigger outside world than it otherwise would with a brain confined in a tiny speck of a head. A bigger head or heavy structural material held far out in front would have thrown the insect off balance, and that would have necessitated a bigger body, heavier wings—a complete redesigning. In that case grubs could not have turned into flies, caterpillars into butterflies, underwater tigers and nymphs into beetles, mosquitoes, and dragon flies, and hidden grubs would never have come forth as ants, grasshoppers, and bees. But, equipped with their antennae, insects are triumphant as the most widespread, active, running, jumping, zooming population on land and in the air.

In the long run the River of Life never wastes any of its

materials and always exacts the utmost efficiency in every operation. In size, weight, and usefulness each part that goes into the making of a tree—root hair, pore in wood, food canal, bud, leaf, stamen, pistil, fruit, seed—is designed to fit and work perfectly with the other. The same is true of every insect, fish, bird, and animal. Each has the particular kind of heart, breathing apparatus, sense instruments, and every piece of equipment best suited to its particular business of living and the protection of its kind of self. Every item, from the invisible complexities of the nucleus of every cell to the whole astounding assembly, is a model of utility, fitness, and economy.

It may sound odd in the face of the multitudes of expendables and excessive productions of mosquitoes, people, seeds, sperms, pollen grains, for example, to say that there is no waste. But these signify the surge and creative power of protoplasm, which frequently boils over, and all excess or anything that has lost its usefulness is swept back into the mixing pot, where it adds its full elemental power to the reservoir in the soil. The bodies of mosquitoes, the surplus pollen of a pine, the robin's egg that fell out of the nest, will contribute their utmost to raising a fresh field of daisies.

I have seen my companion isolated by a broken outboard motor in a small, open boat among icebergs in a polar sea use a piece of wire and a screw driver in ways for which they were not originally designed, to fix the engine when it was necessary to survive.

The same is true of animal equipment. Once an animal has a good projection it can be put to a variety of uses. Horses in time of stress deliver a kick with legs that they walk on. Crabs and lobsters pinch their prey with their huge pliers and also brandish their claws in the air menacingly to scare off an enemy. A bee uses its wings for flying and also as electric fans to ventilate the hive. Beetles find that their wings can make clicks and katydids find how to make strident noises with their wings, using them in lieu of vocal cords to communicate with other beetles and katydids. A woodcock uses its long, slender bill not only as jaws for eating but also as a straw to thrust deep into mud to suck worms, like a kid with a straw in a soda. A wasp can turn its egg-laying tube which projects from the rear of its abdomen into a dagger and hypodermic needle.

The front tooth of a narwhal grows straight out in front of its face in the form of a slender eight-foot spear. I have one in the corner of my study and continually enjoy the sight of these exquisite spiraling ridges of ivory, thereby making aesthetic use of another animal's projection. There has been much speculation about the original owner's use for this tool, which certainly is not to tear and grind food according to the standard function of a tooth. Does the narwhal charge and impale its enemies on this mighty spear? Does it caress its mate by fencing with her—a sort of friendly joust of King Arthur's knights? Does it merely brandish the ivory to protect its feeding territory with a ghostly white sword that it brandishes back and forth?

The evidence is that the narwhal, whose favorite food is halibut, stabs this flat fish as it lies on the bottom. Then, if you please, it thrusts forward through the water, leisurely swimming while the halibut, impaled on the spear point, cannot escape because of the pressure of water against its flat body and whirls around on the spiral ridges as it travels along the spear until it pops into the narwhal's mouth. That is just another way to use a tooth, and it works beautifully in behalf of the narwhal. The halibut hides by standing still on the bottom; the narwhal's food is halibut; how else could the narwhal, which is unable to get its face within eight feet of the fish because of that rigid, nonretractable projection, get the halibut into its mouth?

Claws are great projections that can be used in many ways.

A bear claws its prey, climbs a tree, digs—all with the same useful little tools at the tips of fingers and toes, which are projections at the ends of projections. There are many uses to which the antenna can be put. This is not a physical tool or weapon, like limbs, wings, tusks, and claws, but it serves exactly as the TV antenna on the roof of the house in the way it can bring to its owner a variety of sensations from which to piece together a picture of what is going on in the outside world, an education in living. This is quite a lot for one little speck of a head to receive.

Touch is the commonest use of antennae. No seeing with eyes is needed in the darkness of ant tunnels. Touch talk is so fulfilling that by the sense of touching antennae ants can carry on all their affairs. They converse with antennae as to where to get food, and they keep up an almost continuous running gossip and news-spreading. An ant is so used to using its antennae instead of its eyes that it continues to carry on its activities with touch even in the daylight.

I have just been down on my stomach in the grass watching an ant do the impossible. It had a dead moth much bigger and heavier than itself to carry through a dense tangle of grass. Two inches above the ground presents as great a problem to an ant as your carrying a piano through the branches of trees in a forest. The law of gravity becomes a serious problem. To make matters worse, the wings of the moth carcass extended far out rigidly so that the blockade and interference in the tangle of the grass was terrific.

I shall never forget the strength, perseverance, and intelligence of the ant in coping with the problem. The wings of the prey caught at every step—the body had to be shifted, pushed, pulled, jammed, to keep it from falling, while the ant dashed to front, to rear, to side.

All by itself, it caused that ponderous moth body which was

about to yield up its dynamic elements to produce more ants, to travel haltingly, jerkingly, but continuously through the grass tangle. All the ant's sense, all its measuring, all its sizing up of the situation, came from a rapid-fire touching of grass, carcass, wings, space by two exceedingly busy antennae. If the ant had been surrounded by observers shouting instructions for each step of this manipulation, it couldn't have done better—not nearly so well, of course.

Mosquitoes use antennae to hear with, for an antenna can hear by recording sensations so delicate that they are far beyond our senses. A tiny thorn on the antenna is bent or vibrated by sound waves which give a pressure signal to the nerve. This thorn is microscopic beyond imagination, but the electric current it discharges as a sound wave can be measured by amplifying with a transistor.

The mosquito's antenna not only picks up incredibly tiny sounds but also selects what it wants to hear. There are many big noises in the world—but these it pays no attention to. Who knows but that it enjoys the tinkle of blood flowing through a capillary even more than we enjoy the sound of a splash of a mountain brook? The most enjoyable sound to a mosquito is one which we hear as a thin, high pitch, perhaps an octave above a peanut whistle. This is the buzz of the female mosquito high in the air calling to the male mosquito hidden in the grass. If you want to be mean to mosquitoes set a tuning fork to humming in middle C at exactly five hundred and twelve vibrations per second. This will create visions of valentines in the antennae of male mosquitoes in the grass.

A mosquito also uses its antenna to test the water before laying eggs. This is a chemical test, like taste or smell, to see if the water is too salty; its eggs must have quiet fresh water, not brackish water.

The capacity of an antenna to smell seems more wonderful, if that were possible, than all its other abilities. A smell is a chemical in the air or dissolved in water which can be detected by our noses, or by the cheeks of a fish, in very minute quantities.

Smell is one of the big sensations for all animals. Your dog can smell you out in a large crowd, and probably a dog can smell its master's moods, whether he smells happy or mad. Police dogs given a whiff of something a criminal has touched can smell out the footsteps of the criminal after his getaway. Bees smell out a certain species of flower, selected for collecting nectar on that day, in a vast field of many different flowers.

A pig can smell truffles (subterranean fungus which is a table delicacy in France) buried deep in the ground. Soil is a strong deodorizer, but the pig somehow gets a whiff and then excavates an area around the base of the tree. Dog and pig smelling is wonderful—far beyond the range of our mediocre noses. But it is not pin-pointed, while the miracle of an antenna is the way it receives odor as though delivered through a fine wire that leads straight to the minute spot where it comes from.

This is the genius of a little black beetle the size of a cherry stone which also likes truffles. In the evening (apparently bright sunlight scatters the mysterious signals) the beetle goes forth and walks around until suddenly it stops stock still. It then drives a shaft rapidly, burrowing straight down, invariably hitting the truffle on which it feasts. There is no hesitation, no trial excavation.

In human experience the only power that seems comparable to this, which has never been explained, is that of the water dowser, a man who looks for water by walking around holding a forked witch-hazel stick horizontal. When he stands exactly over water it turns in his hands—he can hardly hold it tight enough to keep it from turning—until the stick points straight down to the underground water.

This is no fairy tale. I have a friend who is a hardheaded businessman. After he built himself a new house water experts told him that there was no water on his property. When he

XI. *The ant pushes, shifts, drags its giant prey, a[*
the while measuring obstacles with two
busy antennae

PLATE XI

BERNARDA
BRYSON

heard that a dowser was locating water for a near-by church he invited him to come over and try it on his place just for fun. This dowser used a linesman's pliers instead of a witch-hazel twig, but they worked perfectly, locating where two underground streams met at a depth of seventy-five feet. The dowser said that anybody with an X in the creases of the palms can do it. You take it from there.

A common fly with a Greek name, *Ichneumon,* meaning "tracker," can track down a maggot in an insect tunnel inside a log by its antennae. It alights on the log precisely above the maggot, and without shifting its position it drives a needle vertically down through the wood, stings to death the prey, and lays eggs on it through the same needle. When the fly's eggs hatch, the babies find themselves on a pile of good food. How does the fly unerringly pick up the signal that comes through the wood? Its antennae must be adjusted for direction pickup so precisely it makes our TV antennae seem crude.

Of all the miraculous smelling the most startling is related to the antennae of a moth. Indeed, having stretched the idea of an odor far beyond imagination, we have recently arrived at a hint that radar is used by moths, and probably by other insects. When odor reception has reached its amazing ultimate limits, radar signals take over. Or, since we are dealing in a strange sense that is beyond human understanding, perhaps odor and radar are the same phenomenon.

A reliable scientist was delighted to find the cocoon of a rare species of moth. He put it in a bureau drawer and when it hatched he enjoyed studying the big moth as it flapped and collided around his room with the windows closed. He put it back in the bureau drawer for the night. Next night a number of males of the species appeared and tapped on his window pane. The experiment was continued, and for a week males continued to arrive, until there were upward of a hundred of these rarely seen moths in a frenzy at his windows. In a frenzy too were the professor's family and the whole neighborhood.

It is reasonable to suppose that the male moths of this rare species must have received from across the miles a signal including direction from the prime virgin moth imprisoned in the professor's bureau drawer. This is a miraculous example of odor detection.

In studying the gypsy moth to outguess it and stem its rising tide, a carefully planned smell test was made on the wind-swept pine dunes of Cape Cod, where it was a certainty that there were no gypsy moths at that time. One female in her prime was put in a cage and attached to the trunk of a pine. A marked male was released two miles away. Think what two miles of drifting across country exposed to the winds along the seashore can do to a wisp of odor from one little moth in those wide-open spaces. This odor is so faint that we can't smell it an inch away. After allowing for the average miles per hour of a moth's eccentric fluttering, observers were delighted to see the male gypsy show up at the right tree on schedule. This was duly recorded by a leading odor scientist. But was it odor as we know it?

The female appeared to be doing nothing except sitting hopefully in her cage. Now a spectroscope reveals that the female moth broadcasts mating calls over ultrared wave lengths. Those are heat-light waves, invisible to our eyes but not to our sense of warmth. The moth doing this broadcasting is eleven degrees hotter than the air, and the broadcast rises and falls with fluctuating peaks. She's playing a red-hot piano in the infrared octave. This love story has an astonishing climax —the points of the feathery antennae of the male moth vary in length in the same proportion as the wave lengths of the female's broadcasting.

These miraculous projections of insects' brains lead us from mystery to mystery. If insects are equipped to polarize sunlight for a compass course across an unknown countryside, as with bees, a moth beyond the range of sight and sound and odor can resort to sending out infrared waves.

ANIMALS THAT FIND THEIR WAY HOME

Related to this is the mystery of animals that find their way home. I have a friend named Marie who lives in traffic-packed, house-crowded Westchester County with a small, cherished fox terrier named Terry. Five miles away the dog was inadvertently left on the porch of a friend's house. Arriving home, Marie was upset to find the dog missing, and a phone call established that it had vanished from the friend's premises. The dog was given up with a sigh, for an intelligent human adult who had not walked the course before could never have found the way without asking questions, across five miles of mazes of houses, concrete roads, right through a jammed shopping district. (Westchester County is perhaps the easiest area to get lost in in the country.) Ten days later a bedraggled, whimpering, exhausted little Terry turned up at Marie's house. How did he do it? What traffic cops did he ask? What street signs did he read?

Eels are experts at global travel. When ten years old, every fresh-water eel in Europe and North America will go downstream, find the Atlantic, swim out hundreds of miles, and lay eggs in sargassum seaweed in the middle of the ocean. After two years at home their children will then swim back to the *same* streams where their parents came from. So do eels from Egypt, which first have to traverse the Mediterranean and go through the Straits of Gibraltar to gain the open sea and then lay a course to the Sargasso Sea, floating around in the mid-ocean whirlpool.

Monarch butterflies, the only long-distance migrants among insects, have a marvelous sense of direction. It is so unbelievable that a weak, helpless, fluttering butterfly could make a thousand-mile trip from one point to another that two hundred and fifty butterfly watchers were alerted in Canada to put gummed labels on the wings of thirty-three thousand monarchs.

One labeled monarch which was recovered had gone a straight-line distance from Hanlan's Point, Ontario, to Virginia Beach. Without any previous experience, so that they cannot know the landmarks, thousands of monarchs go south for the winter and return to their birthplace in Ontario. We must believe that this incredible feat is due to the antenna. If an adventurous hypothesis is in order, I would suspect that northbound monarchs tune in either by odor or by radar with milkweeds en route. You always see them fluttering around milkweeds. I have no guess as to how the southbound butterflies reach their destination.

Bird migrations are the crowning exhibit of long-distance navigation. Homing pigeons go straight to their home hutch over hundreds of miles. Racing home pigeons is a popular sport of people in New York City. They keep the hutches on their apartment houses, then carry their pigeons far out over the super highways and thruways, and let them scoot home from fixed racing points. The sport is known as a chuck-up.

The shearwater, or stormy petrel, lives far out at sea over the cold North Atlantic. I have watched them by the hour from the deck of Admiral MacMillan's schooner in stormy Davis Strait. They zoom swiftly, undulating up and down just above the contours of the sea, as though on a vast and glorious roller coaster. Sometimes they playfully tick the crest of a wave with a wing and give a little splash. The splash is always the same size, although every wave is a different height. They seem to be having a wonderful time and it is exhilarating to see such swift, frictionless motion, such free grace and precise control. Of course they are looking for something to eat and I only thought they were having fun because I would have loved such buoyancy and freedom myself.

Shearwaters have a nesting place on a little island off the Welsh coast. At mating time in the spring two marked birds were taken from home in covered cages to Venice and released. Now this seems to be an impossible proposition. The shearwaters had never been to Italy, nor had their ancestors. No shearwaters have ever been seen in the Mediterranean. It's a different world, a different climate, smells different, looks different from a rocky island on which North Atlantic waves crash. The scientists who had outsmarted the birds from two nests kept close tabs on their nests—and on the fifteenth day, after the chuck-up in Venice, one turned up.

What about the other? No sign of him all summer. When breeding time is passed the shearwater ranges far from its nest over the ocean rollers, so a patient bird watcher kept an eye on the empty nest just in case. No luck. A year passed, and at breeding time the second spring a watchman was posted at the empty nest. It seemed hopeless, and the watchman was hardly paying any attention to the nest, although he was fascinated by the birds and seascapes, when suddenly the second shearwater shot past his nose and settled on its personal home that it had built more than a year before! How did it do it? The shearwater didn't say.

Neither did the female moth tell us about her infrared signal, but we found out about it recently. And we have found out how a bat can shoot swiftly through the dark without seeing anything yet without hitting anything. I saw bats in a limestone cave at Twin Lakes, Connecticut, when as a boy at Hotchkiss School I went exploring with candle and cord. Crawling through a tight squeeze, I confronted the bats a few inches from my face, where they were hung up on the ceiling. As there was not much room to dodge, I was terrified that they would strike my eyes or pop into my mouth. When one of them was jostled it woke up, and I gave my head a crack that still hurts trying to dodge it. As it shot through the small space around my head, I could feel its wind but was not struck. This seemed like great luck. I didn't know until years later that bats just don't hit things when they fly in the dark.

I was too scared of bats in the dark to do anything about it, but an Italian scientist named Spallanzani three hundred years ago was so curious he did something. He hung a forest of strings from the ceiling of his room, each string far enough from the next to give clearance to a bat's outstretched wings. At the end of each string was a small bell. The bat was set free in complete darkness. It was heard flying all around the room swiftly, darting in every direction, but a bell rang faintly only twice.

Now we know that bats send out a constant stream of squeaks pitched at fifty thousand per second or more. People with keen hearing can detect up to forty thousand vibrations per second, so bat squeaks are so high people can't hear them. These supersonic squeaks hit an object and bounce back into the bat's tall, sharp ears. The direction control is so precise and so fast that, as Spallanzani proved, a bat can fly through a forest of strings and rarely touch one. This is the same principle as echo soundings for a ship in uncharted water, where the depth of the water is measured by the time it takes for a click to go down to the bottom and bounce up into the instrument. The same idea is called radar when electromagnetic waves are shot into the sky to detect enemy aircraft at night. It is exciting to discover the echo-sounding exploits of bats, but it doesn't tell us how or why these little mammals were equipped this way. Protoplasm, which did it for the bat, holds the mystery. It also holds the mystery of animals finding their way home and migrating birds finding their paths over thousands of miles of sea and land.

It's hard to imagine what a mile feels like to an insect—it is infinite distance. We rush a mile in a car or a hundred miles in a plane and think nothing of it. We giants possess power and instruments for direction finding immensely greater than the body. One of the most important is the ribbon of a road. With a highway number you can go from a red spruce beside Lubeck lighthouse in Maine, the most eastern tree in the United States, to a cypress on Monterey Point in California, the most western.

Such equipment is causing the human population to expand into all corners of the world. From 1850 to 1950 people increased from 1,200 million to 2,400 million, a startling rise compared to the historic past, when it took the human population ten centuries to increase from 100 million to 200 million. To increase, a new population must continually tap new sources of food, and this we do both by discovering new supplies and by using our chemical and mechanical powers to excite soil and sea into ever-greater production. Producing people and producing food are the prime necessities and represent the fierce and fantastic struggle inherent in protoplasm itself.

If a mile is infinite distance to a tiny insect, the span of a continent is interstellar space. With antennae erect, a tidal wave of life has rolled around the world, and its floods have filled every cranny of rock and soil, so that weird populations exceeding in strangeness anything we can imagine on another planet lurk in every shimmering shadow of tree and bush and field, abide in moist cracks of bark and wood and under stones. Because there is no way to increase the size of the earth, the best way to accommodate a vast population on this planet is to make little bodies.

In this respect insects are the crowning success of protoplasm, and, moreover, because tiny eyes in tiny heads can give their owners a world of only a few inches round about, the antenna is the magic key that unlocks the gates to vast vistas of worlds.

At this point we encounter the law of life that almost no food is ever left unused; that every speck of life energy stored in the bodies of animals and plants shall be used by protoplasm for other animals and plants. A big body such as that of a dead elephant lying in a swamp among the reeds is an immensity of food for generations of millions of little creatures. So are leaves from a tree, or stumps. You can think of nothing which has been part of a living structure which is not destined to be part of another living structure. The law is the same for all, whether fish, dogs, eagles, people, or oak trees.

From our viewpoint we may think that we can discover an unused source of food. Peat moss, dug raw and rich, is wonderful food for the garden. It is the bodies of what had been living moss now converted into roses. The life energy of dead pine needles, rabbits, and woodcocks mixed with soil to make sediments washed out to sea is not lost. Protoplasm in the bodies of diatoms pounces on this washed-away food. This, in turn, is swallowed by fish, and eventually the insects and we may get it back if we eat the fish, or it may be routed through beavers and bears and not reach us.

Lush spaces of incredible immensity, opened for the use of tiny insects by the invention of the antenna, demand a tremendous acceleration of procreation.

The multiplication table used by flies, ants, and mosquitoes is in the order of the arithmetic of the Milky Way. It is not the same as the multiplication table used by the elephant. One pregnant housefly laying its eggs in spring would have a family of five followed by twelve ciphers by fall if all its descendants lived. An elephant takes twenty-one months to come across with one additional elephant.

But the law which dictates to protoplasm that there must be no life energy unused has a corollary—namely, that every living body must find enough food to live its life or die and yield its body to another. The intense power and drive given to reproduction stimulated by an abundance of food soon meets this drastic control, or else insects would be smothered to death by the pressure of their populations.

The River of Life uses the same procedure for curbing population that it used for filling with life the new worlds opened by the antenna—namely, more production of life. Only now the bodies are larger, and different kinds of life swallow the excess population and restore equilibrium to the living world. It is the turn of insects and their eggs to become the fresh supply of food producing bigger bodies, and the balance is held by birds and frogs and bigger insects such as grasshoppers and praying mantes, and beetles which seize aphids, and dragon-flies snapping up mosquitoes like a flash of light in mid-air.

Still the tiny insects possessing the antennae dominate. The antennae give them mobility and a power of discovering hiding places, food places, breeding places that anything bigger cannot match. On this level flow the strongest and deepest currents of the River of Life. One authority with a genius for mathematics that leaves me gasping estimates the insect population as two and one half followed by fourteen ciphers. Before the ink is dry on the report it could be double that for all I know. It is clear that the antenna is a magic wand that summons up abundance of life on earth.

7*

The Halteres

THE SPECTACULAR SUCCESS of the antenna, in making it possible
for tiny bodies to keep in touch with mates, smell out food,
and hold to a far course, led to the whiz type of wing projection. Whiz wings are the most rapid and adroit projections of
locomotion in the living world, matching the keen sensitivity
of the antenna. Antennae and whiz wings are equal and corresponding. The latter operate tirelessly at high vibrations,
being fed energy by a constant supply of raw oxygen taken in
through portholes along the body instead of channeled through
lungs and blood stream. The tissue of the wings is so thin and
light that they have practically no weight at all, and this exceedingly delicate material is supported on a network of veins,
with every space measured and every strut balanced, that is an
engineering marvel designed to meet a rapid-fire variety of
stresses and strains.

In this air-minded age it seems like standard practice that
things should fly. But flying power built into a living body is
an ultimate and superb development. Original models were
localized in their movements, merely being carried here and

there on random currents, then creeping and crawling a few inches, and, on land, walking and running. The gliding of flying fish and flying squirrels pointed the way, but they never got beyond the localized swimming kind of moving about. Flying is super-swimming, but much more specialized and more complicated.

If we do not count populations but animal styling we see that there are only three kinds of flyers. The first, the flying lizard or pterodactyl, which means "wing-finger," is obsolete and no longer with us. It kept building its body heavier and heavier and its wings heavier and heavier to carry the load until it came a cropper. Instead of a delicate membrane on a beautiful network, the wings were made of ponderous skin suspended from the lizard's long, slender little finger.

The pterodactyl's little finger draped with heavy folds of skin shows how protoplasm can also make mistakes. It must bow to the law of gravity like everything else. So the bones of the fore limbs were split and lightened to make a wing skeleton, and on this were arrayed feathers. The feather is a fine new type of projection, light and airy, and extended and compressed not by heavy folds but by a sliding fan action. Wings can increase their surfaces both by fanning out the feathers themselves and by opening and closing the little segments of one feather, each of which is supported and moved on its individual pin. This gives immense strength and delicate control with so little weight that a feather by itself hardly falls to the ground. This remodeling put birds in the air in place of wing-fingers and kept them there.

The bat is a curious little compromise between the wing-finger flyer and the bird. The bat has a little mouse of a body, with slender bones and thin skin. This lightweight skin is spread over long, outstretched fingers. All the fingers except the thumb are used to support it. With its four very long fingers operating as a wing, the bat can fly like a bird without feathers. We have just seen how the bat does blind flying in the darkness when it cannot use its eyes for guidance and how it has a peculiar radar for a direction finder. (The antenna is reserved solely for insects.) The bat has a warm-blooded body and suckles its young, belonging to the body group of the dog, the tiger, and the human being. With its skin stretched on fingers for flying and its echo sounding equipment, the bat is unique among all the earth's animals. Too bad we can't see its miraculous flight as we can see and thrill at the sight of other kinds of flying bodies in the sunlight. It wakes up and flies only at night.

THE GOLDEN EAGLE

How earth-bound you can feel when you stand on a rocky cliff in mountainous country and watch the golden eagle swim the deep of heaven! A shadow glides frictionless across pine slopes, ravines, crags, and snow patches, and, looking upward, you see the golden eagle wheeling, searching, flowing dark and buoyant against the sky with feathers spaced out widely. It glides into the brightness, turns, and is borne back again on a current deflected from the cliff. The pulse quickens, for in the cockles of every heart there is a yearning for such freedom and scope in the clear, clean high air, for riding the spacious winds.

Sometimes the eagle appears to be suspended motionless a mile up in the air. This is its skill in measuring and executing a glide in perfect unison with the winds. An eagle never hovers. With the mere effort of a feeling, it can make slight adjustments this way and that through widely separated feathers, easily compensating and holding a position against a horizontal stream of air.

The golden eagle and its mate take title to ten thousand acres (overriding the claims of bear and deer and rabbits and foxes), with vertical rights to the flying ceiling some four miles up. This great block of biosphere belongs to the golden eagle according to all the natural laws. With fierce eyes above a beetling, curved beak, the emperor can easily watch over the domain he has staked out for his family. When called upon he can pour tremendous power into those wings to drive upward, chasing off any trespasser that presumes to look down upon the owner. Or in a flash he can dive to attack with deadly accuracy.

Most of the time the golden eagle conserves his power. The massive body floats buoyantly and effortlessly between seven feet of wingspread. Movements are slow and executed with disdainful dignity. Scotsman Seton Gordon, who watched the golden eagle all his life and wrote a beautiful book on the subject, says that the golden eagle, in its own way, is nevertheless the fastest bird that flies. He reports a golden eagle's flying at ninety miles per hour beside an airplane at four thousand feet. There are small birds that dart fast and move along fast in still air. The golden plover, the mourning dove, and the homing pigeon have been clocked at sixty-five miles per hour when in a hurry; ducks and geese at sixty miles per hour.

But the golden eagle can never be hustled. He regards every situation with majesty and calm. If he wants to go from a spot in the sky to a ledge on a far mountain he does not set a course straight for the destination as other birds do, but instead he mounts higher until he gauges the height for reaching the goal by a series of spirals and glides.

Seton Gordon watched a golden eagle dive five thousand feet. In the first two thousand, while sizing up the situation below, he held his wings half closed, giving enough surface for control of the speed and an opportunity for a quick whirl if the prey ran. Below that, for the last three thousand feet, the wings were tightly closed, making a bullet out of the body tearing at dizzy speed to the kill.

The golden eagle travels with equal speed with the wind or against it. If he is sailing before the wind he simply rides it without turning on power; if he is headed against the wind he takes it with a steep downward glide, keeping wings bent and held close to the body. The golden eagle's dive is often a corkscrew, descending a steep spiral through the sky. Or he may combine the straight high dive with the corkscrew. Near the bottom of a headfirst dive the eagle may twist its body faster than the eye can see, and suddenly it is falling feet first, with bright yellow legs and claws extended, and alights lightly on a perch, without overshooting the mark.

Such skill in landing from swift flight on a spot without any running, in perfect control, shows the eagle's perfect command over the forces of gravity and kinetics.

THE HOUSEFLY

On the other hand the antenna and whiz wing combination gives matchless supremacy of flying skill and power, and irrepressible protoplasm has found a dazzling variety of ways to apply this combination. But if we are to select the most adroit flyer of all it must be *Musca domestica*, the everyday housefly. It has a most ingenious projection added for its special use, in addition to the antenna and whiz wing equipment. This projection gives the housefly the title of world's champion flyer.

Its body is compact, muscular. More than half its weight is devoted to its flying mechanisms. These have power and drive and always alert control. A fly cannot glide and soar and rest in mid-air. In the air its wings must vibrate without missing a beat; it does not even glide to a stop when it lands.

If any mechanism ever came close to perpetual motion, it is the musca domestica's. It can sustain flight without a pause for one and one half hours. During that time, the fly's wings beat continuously up and down a million times. Such energy must come from somewhere. Some of it uses up the carbohydrates stored in its tiny body, because after such a prolonged buzz, the fly is 3.5 per cent lighter. However, when a mechanism consumes its own body, it must have a way to refuel while in flight. This is accomplished very simply, not by the arrival of another fly to pump fuel to the long-distance round-the-room

contender, but by a simple arrangement for oxygen to reach the
wing muscles directly. This is accomplished by the little
portholes along the insect's body. These catch oxygen from
the swiftly passing air and carry it directly to the wing
muscles.

Moreover, this magic flyer has the most efficient walking and
running mechanism of any animal. This is in contrast to the
penguin, which, so beautifully perfected for swimming, wad-
dles awkwardly when it walks. It is also in contrast to his
majesty the golden eagle, who with all his conquest of the
open sky runs on the ground with teetering, choppy, short steps.

The fly's legs are in three segments, with claws at the tip
of the third segment. It always walks on the tips of these
claws—in other words, on super-tiptoes. They are wonderful for
grabbing hold of any surface that is not slanted more than 45
degrees. Walking on a surface steeper than that is also no problem because behind the claws there are two little pads which
excrete a sticky fluid. In fact, one of the fly's happiest ways of
walking and running is upside down on the ceiling.

A fly tastes with its feet. This saves time when it lands on a
lump of sugar. The instant its feet touch the sweetness, its
mouth, made up of nine parts, begins to extend like an extension ladder. Two half pieces of pipe come together to form a
tube. At their tip there is a file which scrapes the food, releasing
the juices to be sucked up the tube. A fly can eat only liquids.
When it's through with that course, the mouth parts retract and
fold up under its chin. If you want to make a fly eat something
tasteless or anything inedible which it might reject, all you have
to do is to let its feet touch sugar and it will automatically eat
whatever you offer it.

To enjoy an exciting circus performance, watch your housefly carefully before you smite it. When you do smite, the
chances are it will perceive that swiftly descending hand in
plenty of time to hop out and buzz around your head, with
quick, sharp turns in the air, sudden spurts up and down, figure

eights, take-offs without a running start, and land at terrific speed, more lightly than a drop of water, without a staggering step for adjusting its weight. It alights and takes off upside down, rightside up, or at a steep angle.

The portholes for taking in energy directly from the air, the sticky pads for landing and walking upside down, wing muscles much heavier in proportion to its body than a bird's—all this gear is under the direction of the wonderful antennae. But something else is needed.

This insect item that appears to defy the laws of gravity, inertia, and momentum cannot defy them of course. Nature is never supernatural. For the same reason that you skid on a wet pavement, a fly would tend to skid on landing at an angle; just as a boat approaching a dock on a curving course will sheer and haw—that is, swing out and pivot in—a fly would do so; if an airplane will pitch when buffeted by air currents, how much more readily would a lightweight oval body of a fly pitch.

This brings us to the unique little projection that makes a fly such a frisky freak. The halter of a fly is an ultimate and unique gift to implement the power of the antennae. I say ultimate because I cannot imagine why any creature on earth would ever have to fly better than musca domestica.

Most insects have four wings, one pair attached just aft of the other. The housefly has only *two* wings, the after pair having been completely transformed into heavy clubs with knobs formed like drumsticks from a roast chicken. However, the halter clubs are not bone but nerve fibers—over two hundred fibers are pressed together to make a short length of cable. The knob at the outer end is distended with protoplasm. Fly halteres add nothing to the body weight, as the slightest increase of weight would have changed the aerodynamics of the whole establishment of antennae and whiz wings. Instead, the fly has only two wings while other insects have four. The after wings were converted into halteres, a transaction that keeps the total weight of the animal the same.

PLATE XII

XIII. *Eagle descending.*

PLATE XIII

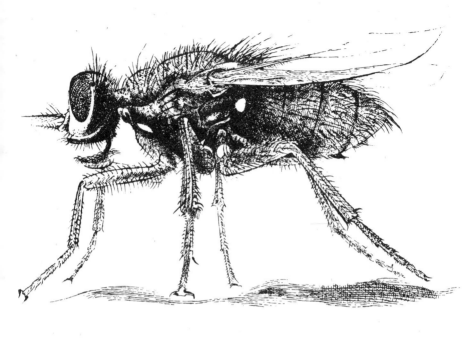

PLATE XIV

Halteres perform as gyroscopes. They are synchronized with the wings, beating at the same rate of around two hundred times per second—but on the opposite beat to the wing beat. When a wing goes up the halter comes down.

These alternating halteres are far more than gyroscopes which keep the fly from hawing and sheering and pitching. They are highly sensitive receptors of air currents. They have a strong balancing sense and convey this feeling to the rest of the body. The fluid in the knobs corresponds to the fluid in our inner ears which takes stresses and strains of changing position and translates them into the sense of balance. Although halteres vibrate with the wings, they may also be controlled independently and perform like freewheeling in a car. Wings beat with the same vigor if the halteres are cut off, but then the fly loses its balance, skids in mid-air, goes into a spin, tumbles headlong. When a fly rests or walks the halteres vibrate to keep the balance, while wings are still.

This great musca domestica system surpasses the perfection of our marvelous electronic flight instruments. The body of the fly itself is an important moving part of the mechanism. It has no interior bones, but, according to the insect plan, its body is a firm plastic that vibrates and communicates these vibrations to wings and halteres.

This high vibration of halteres is super-rhythm. When connected to an electronically fine phonograph needle and amplified, they give a clear musical note. The pitch of this note picked up by a tuning fork shows the rate of two hundred per second. If the knob of one halter is pinched in as though it were a rubber ball so as to reduce its oscillating mass, making it vibrate more rapidly than the other, the result is a musical chord, with two harmonious vibrations. Every engineer must achieve inherent resonance in a vibrating system or the vibrations build up until the device destroys itself. A bridge at Seattle shook itself to pieces when the wind set off its resonance; the vibrating response built up like an ever-mounting

xiv. *The everyday housefly is the most adroit flier of all insects.*

wave. One of the greatest problems of engineers dealing with vibration is to keep the resonance from building up. The fly is equipped naturally and easily to do this with inherent damping in the muscles at the base of the halteres.

The little fly obeys precisely and in the most efficient way all the laws of flight. There is nothing miraculous except the laws themselves.

The Elephant Trunk

I DO NOT KNOW how many flies it would take to equal six tons of elephant. H. G. Wells says that an elephant is a million times as heavy as a mouse. Nature is not concerned with such statistics, and if any mathematician wants to figure it out we can consider him an authority. While this number of flies might darken the sky locally, it is a safe guess that the total weight of all insects alive today in the world far exceeds the total weight of all elephants, and probably you could throw into the scales all the lions, tigers, gorillas, and their kin. The antenna, then, is the most successful of protoplasm's means for making the most living meat in the world. On the other hand, the trunk is the most successful instrument for packing the most volume into the body of a single land animal. The sea offers even greater opportunities, so a blue whale, the biggest animal living on earth today, assembles life materials seven times heavier than an elephant.

An antenna and a trunk seem utterly different. It takes a magnifying glass to see the details of one, while the other is a massive, swaying thing eight feet long, looming up above our heads. Yet both fly and elephant live by the same basic laws of existence. Both their projections have the same functions of mating, feeding, communicating, although each of them arrives at these ends in a different way.

Few people have ever seen an elephant in the wild; we think of them as they look standing around with poker faces in a zoo, or shuffling along in a parade, or going through a military drill in a circus ring, seemingly only partly awake and too ponderous and tired to resist going through their routines automatically. The elephant's eyes look small and almost closed. The giant blinks his eyes but makes little effort to see with them. He or she (it is impossible to tell the sex of an elephant at a glance) stands and stands, sways and sways, shifting slightly, with hushed padded sounds. The beast is imperturbable, very old and very wise in contrast to pesky little people. The body is not trim and styled for action; its massive hide is wrinkled and loose, like an unpressed, baggy suit.

The restless trunk has the sinuous elegance of a huge snake as it gropes from side to side, curves and lifts suddenly, and reaches toward you with two dripping nostrils on a flexing tip. This huge phantom snake is uncanny and menacing, yet its action is as neat and gentle as a loving touch when two sensitive fingers at the tip of the trunk pick a peanut from your hand.

Everything about an elephant is incongruous. For one thing, it seems to have no fore and aft. The trunk gives the front end its personality, whereas most animals get their expression from their eyes. At the rear end a tail almost six feet long looks all the bigger with a fifteen-inch tuft of bristles. Buttocks and head are about the same shape. Thus, the animal seems to be made with two rear ends. So, when you meet an elephant standing in a shadowy forest or among tall reeds you may not be able to tell which end you are looking at.

Another incongruity is that the sperms of this massive mountain, which pack all the potentials and potency of the giant bull, are the same size as the sperms of a fly. Moreover, unlike all other land mammals except a cony rabbit, the testes do not descend into a scrotum, so only an expert elephant observer can tell whether the animal is male or female.

Few people have ever seen wild elephants free and raw in their native primeval fastness so as to discover all that the trunk was invented to do and how it made possible this kind of animal among our fellow passengers on our trip through space. A few herds at large in reservations of the Belgian Congo are protected and can be photographed from car and plane. But the biggest elephants left in the world are living in what survives of a vast primeval jungle between the southern boundary of the Sahara Desert and the Equator, around Lake Chad.

Lake Chad has shrunk to one fifth of its former size, while the great tropical rain forest of mid-Africa is seared and drying to one third of its former extent. The mighty hardwood trees, with the finest, strongest wood graining, are shriveling as the rainy season brings less and less recovery from the searing monsoons. Formerly a jungle such as this was able to protect its own climate by retaining moisture and producing its own local showers and upkeep. But African climate is changing, and the change is quickened by the deeper and deeper penetration of burning forests on the fringes of the jungle, where man is clearing land.

This area was not considered penetrable by man until recent years. Chad is the greatest reservoir of water in the heart of this tropical battleground between scorching dry and drowning wet. The territory is inaccessible and unspoiled not only because of its location within hundreds of miles of torturous country from every direction but also because Lake Chad itself has no fixed shore. The lake is nowhere over five feet deep, and when torrential downpours fill it to overflowing it pours over low banks and floods thousands of square miles of reed and papyrus swamps. The mighty swamp of outer Chad, where water stands a foot deep and is hidden by the reeds, is still thirty thousand square miles, while the inner Chad, the lake proper, is less than ten thousand square miles. The surface of the outer Chad is an ocean of waving reeds from horizon to horizon. This elemental swamp with its invulnerable islands is the last sanctuary on earth big enough and lush enough for giant elephants to be primitively free, and where they can hide so that no man may know or touch them—except one.

Fortunately there has always been, at each barrier to learning, one man who dares to breach this barrier. Everybody else must live life as it comes—some contributing more than their share, but all working, playing, loving in the given pattern. The pattern itself is an organism that reproduces fixed characteristics by its mores—a city and its commuters, for example, or a county or small town, are all devoted to the same pattern of life as it is handed to them. It takes a wrench and courage, or foolhardiness, to break the cast to discover more broadly and live a little more richly, though not more importantly unless one is able to share. An individual is bound to the pattern by obligations, to family, to church, to the block, to pay the installments on the car and television, and it is usually not within his power to break the inevitable train by which he must live and die with respectability.

The few who come to renounce life in order to find it leap over the barrier, live with curiosity, seek suffering in order to know the beauty and the pain of living things. On the stormy seas, in the polar regions, on the highest mountains, in tropical wilds they seek, haunted by hours that cry and winds that call.

One man mingled with the phantom herds at Lake Chad and for four years contended for mastery with the animal that no one else had ever seen with understanding and lived to tell it. Oberjohann was born in 1891, the son of a village blacksmith in Westphalia. He had Herculean strength and became a legend of reckless daring among the tough characters of his countryside. He burned with a passion for animals, and out of his pride grew a belief that there isn't a beast on earth which a man can't cope with and outwit. At eighteen he set forth as a sailor and brought back animals from far ports to Carlo Hagenbeck, the animal trader to zoos and circuses. Hagenbeck knew about the deep mysteries of the Chad elephants and how impossible it would be for a man to get in there and out again alive with a six-ton, untamed live mountain of flesh in tow. But Oberjohann offered to go to Chad and bring back baby elephants. To capture babies alive he would have to run with the herd, live with the beasts, study their behavior, know more than any man had ever known before about elephants—and this would take four years. If Hagenbeck would back him for four years . . .

So this reckless, obstinate Tarzan who held death as less important than exploiting an iron will set forth for Chad, the one white man to go. He cajoled, beat, roared at, and by the sheer awe of a big scrawny beard persuaded a few natives to go along and help. Fortunately one named Colo matched his spirit of daring and had, moreover, an innate compassion for all living creatures. The dark man, while saddling the semi-wild stallion for his master, would stroke it with rough hands and talk to it with indrawn hissing sounds that the horse understood.

During four years in the jungles and swamps around Lake Chad, Oberjohann caught nineteen baby elephants, usually by stampeding the herd, for the babies can't travel over ten miles per hour. He would then rush up, grab the baby elephant's tail, vault its rump, mount its back, and somehow make a towline fast to its forelegs. The performance bears some resemblance to steer wrestling in a rodeo. Baby elephants were always cozy after being caught because, like all babies, they have a strong sense of dependence, and the man is the substitute when the mother elephant isn't around to take care of it.

But elephant catching never ended as peacefully as that. There was always a terrible aftermath, because somehow the mother elephant knew exactly where her baby was. The man with the baby elephant made long journeys into hiding. The mother might be miles away—but inevitably she would return suddenly, unexpectedly, and rush the people. With a baby elephant on their hands, Oberjohann and his little band of natives led lives of nightmarish suspense. They traveled at dawn after a sleepless night of watching; went into camp at the heat of day. But always the mother came back, no matter how far they had gone or how many days had passed, and gave them the bum's rush.

It was as though the baby sent telepathic messages to its mother as to its whereabouts. Like the insect's antenna, an elephant's trunk is a sensitive smelling instrument. An elephant's world is not a world of visual images but of feeling and smelling images, all summoned up with the wonderful trunk. Eyes are only a supplement of the trunk, providing a vague vision at close range which helps to knock down and trample a little thing like a man or wild horse. An elephant can't see more than seventy-five feet.

In the wild it opens its nonfocusing eyes wide; they become big, round, and terrifyingly white and fix you with a stare. This is an ominous—in fact, fatal—sign, especially when the rumbling of its bowels, which always goes on inside the elephant and which can be heard for a quarter of a mile, is turned off and the monster is absolutely silent for a few moments.

Suddenly the trunk whips up vertically and is held stiffly, with the tip directed at you like a periscope. The ears stand out at right angles, rigid as steel doors, not fluttering as you see them in the zoo. At such a time all the rest of us are goners No use to jump into the nearest acacia tree even if its wood is a foot thick, because the charging elephant—six tons at ten miles an hour—can easily push the tree over.

Only Oberjohann knows what to do. He waits, surrenders to his fate if that must be, even feels a comforting submission to death until the uproar of mud and mad meat is only a few feet away, when he throws himself to the left, while all hell rushes by. Once he was a fraction of a second too late, and the sinuous, sensitive trunk, now a brutal club held on high and swinging down, glanced off his shoulder. When he came to, his injuries were diagnosed as "a few fractured ribs and a broken leg." A mere brush with an elephant.

So the elephant stares at you with glaring white eyes just before charging. Probably those sleepy little slits at the circus are not trying to see much when no charge is contemplated. You do not figure in the elephant's world even when you are so kind as to offer her a peanut. Elephants in zoos and circuses are usually female because they are more easily trained and do not have the cyclonic tempers of males. The fragrance of the peanut guides the trunk. This unique appendage can be used as a brutal club or it can pick a daisy with two sensitive little fingers.

Elephants talk to one another when they are in a huddle by low mutterings and rumblings. It is hard to distinguish the deep rumbling voice from the rumbling of the alimentary canal. Both are controlled by feelings and can be turned on and off at will. When an elephant is surprised and alerted, and when it is charging, it becomes silent.

One of the most mysterious of all communications between animals is trunk talk over the long-distance circuit. Like birds which respond to the orders of a flock leader, like the moth which summoned her mate from miles away, this is animal communication which man knows little about. Moth antennae catch a kind of radar signal, and perhaps the elephant trunk has another invisible power.

Members of a herd of Chad elephants mysteriously signal to one another across more than a hundred miles, perhaps much further.

Oberjohann, with all his instinctive feeling for elephants and his daring and skill to travel with the herd while observing them, could never understand this long-distance communication. Lifting their trunks high to trumpet with sound signals, or erecting them and revolving the nozzle in all directions to catch an odor, is more understandable to us but it does not explain the "telepathy" at all.

The antenna gives insects the image of their world by touch, smell, and communication, which hold together the same kind of individuals for procreating and for the sheer elixir of having company—an almost universal necessity. Few creatures can endure a way of life such as the rock-boring clam (*Lithophagus*), which uses its body as a gimlet to make a hole in rock. Then the clam slowly revolves as its body grows, and the hole grows bigger as it gets deeper until the clam is entombed inside a bottle of solid rock that fits its body but leaves only a tiny hole above to the outside world where it entered as a baby. Generally loneliness is as despairing and corroding as hunger and thirst.

The elephant's trunk renders services similar to those of the antenna by creating an image of the world for its owner through touch, smell, and also by maintaining herd communication. Also like the antenna, it is basic equipment around which is built a certain kind of body to live under elephant conditions, but with more uses than the antenna. The result is another triumph of protoplasm that puts upon earth some creatures which are just as astounding and dramatic, in an entirely different way, as insects.

Elephant living space is hard to find, because of the limited size of the earth. The only place that animals the size of elephants could exist in numbers like mice is on some unknown world beyond the Milky Way that is a million times bigger than the earth. Moreover, because elephant living space on earth is shrinking, we are just barely able to catch a glimpse of these grand animals before the last trunk trumpets and the last monstrous periscope above the reeds crashes into the mud.

The poor dulled animals in captivity may breed for a few years a few more dulled animals in captivity, but the great muscular trunk throbbing with sensitivity was not made to sway like a lazy pendulum in a street parade and pick peanuts, and those sleepy slits of eyes will lose their power to pop open, round and glittering white, to eye a wild horse or a man while stamping them into the mud.

We have seen how living projections come in great variety. Limbs and tails are examples of the commonest; the fly's halter is an example of the most specialized and precise mechanical gadget; the antenna and the elephant trunk are the most versatile and exert the greatest over-all effect on the design of their creatures' bodies.

The elephant trunk, instead of being, like the antenna, an extension of the nerves of the brain, is made by welding together the nose and upper lip and then pulling this merger far out and equipping it with a series of muscles which already existed for the nose and upper lip. We can move our upper lips a bit, and our noses a little less when we snuffle, but few people can ever wave their noses. So we can hardly consider their muscles as a mighty force. In the elephant trunk these muscles are assembled and multiplied so that there are forty thousand of them, with the power to lift a ton of teak.

Many creatures have long snouts. A tapir has a fused elongated nose and lip that looks like a curved, stubby trunk beginning to grow out of its face. By coincidence, or because there is a weird correspondence between the two ends of the animal, a tapir also has a short, stubby tail. The aardvark strides clumsily into a termite's hill and thrusts in a snout a foot long, whips out a tongue nine inches beyond that, laps up and sucks in termites—devouring them thus without any teeth. This is an efficient little trunk in its way. Borrowing other projection ideas elsewhere, the aardvark also has the ears of a donkey and the tail of a kangaroo fastened to the body of a bear. A certain snail (*Cyclostoma elegans*) has a muzzle called a trunk that resembles the trunk of a tapir. A four-foot turtle in Africa has a pair of trunks. You find trunklike projections on many kinds of animals, but they are only reachers for food, like long bird beaks. With its many uses, the elephant trunk is the most important part of the animal because the trunk is the elephant, and every other part of the animal is an accessory to it.

THE PENDULUM THAT MAKES AN ELEPHANT GO

When the animal is on the go the trunk moves restlessly back and forth. While grazing, members of a herd may become far separated. Then up goes the trunk, erect tip revolving, the signal is caught, and all the elephants head straight for water, making fifty miles in a night. As an elephant steps along at its usual rate of about six miles per hour, the trunk is repeatedly erected to check direction. Now it searches bushes and ground for the scent of an elephant which has preceded it, much as a dog follows a trail; most of the time it sways like a great pendulum, balancing the body, giving swing and pace to six tons of meat.

Nature did not achieve such tremendous weight in an animal without arranging for it to move easily. Actually the elephant is as deftly balanced in its way as the housefly is in its way. The principle is that of counterbalance, or seesawing.

An elephant's forelegs are mighty vertical pillars that support the weight of the body like a fulcrum. The elephant gets no sleep in the sense of losing consciousness but stands occasionally completely relaxed on its foreleg pillars. The big mature African elephant never lies down. It's too much effort to get up again. It just stands up for the last thirty-five years of its life.

Hind legs push the animal forward, although they must also receive weight from each foreleg momentarily when the elephant takes a step. Almost half of the weight of an elephant is in front of the forelegs, so that with comparatively little effort the weight seesaws on the forelegs when it moves.

The pendulum of a heavy trunk helps greatly in this movement. When held out horizontally for a moment its leverage helps the elephant to step on the accelerator and run in an emergency. Most of the time the rhythmic swaying of the trunk makes it walk. However, massive head, neck, chest, and trunk are not quite enough weight at the bow, so enormous forward-thrusting tusks are added to counterbalance the afterpart of the body. An elephant gets little use out of its tusks in digging and tearing. Tusks are all the more important for balance when the trunk is erect or straight down, reducing its leverage.

A pair of African elephant tusks ten feet long weighs three hundred and fifty pounds. They are not fibers and hairs stuck together like rhinoceros horns; they are solid ivory, the weight and beauty of which created the billiard-ball industry. Ivoryton, Connecticut, had billiard-ball and piano-key factories until a few years ago when the tusk supply all but ran out. The industry was established in colonial New England when ships brought tusks from Africa into the Connecticut River, and the marvelous elephant counterweights were trundled up to the factories of Ivoryton on ox carts.

BEST REACHER EVER INVENTED

The elephant trunk is superior to all other projections as a reacher, though it can't compare with the bee animal's long-distance reaching, which is achieved not by attachments but by detachments.

Without bothering to move its head much or shift its position, an elephant can reach up almost as far as a giraffe to chew the leaves of a tree. The giraffe is not using a body projection; it is just tall. Its neck has the same number of vertebrae as a horse's, but each is lengthened. The giraffe can do a great job of grazing in treetops, but that is all. Its neck is not suitable for grazing on the ground. When it drinks, it has to spread its forelegs far apart, and this makes it helpless and vulnerable to a lion which has been waiting for that giraffe to spread its legs and take a drink. The long neck is far from being always a great advantage. It is a hard necessity which nature has imposed on the giraffe. When erect, its legs are slender and swift, its body beautifully balanced, but when it stoops to drink it must lower the body, and the legs are turned into rigid supports slanting far out. At the same time the ponderous neck revolves downward, almost burying the eyes and nose of the animal. In this predicament it may neither see nor smell its enemy, and its long legs are immobilized so that it cannot spring away and be off in a split second. What a cruel contrast is the long neck of the giraffe to the elephant trunk.

The elephant trunk reaches high for leaves and low for water; it eats the bushes on this side and that. If it sees delicious leaves high up, which would be out of reach to a giraffe, it puts that big bony forehead against the tree, gives a push, and the leaves come down where they can be neatly plucked by the two little fingers at the tip of the trunk.

Drinking with the trunk is pie compared to the difficulty of a giraffe in taking a drink. The elephant stands still and relaxed while the trunk sucks up water, then coils under and squirts the water into the mouth. On occasion, the trunk acts as a great shower bath for cooling and cleaning the skin of the elephant, which is very sensitive, not the tough leather it appears to be. Or the trunk shower bath can be directed at a bystander whom the animal can't stand the smell of.

Eating is big business for an elephant. To take in enough energy to provide itself with strength the giant must eat most of the time. An elephant can't reach food with its mouth alone—trunk and tusks are in the way. Moreover, the massive, firm neck does not permit the elephant to lower its head. So the trunk coils in under to stuff the mouth. Oberjohann says that the Chad elephants, which are always playful, active, and on the go, eat eighteen hours out of twenty-four. To feed a torpid giant of a circus calls for considerable effort on the part of the men who are paid to wait on him. He must be stuffed with a quarter ton of grain, one hundred and fifty pounds of hay, and fifty gallons of water per day.

The monstrous elephants of Chad constantly come down from the dunes and jungles to wallow in the shallow, muddy water and scoop in great mouthfuls of reeds. This is the perfect place for happy elephants to find their combination of food, water, hiding places, and living space on the colossal scale which they must have. Elephants move as easily and surely through the confusion of reeds and mud as you walk on a golf course. Direction comes through signals received by the uplifted trunk. Reeds part like water before an elephant moving freely among them in any direction, but the way an elephant avoids getting stuck in the mud shows how one perfection of protoplasm begets another.

Below the bones of an elephant's foot is a cushion made of tough plastic skin filled with fatty gelatin. As the mighty weight presses on this the cushion expands while at the same time it is buoyant. This on a giant scale is like the plastic bags in which people used to knead oleomargarine to color it. The elephant can walk on these fat-filled bags on hard ground softly and silently to the human ear. It can sneak up and stand but a few feet away, watching you struggle through the underbrush, suddenly appearing at your shoulder like a towering gray boulder. In a swamp, the cushions spread as they sink into the mud, and when one is lifted it contracts, to come up easily without the suction that makes people lose their rubbers in mud.

Continuous large-scale eating requires something more than apparatus for gathering food with the least amount of exertion. It also calls for tremendous grindstones. Fodder consists of coarse branches, leaves, great sheaves of reeds bound together by the big living rope of a coiled trunk. Ordinary teeth cannot handle this grinding operation without wearing out fast. So the elephant carries in its head a parade of mighty molars that move down each side of its mouth in two assembly lines. It has no cutting teeth—incisors—as these are not needed for its kind of eating. Two incisors are converted into the magnificent tusks.

The molars are blocks of ivory dentine compounded out of twenty-four separate teeth, each with its living nerve. So great is the grinding surface that only one pair is needed on each side for the job. As those are wearing down, other grindstones are growing at the rear; and when those in use are so worn down that they must be replaced, the next set is moving up and ready with a new grinding surface. The elephant makes twenty-four of these marvelous teeth in a lifetime. This provides it with six complete changes of grinding equipment.

With all this great equipment—trunk, tusks, pillar legs to pivot on, parade of teeth—there is yet one more necessity for elephant success in terms of the River of Life. That is how to solve the problem of reproduction for so massive an animal.

Because elephants have been, until man came along with a gun, secure and supreme in their own domain, they could breed without fear. With their sensitive and deadly trunks they can easily protect their babies from panthers and all other enemies. Thus, with a low infant death rate, the elephant population has been maintained and slowly multiplied by bringing forth a single baby every twenty-two months. This is exactly the opposite problem of the insects, whose high mortality must be offset by extravaganzas of multiplying. Before man, climate changes to drier or colder have been the elephant's only threat of extinction through the ages, as they have extinguished the mammoth and mastodon elephant ancestors.

The trunk plays an important part in love-making. It is great for reaching food and wonderful for hugging and caressing. The extent to which the trunk is used on such an occasion was not appreciated until the inquisitive Oberjohann stole up on elephants and patiently hid down wind in the early hours of dawn to witness touching and beautiful romances among the Chad monsters. He saw that female elephants are coy when

xv. *The elephant's trunk has many uses, including hugging and caressing*

PLATE XV

in heat, which is very seldom and then for only three or four days. They run away, to be chased by the bull, but arrange to be overtaken promptly. Caressing pairs are very shy, and if they caught the least suspicion of the smell of a witness they would rush to hiding and we would never know all the poetry of a trunk.

Chapter 16

The Eye

AN INTERESTING CAPER of protoplasm in its urge to overload the ark is to create eyes for use at night. This means that many creatures can be out of sight and practically nonexistent by day. Obviously a much greater population can inhabit an area when night animals and day animals are out of one another's way and don't eat one another or bump into one another.

When you go out on a warm summer night there is no telling how many eyes may be turned upon you. Vast mysterious throngs, invisible to human eyes, are hidden in the dark. Yet to them this is the time to wake up and live, to go about their business of eating, mating, or just sitting around enjoying themselves. These are the countless night insects, like moths, and the night animals, like rats, mice, the woodchuck, the owl—all of whom have night eyes. In addition you may be stared at by deer, fox, bear, rabbit, dog, or cat which have both night eyes and day eyes.

Animals with both day and night eyes can change their living habits back and forth to take advantage of the best conditions. Deer and bear are good examples—and man. In big cities some taxi drivers dislike having their nerves jangled by rush hours and thwarted by traffic and they elect to work the night shift. Elephants who "see" better with the trunk than with the eye readily shift their hours of being about to night-time when a man comes shooting his gun or disturbing the herd. They will stand motionless and hidden in the bush, asleep on their pillars by day, and they travel by night.

Fireflies have peculiar night eyes. If you are looking for fire-flies, as I was in the weird weed jungle at midnight, you will see their flashing abdomens. They will not return your gaze unless you light a Fourth of July sparkler, because their special night eyes are adjusted only to see sparks in the darkness.

No eyes can see in the pitch-dark. Touch, odor, sound come into play more importantly in the dark, and there are marvelous devices, such as the bat's supersonic echo or the moth's mystery radar. The night eyes of animals, far exceeding our power of seeing, are designed to collect and use dim light.

A "pitch-dark" night hardly ever occurs. Always the out-doors is illuminated, from the moon, from the glow of the gauze of stars, from the twilight that lingers all night in the time of the long days of the year, from the lights of a city glowing on clouds, from the Aurora Borealis. At any hour of the night, when the sky is clear, your bedroom window in the country will show a dim rectangle of light. Night offers a great and unfailing opportunity for going about the business of living when night eyes are available.

At sunrise the whole population changes. Armies disappear and entirely different armies appear from a billion hide-outs. Then the tortoise, snake, or squirrel in the vicinity will keep us under strict observation wherever we go in their vicinity. When I was out in the weed jungle in the sunlight looking at the gold flies, bees, butterflies, and beetles, their eyes were alert to spot my least gesture instantly. Because of their keen day eyes you can never easily touch these animals. You do not reach out your hand and pick them up because they see your hand coming and bounce away.

8*

A phoebe which had a nest of babies over my studio door sorely wanted to keep an eye on me. She stood high for observation on the garden gate post while I took a stance about twenty feet away and tried to outstare the bird. The two of us formed a triangle with the nest, from which little heads were bobbing. Evidently the other phoebe was near-by and my bird was signaling to its mate with a flip of the tail about my least move, even seeming to read my thoughts. One flip—"Look out. He's *thinking* of moving!" Two flips—"His hand moved!"

The phoebe has keen sight. A bird's eyes are enormous compared to the size of its head. Birds and lizards have the keenest sight in the world. I could feel this phoebe's superiority. No motion, not even the drawing of a long breath, nothing I did escaped instant notice. If I merely shifted my gaze or puckered my lips the fact was telegraphed to the mate by tail flips. At length it was I who surrendered to the champion in this ocular tourney. When I continued on my way to see the gold flies, the phoebe flipped an emphatic burst of dots and dashes and flew off. This was evidently the "all clear."

RABBIT EYES

Often I have tried to outstare a rabbit. So unblinking, so fixed is the big round eye that after you have stared back at it for a few minutes it makes you nervous and you look away. Its gaze seems the more searching because it is the stare of a single eye.

One-eyed seeing is somehow uncanny. The most ruthless sailors of sea stories often have a patch over one eye that makes the one good eye all the fiercer. A race of one-eyed giants that inhabited Sicily were called cyclops, a combination of "cycle" and "optical" that spells "round-eyed." They were terrible. True-life cyclops, their namesakes, living in fresh-water ponds, are almost the only one-eyed creatures on earth. They are unterrifying only because they are $\frac{1}{25}$ of an inch big, just barely large enough to be seen with the naked eye. A near relative, the copepod, much larger at one sixth of an inch, lives in the ocean. This is also a one-eyed creature, but it never fixes anything with that eye. It just bobs around like seaweed, using the eye as a direction finder to help it move toward the sunlight. Far from terrifying its enemy with one eye, this minute one-eyed monster is the chief food of the world's biggest animal, the whale. It is scooped up in hundred-gallon mouthfuls and strained through huge bone strainers in the whale's mouth. The massive whale pays no more attention to the one-eyed copepod than it does to the salt in the water.

The rabbit stares with one eye because he never faces you. His eyes are fixed orbs that look out from opposite sides of his head. To look straight at you the rabbit must always present a silhouette, right or left. If you happen to encounter him head on he will instantly hop around to turn the side of his head toward you. Unless you have a skeptical nature, you know the other eye is looking out on the other side.

When the late President Coolidge was riding through the streets of Detroit his military aide by way of pleasant conversation said, "I see they have painted the streetcars in Detroit." To which the President replied, "At least on one side."

When you look at a rabbit you will see how the field of vision of its two eyes is a complete circle. It can see an enemy approaching from any angle while at the same time holding absolutely motionless to avoid detection. Motionless eyeballs, encompassing a three-hundred-and-sixty-degree circle, contribute to swelling the rabbit population because rabbits always see the other fellow first.

Newborn rabbits are naked, helpless, blind, and so tiny you could hold one in a teaspoon. They nurse only at night and are covered by dried grass and leaves in daylight. But nature equips them swiftly for playing their part in the rabbit world. In ten days their eyes are big and round; in fourteen days they are out bouncing the cotton balls on their behinds.

Cunning enemies who are skillful finders of baby rabbits always lurk near. This contest to live in the grass jungles, with its triumphs and tragedies, is little known and appreciated by us. Only the big, round rabbit eyes tell the story—of how across the prairies where rabbits abounded before they invaded our eastern meadows the mothers watched stock-still by the hour, ready to strike or to lead the enemy away from a nest with the lure of a bobbing white ball. Nevertheless, wildcats, foxes, weasels, raccoons, hawks, eagles, and woodchucks took their toll. But the coyote, which can run at forty-five miles per hour, is the only animal fast enough to catch the rabbit.

As you stand stock-still and fix the rabbit's one big eye with both of yours, you can almost see the animal making up its mind when to cut and run. The rabbit's muscles give sporadic jerks; it is constantly ready to leap, like an eager runner at the starting line. Alternately with this jerking, its nose twitches— probably not because it itches but because it is filled with impulses to eat grass or leaves or your garden lettuce. I believe that a rabbit on the alert watching your motionless figure is torn between running and eating. In fact, with a little practice, you can watch the rabbit and it will go back to nibbling, but without ever taking its eye off you. But flick a finger, move a foot, and off it goes.

What does the rabbit see when it looks two ways at the same time? Is your fine figure a sort of ghost or transparent object?

The answer may be found in the way our own eyes see one object at a time, although our vision covers almost half a circle when we look straight ahead. You don't see what your eyes are looking at but only what you are concentrating on. For example, you don't see all the people in a crowded bus but only what you are thinking about—the pretty girl or the newspaper headlines in the hands of the person next to you. So what does an animal see if it is not consciously thinking? By concentrating its emotions, a rabbit can probably see one side at a time and the two views never get scrambled. In the subconscious, various senses concentrate on what is of interest, and eyes, ears, nose, and skin throw away the rest. A dog may "see" its master's voice and footstep as well as the height of his shadow and the way his legs move, which add up to even clearer identification than seeing his blue eyes and chin and the sparse hair on top of his head.

We have a situation similar to the rabbit's two views when we look straight ahead and see things moving in opposite directions at the same time. While we are walking and driving a car, things move from right to left on the left side and from left to right on the right side. Our eye systems are so accustomed to this alarming sight that they have learned how to co-ordinate it easily on the subconscious level. In the same way, the rabbit must have no confusion at all with its two separate views at the same time.

But, if, while the rabbit and I are trying to outstare each other, another human apparition were to loom up on the opposite side, the rabbit would not stay frozen to look at both of us, but with a twitch of its nose and a jerk of a leg it would be off. The rabbit doesn't even try to see two things at the same time and, leaping through the grass, it stops depending on its eyes and uses the long sensitive hairs on its face to keep from bumping into trees and bushes.

HORSE EYES

The horse's eyes are set on each side of a high nose and also cover separate scenes. Look a horse straight in the face and you will see how extremely walleyed the handsome animal is. Protoplasm put the horse's eyes in this position for the same reason that it put the rabbit's eyes on each side of its head.

In past ages when rabbits were nibbling the grass of the prairies, little wild horses were grazing those grasses, and the two of them were ideal animals to share the lush domain.

The rabbit had its foxes, weasels, and coyotes to look out for, while the horse had bison and wolves—and gadflies and big green horseflies. To cope with the latter it was given a long tail, and to survive the animals with claws and tearing teeth it was provided with the peculiar eyes that stand on guard while it grazes. The mild-mannered horse has no other defense except to take to its toes (not to its heels, as a horse walks and runs on its tiptoes). The horse survived through this combination of wide viewing and super-running—and also because of the long tail, as there is no doubt that flies left to themselves would have destroyed the horse.

Horse eyes do not quite see a complete circle without turning the head. The powerful running mechanism is housed in a high rump which gets in the way of seeing straight to the rear. To sneak up on a horse without being seen, the only way is from the tail end, where an arc of fifteen degrees is a blind spot. The deer, which has the same eye arrangements as the horse and for the same reason, sees in a circle without a blind spot. It grazes mostly on leaves of bushes and trees with head up so it can see over its rumps. The deer can stand stock-still like a rabbit and watch from a lookout tower, but the horse must keep shifting its position to see around its rumps.

TRAVELING EYES

You would suppose that a flatfish, such as a halibut or flounder, which lies on its side on the bottom of the sea, would have but a single eye available to stare upward at a passing fish. Why isn't the down eye, pressed with sand or mud, uncomfortably useless?

The weird part of this story is that just after hatching, the young flatfish has eyes on each side of its head like any ordinary fish, and it swims around in the usual manner. Then, as it grows, it develops a tendency to lean more and more to the right side, for its skull is twisting. It swims awkwardly for a while, holding its head like a person with a stiff neck. The twisting of the skull persists to such a point that the whole body must surrender to a new position, and so it stops trying to swim like other fish and lies on its side. The internal forces that twist an animal in this way while it is growing up may seem cruel to us, but halibuts and flounders are used to it.

During the days of the twisting skull, the down eye has been gradually moving up toward the top of the head. Then it goes over the bridge of the nose, traveling from the right side to the left side. When the eye arrives on the other side of the head, which is now the top side, it finds an empty socket waiting for it. The eye that had been there originally had quit the socket and moved down toward the nose into another depression. Thus, the flatfish can lie on the bottom and now has two eyes side by side on top looking up, ever alert for a dogfish that may come as a slow, black, sliding shadow or a giant narwhal's spear pointed at its heart.

Besides these marvelous traveling eyes the flatfish's protoplasm has done something else for it. For the down side is white and concealed, while the up side has color pigments created where the light touches the skin. The pattern and color of these pigments render an exact copy of the bottom where the fish is lying at the moment. When it changes location, the flatfish continually slides around the bottom, and its spots and colors change, duplicating fine gravel, coarse gravel, or sand, as the case may be.

The traveling eyes of flatfish are a vivid example of how protoplasm pulls, pushes, presses, and twists the bodies of its creatures to make each fit into a particular place where it can find its opportunity to live. The changing of a body after it is already in being as an established type of animal is a finishing touch by that secret genius which begets a vast array of entirely different kinds of living things to fit entirely different sorts of places to live in. The process first fills the recesses of the earth, and then, as in the case of the flatfish, layers are built on layers.

The flatfish were twisted into shape to find their opportunities on the bottom tier.

A great deal of thought must be put into such a project—thought combined with skill and force. The flatfish is never thrown off balance; it must function continuously while it is methodically transformed from a fish swimming about in the ordinary way with its backbone on top to a fish that lies on its side with its backbone on one edge and the rest of its body spread like a puddle. The standard fish is hung from a top backbone like a roof girder, just as an elephant is. The imagination that went into converting a fish to live on the bottom dares to lay the top girder down on the ground. Also it takes force applied with great care, for it twists the girder system at the same time that it causes an eye, a complicated piece of precision equipment of the utmost delicacy, to move from one side of the head to the other without a blink.

CITY-PIGEON EYES

I cannot imagine where else a flatfish can live except on the bottom under water, but there are other creatures with body tools and equipment which serve their owners well in an entirely different kind of living place from the one for which they were originally designed. City pigeons are a remarkable case in point.

Pigeons, like all birds, have keen eyesight, which enables them to bring things into focus quicker than man and keep an object rushing toward them in clear focus. At the same time pigeon eyes, like those of the rabbit, horse, and deer, are located on each side of the head, so the big bright orbs can stare out in opposite directions at the same time. A pigeon must be constantly on the lookout while it snaps up grains or takes a drink of water, its eyes covering all the points of the compass, or hawks would long since have extinguished from the earth this luscious, mild-mannered bird with its slow, flapping flight.

Such eyes also equip the pigeon to escape the perils of on-coming cars and people to live safely in the anarchy of a city. With food enough, pigeons can maintain their natural life in the city.

One of the more entertaining shows in New York is staged daily at the corner of Lexington Avenue and Forty-fifth Street. This is the most pitiless, rip-snorting corner on the face of the earth, with a melee compounded out of Grand Central Station, post office, and the usual street traffic, plus masses of people debouching from skyscrapers for lunch. Here a flock of pigeons is based on a seething restaurant where sweepings, crumbs, and ruins of food are forever being hauled across the sidewalk. Moreover, pigeons have sense enough to come in out of the rain and here are many cozy retreats and alcoves, including a row of glowing, warm neon letters, on the top of which the pigeons line up in chilly weather, thus converting the sign into warm rooms without rent, while adding considerable life and dignity to the sign.

At the height of man's noon mob scene the pigeons descend to the sidewalk and street, pecking and strutting, happy and free, walking around with chests out and heads synchronized with footsteps, nodding back and forth, in perfect balance, a vision of rhythm. They strut between thousands of relentless legs and flap easily and carefree among the thousands of trucks and taxis bearing down on them.

When a soul turns up with a paper bag of bread crumbs, the same wonderful eyesight that saved the pigeons from destruction by wheels and feet spots each crumb. Then, with one accord at the squawk of its leader, the flock descends and snaps up the crumbs. The birds are constantly turning, flapping, running, and stooping, while never taking those eyes off the lethal blows aimed at the funny birds from every direction—all deftly dodged so there is not a single collision—and presently the crumbs are all picked up.

How do these high-strung birds stand the awful noise? The

same way that people do. When you are "used to" a sound, be it gentle or loud, you tune it off. You don't usually hear the clock ticking, or trucks going by if you live on a highway. No being, man or pigeon, could live on the corner of Lexington Avenue and Forty-fifth Street without tuning off the cacophony, or the nervous system would soon be wrecked.

Keen sight sharpened in pigeon ancestors for the hawk days has been kept in a high state of efficiency and probably made keener by dodging legs and wheels that rush at the pigeons from every direction. On the other hand, hearing has had to be altered for the city model. The shriek of a hawk streaking down from high in the sky does not trigger the city pigeon to flee in terror, else it might have a fit every time a brake shrieks or a boorish driver leans on his horn.

Some people want to rid the place of pigeons. Since they have no way of selling the guano on the window sill, they call in the bird shooers. These think they have the answer because they have done a job in Middle West towns where starlings kept people awake by their raucous cocktail-party chatter. It was discovered that when a trapped starling is suddenly turned upside down it yells bloody murder—whereupon all starlings in earshot leave town. The yell of the upside-down starling was recorded and broadcast from a ward heeler's sound truck to the starling guests of the towns that called for rescue—whereupon they left town.

The same general idea was tried on pigeons. With considerable trouble the scream of a diving falcon was recorded and blared at the city pigeons. All the shades of their ancestors could not make them hear this horrendous sound. They continued to nod their heads as though saying, "Yes, so what?" and to warm their feet on the neons and to park under parked cars. Screams and shrieks are an old story with city pigeons. The smart bird shooers could not outsmart protoplasm, which had altered the birds' hearing so they would not hear shrieks, whether city or falcon.

Every living thing both sees and hears according to its consonance with its surroundings. John Compton says that the Chinese are spellbound by music that sounds like pigs being stuck, while they double up with laughter at "Ave Maria" or "Nearer My God to Thee." So inherent is this adjustment mechanism in the River of Life that a spider which takes off in fright the first time a tuning fork is sounded by its web quickly learns to disregard it. On the other hand, a spider likes certain kinds of music. They say that when Beethoven was a little boy practicing his violin a big spider would drop down from the ceiling on a silk thread and sit on the violin.

SQUIRREL EYES

What a bird can do with special eye equipment a mammal can do also, but the art is quite different. Pigeons live in flocks; their charm is their color and rhythm of strutting and nodding; they are a ballet. Anton Dvořák, the great composer of symphonies, found some of his chief enjoyment and inspiration in watching and talking to pigeons. On the other hand, a squirrel is a solo acrobat and comedian.

Squirrel eyes are as keen as a man's in the way they bring things into clear focus. Both squirrel and ape eyes are directed forward, not to each side, and merge two images to focus on the same object. This stereoscopic or binocular vision not only sees an object but can measure its distance. Watch a gibbon or a spider monkey swing across space effortlessly, touching and grasping a spot on a limb with never a miss. Nor does the squirrel in all its life ever miss when it jumps across various sizes of spaces in the treetops. A squirrel comes tumbling to the ground only when the branch to which it jumps breaks.

Two eyes lined up a few inches apart side by side, seeing the same object from a different angle, are fine not only for jumping from limb to limb but also for picking fruits without groping. The disadvantage of this kind of seeing is that it narrows the field of view, reducing the chance of catching sight of an approaching marauder.

However, those of us animals who direct our eyes forward to see in focus have a much broader view which is not in focus. Fix your eyes straight ahead and while keeping an object in focus think about all you can see not in focus way out in the wings of vision. You will realize that your view extends from shoulder to shoulder. I often cross a street by looking straight ahead while thinking about the traffic to the right and left. In addition, we and monkeys can roll our eyes in their sockets and so without moving the head increase our view from one hundred and eighty degrees to two hundred and forty degrees. But that is not wide enough for a hunted being such as the pigeon and the squirrel.

The squirrel survived because it had the eyes to escape martens—at least enough of them escaped to keep the race of squirrels alive. The marten can run faster in the treetops than a squirrel. A tangle of underbrush and lofty branches is like a broad highway for a marten, which travels through them so swiftly the eye can hardly follow. This means that the squirrel must see the marten first so as to take steps.

As the squirrel cannot roll its eyes, other arrangements have to be made. So the squirrel's eyes are placed on each side of its head on a forward-sloping cheek. It sees both like a rabbit and like a monkey. Even more remarkable is the way the squirrel's eyes are adjusted for a good look when its body is vertical going up the trunk of a tree. This is a dangerous position as it must look down on the ground to the rear to see if it is being pursued at the same time that it must look up to see where it is going. A little more careful placement of eyes is needed to take care of this situation.

Squirrel eyes are to the flank and forward positions and also high near the top of its head, almost on a level with the flat crown. When you are standing directly behind a squirrel going up a tree, it can look backward over the top of its head and down its spine at you. This high eye position also lets a squirrel running along the ground look upward at a descending hawk or scan the high tree branches for a marten. You can't sneak up on a squirrel; wherever you are it can keep an eye on you without moving its body.

The squirrel's requirements vis-à-vis the marten are met by a particular placement of eyes in the head, but the sloth's problem can by no means be solved in this manner. That eerie animal lives suspended upside down in the darkest shadows of tropical treetops. To survive in this outlandish situation it must maintain a gaze in full circle in every direction, both around and up and down. This could not be accomplished by any position of eyes in the head, so in this case protoplasm provides a revolving neck, enabling the sloth to turn its head and look in every direction. To perfect this masterpiece, the sloth's hair runs in reverse, from its belly to its back, so as to shed the rain that cascades down through the leaves of the cecropia tree upon this upside-down body.

The super-eyesight of pigeons and squirrels is for daylight, and they have no night life. They depend so much on their keen eyes to see bread crumbs and peanuts that their smelling and touching equipment is dulled by infrequent use. They can see by powerful floodlights, but in order to get their accustomed sleep they generally shun Times Square and night baseball.

Few people stop to wonder where these populations of city wild animals spend the night. City squirrels vanish into holes in trees according to the time-honored squirrel custom, or into squirrel houses provided by the Park Commissioner. City pigeons retire to nests tucked away on ledges and in crevices of the city canyons. The city-pigeon mother produces two eggs per accouchement, which hatch in a little over two weeks. As city male pigeons are highly polygamous and always strutting, and female pigeons are highly fickle and always running after a new mate, the population is maintained at the rate of about ten broods per season. Nests are built with grass and twigs, but protoplasm, which fashions pigeons so well for city life, also inspires them to use paper clips and rubber bands.

Compare those eyes of the hunted with the kind of eyes which are given to the stalkers of lively meat. Instead of eyes looking in different directions and set wide apart to sweep the whole circle of the surroundings, the hunters have eyes set close together, directed forward, and able to combine two overlapping views into a single picture in clear focus. This binocular vision not only makes the prey crystal clear for grabbing or spearing but also separates the thing looked at from its surroundings and gives it three dimensions by which to judge the distance. This is also called stereoscopic—but whatever the name, it is one of protoplasm's most thrilling inventions. All the true stalkers have wonderful binocular eyes—including the dog, cat, fox, weasel, skunk, lynx, wolf, tiger, coyote, ape, and man. Interestingly, the ape and man are included in the list not because they are stalkers but because they are grabbers. Hunter eyes are great for making a place on a branch stand out clearly, for jumping to it without missing, and for giving distance to a fruit dangling on a limb.

All ordinary fish are in constant danger as the prey of something bigger, so they have big, round eyes that see separately and look in opposite directions. Fish eyes do not have eyelids, so they can't blink, which shows the fitness and economy of protoplasm's ways, for eyes that are under water all the time do not need eyelids to wipe off dust and protect the eyeball from bright sunlight.

The dogfish, however, has hunter eyes that can be directed straight ahead and focused on a distant spot. Dogfish eyes are like the eyes of human beings in the way they operate. Every photographer knows that to bring a close-up object into focus the focal distance must be lengthened—that is, the distance between the lens and the back of the eyeball where the image is formed. The closer you get to an object the more the front of the camera must be pulled out to bring it into focus. This the dogfish does by pushing forward the lenses of its eyes for close-up seeing. We get the same result by changing the shape of our lenses. This is intended to work automatically, but when it doesn't we can get the result with eyeglasses.

The owl sits on a limb up in a tree and sees a mouse on the ground ten feet below by dim moonlight. And since its big eyes stare forward with great binocular power, it can measure the distance to the mouse exactly. To go with these eyes the owl has a neck that can revolve three quarters of a circle because the mouse in question is not just sitting there looking back at the owl but is very much on the go. With the addition of the wide angle covered by the big eyes to the two-hundred-and-seventy-degree swing of the head, the owl can see far more than a complete circle without shifting its position, which might alarm the mouse. These are pursuit eyes that can hold the moving object in focus, going farther than a circle with the fixed look.

We find the championship eyes of the whole animal kingdom high in the daylight sky—they are the eyes of the eagle, the vulture, and the hawk. So keen are they that they can look down from a thousand feet in the air and spot a rabbit or a grouse half hidden in the grass. Sharp eyesight of the hunter eye is caused by the reflection of the object falling on a dense clump of pointed, cone-shaped cells. This tiny spot in the back of the eyeball absorbs light rays from the object through thousands of points, in a special manner which summons up a clear image in the mind. For almost all hunters, such as the skunk, the cougar, and ourselves, the single spot of cones is enough; we look straight ahead and approach directly the object of our gaze. But not so the eagle or the hawk, which, having fixed the rabbit in the grass with its sharp focusing cones, may then approach by a long, slanting dive. This causes the image of the target to move across the back of the eyeball on a curved path. Such a path is precisely plotted for the eagle eye so that instead of a clump of cones the diving bird has a curved path of cones. As the eagle zooms down, the rabbit in the grass is thus held in constant focus. It may seem to be a very small point that the curving path of the focusing cells in the eyeball corresponds exactly to the curving path of the dive, but it is of great importance to the individuals involved, and I wonder who thought of it.

Another fine optical problem is solved in a different way for the robin. As it stands on your lawn, its sharp eyes must spot a worm that is the color of the soil and of a shape to insinuate itself among the shadows of the grass. A robin can do this easily and even spot the little worm hole in the ground and wait for the worm to come out. However, the paths of the robin's binocular eyes cannot be crossed to see clearly within three inches, any more than you can see clearly to read this page if it is held at the tip of your nose. To take care of this, the robin stands very erect and stretches its neck as far as it can, tilting its tail upward to maintain balance. You often see a robin when worm hunting is in progress stretching up in this funny way. It is trying to increase the length of vision so as to see a worm or worm hole at its feet. When the robin is stooping over with its face near the ground, it is listening for worms instead of looking for them.

THE JUMPING SPIDER'S EYES

The logic of the flatfish's traveling eyes is comparable to the logic of giving the jumping spider a special setup for its special use.

Other spiders have four pairs of eyes distributed on a round head so that eight eyes point in different directions. This arrangement is suited to their way of life, which consists of sitting in the center of a silky orb in mid-air and taking it easy while the prey catches itself. These ordinary spiders do not need eyesight for stalking, for when the prey catches itself it sends a telegram with a jerk on the threads, and the patient spider can proceed at leisure in the direction of its meat. I imagine that the eight eyes which take in eight separate, vague views are useful when, having come to rest in strange territory after a long aerial trip in the wind, the spider scans surrounding objects and their relative positions by their lights and shadows, an engineering survey of the utmost importance for locating attachments for the web to be built in that place.

But the jumping spider has need for entirely different eyes because it stalks frisky meat, personally and bare-handed. To jump winged, bouncing crumbs calls for rare eyesight. The usual nonfocusing spider eyes are not stereoscopic—that is to say, are not side by side for measuring distance. On the other hand, the jumping spider gets its own version of hunter eyes. First, the head is redesigned to be squared off in front. Then two pairs of eyes are moved from around the head and placed in a row on this square front. These are evenly spaced so that when focused on the same point straight ahead they give stereoscopic vision for measuring the distance. The general effect is that of four headlights in a row attached to a wide board on a front bumper. Why not two? Well, I suppose that it is easier for protoplasm to keep the established distance of spider eyes and move them in pairs. If only one pair had been used, the distance would not have been wide enough to get a parallax angle for distance judging.

By the same principle, when we want to measure the distance to a star, we cannot get far enough apart with two observation points on the earth's surface. So we look at the star with a telescope on a certain date and then wait half a year to look at it again with the same telescope. In this way we get the same effect as stereoscopic vision, with two eyes set a distance apart—the distance in this case is between two opposite positions of the earth's orbit, separated by some 186 million miles, which gives a binocular glimpse into the heavens. The jumping spider uses the same principle without waiting six months.

We can call this quadrinocular instead of binocular vision. Nobody has ever asked a jumping spider how it feels to focus with four eyes instead of two, or whether it mentally throws away the images of the two interior eyes. But we can be sure that it works just fine because the jumping spider is the only animal on earth that can stalk dead prey with its eyes. Other hunters, whose vision depends largely on motion, stalk dead prey by smell when the wind is in the right direction. I am told that if you stand perfectly still down wind in front of a rampant lion you will appear as nothing more important than a tree trunk.

THE PERIO EYE

Suppose that you are taking a stroll along the water's edge near a mangrove swamp in tropical Africa. In such a place you expect weird events so you are not too surprised when a fish about six inches long comes out of the water and wanders along the beach ahead of you. It moves by lifting the forward part of the body and placing two fins side by side, using them as crutches. You are witnessing life emerging from the sea to become a land animal as it did millions of years ago.

The drive for food must have been terrific to cause a fish to use its fins as crutches instead of the smooth, easy swimming motion for which they were made. It seems to be a far and miraculous cry from these fin legs of the fish tottering over the sand before your eyes to the legs of a girl on the beach. But if you feel a little sorry for the poor fish out of its element which has not yet converted its fins into legs but must move like a cripple, try to catch the fish. Hops will take it out of your reach as quickly as the four legs of a rabbit. The fins bent under the body like limbs are operated by powerful muscles, which carry the fish on a swift hunting expedition for baby land crabs, sand fleas, and insects.

This land-hunting fish is named *Periophthalmus*, well-turned Greek for "revolving eye." Naturally, the situation calls for hunter eyes, and the perio has most wonderful and surprising hunter eyes. They are very large and bulging, affixed on the top of a turret that rises from the top of its head and is equipped with universal revolving joints. These are air eyes; they do not focus under water. The turret acts like the periscope of a submarine, and the eyes can scan the horizon when the fish is submerged just beneath the surface. When it walks on dry land the uncanny eyes bulge out and rotate in every direction, moving independently, sweeping all horizons at the same time. Besides the perio, the chameleon and a toad can roll their eyes independently, but this is as rare as it is for a boy to wiggle his ears.

When the perio spots prey, the eyes are rotated so that they stare straight ahead side by side. Because these protrude so far, it looks as though the fish is using binoculars. Thus it fixes the prey with a stare that should paralyze it with fear; then, measuring the distance, it gives a hop and a gulp. It can see a termite clearly ten feet away, and it can catch a fly on the wing. I can imagine no fate more terrifying than to be fixed by the binoculars of the all-seeing eyes of the perio.

You may wonder how such fine, outstanding optical equipment can survive damage from twigs or attacks from insects on shore leave, or what becomes of these protruding turret eyes if the fish wants to act like a fish and dive for safety.

Eyes are vital and delicate, and much body protection surrounds them. Even an elephant, with its deep-set, moribund eyes, has superb thick and bushy eyelashes over five inches long. A glance in the mirror tells us the ways and means which protoplasm thinks up to protect eyes—some of which we think are very artistic—the sculptured skull with its receptacle of reinforced bone, brows, lashes, lids, tear glands which turn on sanitary window-washing at the touch of a grain of dust or at the whisper of an emotion.

The perio eye turret also has special protection. It is cradled in a hammock of crisscrossed muscle ligaments. When the perio is eager to see well—in other words when it is very hungry—these muscles are drawn taut, with the result that the turret is lifted and the hungry perio can scan the horizon from a higher vantage point. On the other hand, if the prey is almost underfoot the operation is similar to the robin stretching up its neck to see an earthworm clearly. A bird hunting on land always has a most flexible neck, and the turret arrangement lends the perio the advantages of a neck. When the fish is ready to return to the water, or when its turret is apt to bump into twigs and things, hammock strings are relaxed and the turret drops. When it is retracted in this way a fold of tough skin is drawn across the eyeball; thus, with hatch covers in place, the fish is ready to dive and carry on the life of a fish.

THE ANABAS EYE

Perhaps as you walk along the shore of tropical Africa or by the Indian Ocean in Siam or Burma you may see another fish—this time a perch—emerging from the sea. This wanders on the beach in a tortuous, erratic course, not using its fins but poling itself along on its stomach with the spines of its gill covers. As gills are short and close to the body, it has to turn from side to side, pushing alternately with the right and then the left gills. This nine-inch perch is good eating and easy to catch, for it travels at the rate of only about one tenth of a mile per hour. If it feels like climbing a tree for a caterpillar it can easily shinny up because the spines on the gill covers stick into bark like spikes on the shoes of the telephone man mounting a pole.

However, if you don't eat it, watch it. This tree-climbing perch (named *Anabas,* Greek for "going up") is another interesting exhibit of a fish coming out of the water and trying to change into a land animal.

Whereas the perio has started to develop legs, the perch has started to develop lungs. It takes in oxygen from air passing over plates in the gills. The anabas does not need quick, leglike action as does the fast-hopping perio because it does not have to hurry back into the sea when its gills get dry. It can breathe air and take its time out of the water. In fact, it drowns if held under water too long. By the same token it cannot chase lively meat. This cumbersome, rolling fish, jerking itself along with gill spines can overtake only prey that moves more slowly than one tenth of a mile per hour—for example, a caterpillar, snail, shrimp on the beach, something dozing. There is plenty of slow and sleepy meat in the steaming stillness of the tropics, and so the climbing perch has succeeded and prospered with a large population during millions of years.

But we find nothing basically different in the eyes of the anabas—only in the way they are placed and operate. Otherwise, however, the anabas is utterly different and exciting. Protoplasm made this lumbering, tree-climbing fish successful by bestowing on it gills that act as lungs. There was no vital need to give it hunter's eyes, as there was in the case of the perio. Regular fish eyes—nearsighted, blurred vision, detecting forms of light and shadow—were good enough for catching sluggish meat. Pushing along with the gills was good enough too. Protoplasm waits for vivid and unusual challenges to create vivid and unusual body tools and equipment—in this case the appearance of air-breathing lungs.

THE HIPPA EYE

Another animal with wondrous eye equipment leads an unbelievable life on Atlantic sand beaches from Cape Cod to Florida. I have seen the *Hippa* in large numbers cavorting in the surf at Point O' Woods, Long Island, in the same place

where Robert Cushman Murphy found it six years earlier and
wrote it up in a pamphlet for the American Museum of Natural
History. This hippa colony is a few hundred yards south of
another phenomenon, the Sunken Forest of Fire Island, a rare
natural treasure, with a haunting story to tell of life survival in
the cup of virgin dunes. At this writing the Sunken Forest is
one of the few spots on the Atlantic Coast not yet violated by
"parkway" or "development." But I venture to say that few who
have explored the mysterious shadows of the woods of holly
and gum and listened to the whistling conversations of the
catbirds have ever guessed that the world's most tireless acrobatic performance is to be seen on the seaward side of the
dunes. Close beside the hippa colony girls in bikinis and flapping, frayed straw hats are more diverting—for one reason because they are larger than hippas. The same is true of the little
children, but they are more like hippas when they dig in the
sand and are tumbled by the surf.

The hippas maintain themselves at the lowest edge of the
sand exposed by the farthest withdrawal of a wave. Here they
line up by the thousands, although you will not see a single one
unless you look hard, for they exactly resemble smooth, oval
pebbles three quarters of an inch long, with a purplish, shiny,
wet hue, and they are tossed like pebbles in the surf. When
not tossing they are buried up to their eyes in sand.

When you are struck by a toppling wave the crash under-
mines the sand at your feet, throwing you off balance at the
same time that it deals a savage blow. This is the treatment
the hippa takes, not for fun, not occasionally, but for a lifetime.
It is forever coping with sudden disaster, forever establishing
and re-establishing its position, advancing and retreating between the lines of the toppling rollers. It can't survive if it
emerges into a quieter area above or below these narrow limits.
Its rhythm is that of the rolling breakers.

Undermined by an incoming crash, the hippa instantly folds
up and tucks away all its appendages, including its long-stalked

eyes, assuming the shape and action of the tumbled pebble. When the rush of water up the beach stops, the hippa is left momentarily under water, like a stone of coarse gravel. Then, as the water around it rushes seaward, it backs into the current, digs like mad with its hind legs to establish a position, erects two feathers in the swift current to strain out the microscopic food from the sand and salt water rushing seaward from the rear, and gets good fresh food in seconds.

When the retreated wave exposes the hippa, it is standing almost upright in sand, facing seaward. Out whip two eyes on long stalks; this is the time to be on guard for gulls and terns. A momentary passing shadow and the animal instantly folds up to become to all appearances a smooth, wet pebble. The hippa's eyes, so sensitive to light, orient it speedily into this position. Tumbled head over heels by every crashing wave, it never grows dizzy, but its eyes turn it instantly to face the bright light of sea and sky and the sparkle of the next oncoming wave.

When I get tired I think of the hippa down in the surf, and the never-ending rhythm of violence which it pursues hour after hour after hour, day after day after day. This brings me a feeling of relief, as I do not work as hard as the hippa.

TOAD EYES

A late-afternoon shower broke a scorching hot day, and when the sun came out an hour before sunset the trees and grass had the brightest possible green. While the pebbles in the path dried quickly, paling from dark glossy marbles to light grays and blues, the grass remained sopping wet after the good soaking down, and the earth in the flower bed was redolent black.

Here and there sunlight patches were spread by a honey-colored radiance that broke through shadowy curtains. Magically, many performers suddenly emerged to jump, fly, run, crawl in each patch. A four-inch toad was spotlighted in one of them, sitting motionless like a miniature Buddha of Kamakura, unnoticed by grasshoppers, caterpillars, beetles, flies, and worms that cavorted around.

The toad's eyes are famous for their jewel-like beauty—"emeralds flecked with red that betoken the fire of its soul." Otherwise a toad, from our viewpoint, is odious because it is sodden, potbellied, warty. This is utterly undeserved abuse for one of the most interesting animals on earth. It sits ready to do away with 90 per cent of the pests in your garden. The toad's body is a compilation of caterpillars, grasshoppers, beetles, grubs, flies, and worms. It never donated a single wart to anybody. It is cold and slimy because, as a thrilling exhibit of an animal that got stuck in the corridor of time and has not yet completely emerged from the water to become a land animal, it must keep its skin wet like a fish to get oxygen through its skin. A bitter milky juice oozes from the lumps above its eyes when it is tormented, but this does not hurt your skin, although it tastes terrible, so a sensible dog never eats a toad.

A snake arranges to swallow the toad without tormenting it. The toad slides comfortably down the snake's red lane, perhaps enjoying a voluptuous sensation. The toad, whole and comfortable inside the snake, does not struggle or squeak, and if it has the good fortune to be disgorged when the snake is alarmed and makes off in a hurry, the dinner hops away, and the incident is forgotten. The skunk, which is the other chief eater of toads, is not so subtle. It rolls the toad roughly on the ground to get rid of the awful-tasting milky juice before eating it.

Meanwhile the toad has some eating of its own to do and this brings us back to the moist, cool summer evening and the sun patch filled with lively meat. I can think of no other animal that collects dinner with so little strain and expenditure of energy, unless it is an elephant in a papyrus swamp, which reaches all around with its trunk, scarcely moving its head to gather in food and stuff itself.

Watch the little Buddha closely and you will see it heave a deep sigh at intervals as though utterly bored with sitting still. It is taking a deep breath through a makeshift lung system to add to the oxygen it is getting through its moist skin—the toad's lungs have been makeshifting for a few hundred million years and it has not yet acquired a pair of lungs worthy of a land animal.

Now and then, also, it seems to yawn—not too obviously, but politely, with slightly opened lips. At each yawn a grasshopper disappears from the grass, or a fly or caterpillar vanishes from a near-by leaf. They have been lassoed by a long tongue that whips out faster than the eye can follow. The toad's tongue is fastened by its tip to the lower lip and tapers to a forked base that lies down its throat while the toad is sitting motionless and watching the passing performance with its emerald orbs. At the instant the meat gets itself into the right spot, out whips the tongue like a lariat. When a good-sized wad of moist food is collected, the toad gives a blink and a gulp, heaves another sigh, and continues to sit on its haunches in satisfied serenity.

With so much wet earth and grass, a blind earthworm will probably ooze out of its tunnel, and, holding onto its hole with one end so as to find its way back quickly, stretch as far out as it can, feeling around for cast-off bits of plants to eat. This earthworm is a vision of steak and baked potato to the toad. Its eyes literally pop out of its head, but in the opposite way to what you would think.

It gives a hitch to adjust its seat; it stares—there is no rush. What makes it act I do not know—probably just the impulse of any hungry person who has been polite long enough—but, at long last, out whips the lariat. Then things happen. The earthworm holds onto its hole for dear life and only lets go

9

when it is pulled out like an elastic stretched almost to the breaking point. The worm, by no means happy to be stretched so far, whips and struggles and puts up such a fight that the imperturbable toad is driven to adopt an extraordinary measure.

An earthworm is muscular from end to end; it can even tie itself in loops; it can change its diameter by pulling together to expand or stretching out to get thinner; above all, it is slippery. It seems that no lips would be able to hold a fighting earthworm, half in and half out, and no toad wants to bite it in two and get only part of such a delicious dish. This would be especially true of the toad which has no lower teeth. The best way to cope with this problem is to hold the worm still by applying pressure.

The toad appears sleepy at this point and closes its eyes. The jewels no longer bulge, for the toad has pulled its eyeballs down through the roof of its mouth, using them to hold the worm firmly.

The toad's eyeballs must be very tough to be used as a wriggling worm press, and so they are. They are made of a sort of rigid plastic that has a little give combined with firmness. This material is the same as that of the skeleton of a human embryo when it must be molded to fit a womb. The embryo skeleton hardens into bone after the baby is born. Nature has a way of conjuring up the same kind of product in different animals for similar purposes. The criterion is: the material must have the texture, weight, and pliability that will do a job the best. If you and I want to hold a worm, the pads of thumb and finger will press it as well as the toad's eyeballs.

To use eyeballs for a food press there must be a trap door in the skull to permit them to be lowered. This is no problem for protoplasm, which is always ready to remodel bones to any shape and size to fit an animal's needs. Body equipment, on the other hand, is usually made out of standardized parts, which, though not interchangeable, are similar in every kind of animal. This is particularly true of eyes. It is an arresting fact that basically your eyes and mine are like the eyes of a toad, flatfish, tree-climbing perch, dog, sparrow, or monkey—evidence that the same powers of creation made the body structure of all creatures on earth.

The muscles which the toad uses to push down its eyeballs are the same muscles which we use to roll our eyes. Eye rolling came into use with binocular eyes, to direct them toward a moving object and keep it in clear focus. It is only a short step between eye rolling and eye pushing. So entirely new and unprecedented sets of muscles did not even have to be created for us and our animal associates who roll eyes.

FISH EYES

A fish cannot roll its eyes, but nevertheless fish eyes must roll in every direction in order to keep looking at something. A fish pursuing prey is constantly turning and twisting and being buffeted by currents. If its eyes couldn't move in their sockets, the image of the prey would dance erratically and make no sense, like a TV picture out of adjustment. I used to stand at the wheel of a schooner in a stormy sea and watch the compass floating in oil in the binnacle appear to twist and turn in every direction. It was merely holding a horizontal position while the ship cavorted around it. This is the way the fish's eye rolls when the body tilts to swim upward, or leans or turns; the eyeball holds steadily in view whatever it is looking at. This compensating motion of eyes inside a fish's head probably originated the whole idea of eyeball muscles—a good idea both for us and for the toad.

Protoplasm's genius is seen, not in the way it does the impossible, but in the way it does everything possible to help its creatures to live. For example, the sea hare has found an unconventional use for its intestines to meet an emergency. Pursued by a fierce dogfish, in a panic, about to be caught, the sea hare escapes by disemboweling in the face of its pursuer, a recourse with aspects more effective than that of the cuttle-fish ink. This is permissible behavior only if it succeeds, and also if, after escaping, the sea hare can grow another alimentary canal fast enough to preserve health. This it can do, and the sea hare lives happily after each clever escape.

There is also the case of the starfish, which has a stomach but no mouth for the entrance of food, no long tongue, trunk, paw, or beak for reaching. Nevertheless its protoplasm has found a way in which, lacking these tools, it can reach, scrape, and spoon up an oyster on the half shell. Oysters clamp themselves so tightly closed that you and I need a jimmy to open them. But a flabby little starfish can open an oyster easily with little suction pumps and lots of patience. Each one of the stubby feet of a starfish is a suction cup. These hundreds of feet are terminals of a vast pipe-line water system that runs all through the starfish, and, when you think it is merely resting on or hugging an oyster or mussel, it is actually pulling that miserable bivalve open. It wraps its big rays with their cup feet around the oyster. In this position, the starfish thinks about oyster meat, in its manner of thinking, and the emotion of anticipation of succulent sea food starts to pump the water out of its body's system, creating a vacuum in each tiny foot cup.

For a while the oyster is strong to resist and nothing happens. All is silent, motionless; you would not suspect that a vacuum machine is at work with a monstrous reverse hug. At length the oyster's muscles tire or its iron nerve is shattered, and resistance weakens in the face of the long, steady pull. It must rest and relax a bit. The closed shells give with a slight jerk. The crack opens slowly with little jerks as the pulling pressure is applied relentlessly, until the oyster is wide enough.

Now the starfish thrusts its stomach through a hole in the middle of its underside by turning its stomach inside out and poking it out like the finger of an inside-out glove. In this way the stomach does its own reaching. The oyster is digested outside the body of the starfish.

When the oyster food is gone, the uncanny stomach finger reverses; the starfish draws it back through the hole and patters off on the several hundred suction cups now turned into feet, to find another oyster.

FLASHLIGHT EYES

In considering special uses for eyes you may think of flashlight eyes, particularly in fishes that live in the dark depths of the sea. This is a fascinating idea from our own standpoint as it suggests headlights on the front of your car at night.

But eyes are made to receive light that enters from the outside world, and no eyes are known to generate light so that a being can let its light so shine before men that they may see its good works. Body lights shine out through skin or from glowing spots distributed over the body, and never through the eyes, which are fully occupied in a wide-awake animal with receiving light signals as to what to do next.

Everybody has seen a cat's eyes glow at night, or the eyes of a night-flying moth outside a window looking in, or the way the eyes of a fish glow at you balefully when it is lying on a beach at night or on a platter in a dark room. Most remarkable of all the night-shining eyes are the eyes of the big-eyed lemurs (named from the Latin for ghost or specter), which are monkeylike animals that hunt at night.

All such eyes appear to glow for the same reason that a polished beer can by the roadside shines by reflected light. No eyes see in the dark, but some eyes can see in such dim light that it looks dark to us. To collect dim light and build it up brighter, a reflector is installed on the back of the inside of the eyeball by a lining of reflecting cells behind the light-sensitive cells. Light filters through the sensitive cells, hits the reflector background, and bounces back through the same cells, stimulating those sensitive cells with double action. Animal-eye reflectors are made of crystal prisms that work better than a smooth mirror. The same idea is used with the lenses surrounding a lighthouse light, which reflect rays back and forth so as to weave a powerful beam. The coating of a cat's eyes is made of glistening, silvery crystals of guanine, the same kind of acid and salt crystals that give the white, powdery appearance to the fertilizer, guano.

Cats are primarily night hunters, although pet cats operate in the daytime because they want to keep company with us and that is the only time they get fed. But you see how the pussycat iris closes to a tiny vertical slit in what we call normal light. In the darkness of night, however, it opens wide and that is when we catch the reflection from the crystal coating at the back of its eyeballs, making them glow like a ghostly apparition.

The flashlight eyes of deep-sea fish are another curious deception. Their eyes are oversized, reflector-equipped, with the eyeball elongated to give it a sort of telescope power as the dim light passes down the length of the tube, striking light-sensitive cells as it goes. This makes them super-sensitive, but they do not shoot out beams of light.

However, fish, like people on the street, usually meet each other face to face. So deep-sea fish always have some of their light-producing spots beside their eyes, and these are the most important and brightest of their lights.

Squids come the nearest to having eyes that give forth light. They have five glowing spots on each eyeball. These are arranged in a crescent around the lower side of the eyeball, never around the upper, although it's fun to imagine how it would look if eyeballs had a circle of lights. Lights on squid eyeballs sometimes glow ultramarine, sometimes pearly white.

HUMAN EYES

The human eyeball is made of tough fibers, densely compact, with enough elasticity to change shape to conform with the lens as it alters for long focus or short focus. Although an eye-

xvi. *The kiwi bird, tailless and unable to fly, has the eyes of a hunted animal—placed on opposite sides of its head so that it can see trouble coming from every direction*

PLATE XVI

XVII. *The toad appears sleepy. He has just lowered his eyeballs through a trap door in his head and is using them to hold a worm in his mouth.*

PLATE XVII

BERNARDA
BRYSON

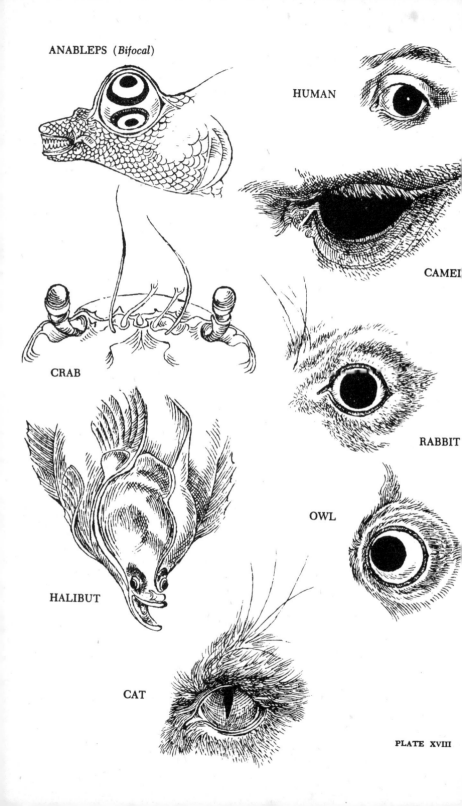

ANABLEPS (*Bifocal*)

HUMAN

CAMEL

CRAB

RABBIT

OWL

HALIBUT

CAT

PLATE XVIII

ball made of fibers instead of bone is lighter, more comfortable, more easily rolled than if it were made of bone, it has the disadvantage of being slightly translucent. To overcome this it is lined with a pigment that resembles a purplish grape skin to make it absolutely light tight.

The ball, about an inch in diameter, has a round opening in the front where light enters it. Fitted into this hole is a lens of clear material more exquisite and more optically perfect than the finest lens glass which man can make, and this focuses the light coming in from a wide angle on a small area in the back of the eyeball. The light coming through is controlled automatically by the iris that opens and closes. This wonderful mechanism, which works swiftly and without thought, keeps the sensitive cells inside the eyeball from being damaged by sharp variations of light vibrations. Bright light suddenly switched on at night causes pain.

Where the light strikes at the back of the eyeball there are countless long cells growing close together, like grass in your lawn, and the light permeates down their length, also like grass blades. The most sensitive of these long cells standing on end are called rods because they are blunt. In dim light these cells fill up quickly with a mysterious reddish-purple dye that makes them far more sensitive.

When you go from bright light into dim light it takes a while for the eyes to "get accustomed to the light"—that is, while your rods are filling up with reddish-purple dye. As the dye accumulates you see better and better. Night eyes consist entirely of rods. They are very sensitive but they do not see colors.

Other long cells which the light strikes, the cones, are sharp-pointed. These are filled with a bluish-violet dye. The cones give sharp vision. They are sensitive to the different wave lengths of light, so it is the cones which see colors. They are for daytime eyes.

The human eye has both rods and cones, so we see black and white by the dim light of night and colors by the bright light

XVIII. *All eyes are the same concept. Variations and additions are made for special purposes, and the eye's efficiency can be tuned up at will when the need arises.*

of day. The numbers of light-sensitive cells assembled inside the eyeball are, in our arithmetic, almost as great as the light vibrations that agitate them. Your eye has about 130 million rods for general seeing and seven million cones for concentrating on a spot with sharp focus.

When light coming into the eyeball strikes this vast receiving apparatus, it plays a tune, like swift fingers on piano keys, by setting up patterns of impulses. This awakens patterns communicated to the brain over an elaborate nerve system. That is seeing.

While we lead our lives seeing our friends and the wonders of the world with swift fluid glances, effortlessly, the vibrations of light coming into our eyeballs from outer space produce a great deal of action. Color pigments gather and disappear; rods and cones elongate and shorten; droplets of oil of various colors sometimes appear as filters to divide the light into its various wave lengths of primary colors. By no means all rods and cones are responding to the fingers on the keyboard at the same time. They are acting in groups, forming combinations and patterns that sketch the moving pictures decoded in the mind, painting in its tints and tones, swiftly shifting from moment to moment. The rods and cones are acting as a system of photoelectric cells which, when vibrated by light, fire off volleys of electric discharges that shoot these impulses of vision along the nerve channels to the brain. At the first instant, when touched with light, or at a sudden increase of intensity, these batteries let go with an extra-strong initial burst of fire, and then, as the pigments rush in, the cells co-ordinate their rhythm with the light vibrations and electric discharges level off.

This is the light machine that communicates the visions and concepts of the outer world to the living body. It can even pass the barrier to the internal, isolated life of individuals by communicating deep emotions. Eyes have an effect on the beholder without a word being spoken. They open wide with horror or amazement; they flood when feelings turn on tear glands; they half close with hate or anger; they shut with fear as well as for sleep.

Eyes began in the First Zoo. The amoeba has no eye, yet it is not blind, for the vibrations that create it permeate its little cell so that it is sensitive to light all over. One of the flagmen of the First Zoo (the *Euglena*) has a tiny rose-colored spot that can be called the first eye. This little spot acts as a light meter, guiding the actions of the flagman in the pursuit of life and happiness.

The vibrations that speed in from the beyond continued to drum with their Jove's lightning the quivering living stuff until something was hammered into shape within it, a device that passes all understanding, the modern eye.

I say "modern" in contrast to light-sensitive spots and pigments. The modern eye was perfected when all beings lived in the sea, and on our calendar that was a long time ago—perhaps three hundred million years—yet the same kind of eye has been receiving light in the same kind of way ever since. Variations and additions are made for special purposes, and the eye's efficiency can be tuned up at will, when the need arises. This was done for the eagle, which has six times more cones in its sharp focusing area than the human eye. But all eyes are the same concept as the first eye made in the euglena by night.

The same kind of light vibrations that gives energy and action to life also powers the chemical forces that create the material bodies of animals and plants. The more you think about it, the more this phenomenon stimulates a sense of profound awe and reverence.

The eye is no more marvelous than a nose or an ear, but it is in a superior position because it is closer to light. The eye is more obviously begotten by waves of light; it is a product of light.

All the light and color of the world would be only black energy without an eye and mind to see it. But it is not blackness when its vibrant waves are caught by receptors that create the patterns of the outside world.

So, as we behold light pouring into our bodies, bringing infinity into us from a long way off, this is the direction we turn in the urge to share. Our eyes are our most emotional connection with our surroundings. They offer us the best way to reach out from our loneliness.

This is a different kind of reaching from that of the other senses—of touch, taste, smell, and hearing. The others are comparatively local and more immediate. But images of the outside world brought to the human brain lend almost unlimited reach to areas and eras among the stars.

Part Four

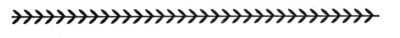

SECRETS OF SURVIVING

Chapter

>>>>>>>>>>>>>> 17 <<<<<<<<<<<<<<

On the Go

LISTEN TO THE NOISE of the city. It is a measure of the clumsiness and waste when the man animal uses nonliving energy to be on the go. A great and interesting difference between nonliving and living things is that the latter move quietly, systematically, and with economy. Nonliving bodies are booted around by the same forces of light, heat, gravity, and inertia that make living things move, but the nonliving waste tremendous energy with sound and fury in the crash of breakers, fall of water, explosion of volcanoes, crack of lightning, and rumble of thunder. As soon as the forces of nature are incorporated in an animal or plant they are stilled and given direction, causing the body to move in repeated patterns.

Protoplasm makes no wheels for its inventions to travel with, though occasionally it does use turning, as when a roundish fruit like an apple or a buckeye rolls along the ground to reach a good spot to raise its seedlings, or the golfball-like volvox revolves through water to reach food.

Compare the roar of the city, the ruckus of trucks, the din of airplanes, with the quietness of living things on the go. The motions of life make a diversity of sounds, but they are a different order of magnitude from the screeching of brakes, the clatter of garbage cans, the roar of engines. The sounds of animals on the go are the hums and rhythms of harmonious motion. They are often whispers of sound, and many, like the sounds of running ants, are below our range of hearing. They are keyed to the most efficient expenditure of energy; they fit each animal as it operates at the rates of speed most useful to it and they are generally silent to us except for an occasional buzz, whir, splash, breaking of twigs, or rustle of leaves. This is true regardless of the size of a body. A panther passes noiselessly through the forest. The giants of Lake Chad appear suddenly and mysteriously a few feet away, so quiet is their movement.

To be on the go is the universal characteristic of life. It is both inward and outward with every living body. The animal body is permeated by nerve impulses and fluids that travel through complicated networks of channels so that every living cell of the body is touched every instant by the passing currents. These movements impel muscles to co-ordinated action and put the animal on its course by making it strive for relief from the inner stress of the drive for food or the drive to mate that keeps animals perpetually on the move.

The outward get-up-and-go is most conspicuous in the Animal Kingdom, but it also affects the Plant Kingdom, though not so vividly and fast. The oak tree and the daisy have the same need to eat and mate, the same compulsion to survive as you and your dog have. The River of Life inside plants, with protoplasm resembling ours, has solved the problems of food and sex in special ways that remove the continual drive for food and the drive to mate from their lives.

Plants are on the go only when the next generation must find another space. This is accomplished by making a miniature model of the plant, complete with root, stem, and leaf, and packing it in a tight parcel that can roll, be carried by a bird or squirrel, or blow away in the wind. This requires no moving limbs, fins, or wings, although some seed parcels, such as those of maple and ash trees, have remarkable nonmoving wings. The blue beech attaches fancy, beautifully designed wings to its seeds. The cottonwood tree, milkweed, dandelion, and others spin silky threads attached to their miniature models to ride the winds. This is exactly the method used by spiders on the go, which spin spiderwebs for parachutes and launch themselves into the air.

The problem of a plant's going after a mate is solved by packing the male sperm, completely equipped with a full set of father's chromosomes, into a package as light as a grain of dust, even though it be from a massive sequoia or oak, so that it can ride the wind like dust. Moreover, many plants are hermaphrodites—that is, individuals that are both male and female at the same time—which makes it unnecessary for them to run after a mate.

In a timeless age, hundreds of millions of years ago, all life was confined to water. This may have been because the entire earth's surface was submerged when the tortured crust buckled and split as it cooled and erupted with volcanoes, or perhaps rock masses heaved out of the sea were parched and sterile long after the water teemed with life. In those days not so many beings were going so many places on earth as they are today.

Underwater organisms are the creatures of a mobile medium. The first animals and plants had little more to do than to keep themselves buoyant and their bodies would be borne on worldwide travels. Life, with all its fanciful contraptions, has never improved on this first and simplest means for going places.

In such an easygoing paradise there need be little distinction in the body of a plant or an animal. All society has the same manners, the same way of life. Plankton animals and open-sea floaters such as the phosphorescent animals of sea waves and the radiant sea gooseberries constitute the most widespread

populations of animal life on the face of the earth. They travel
to and fro and at various levels, being moved not only by flowing currents but also by the pulling power of light and dark,
rising to near the surface at night and sinking to dim depths
by day to hold their balance with changing light intensity. At
the same time the multitudes of diatom plants in their buoyant
glass boxes go side by side with the animals, mingling with
them in their traveling drops.

The traveling throng of plankton is devoured and converted
into fishes and all sorts of weird sea beings on the go. Their
pointed, streamlined bodies flex back and forth to move in a
manner that exceeds even flying in the air in its perfection of
smooth effortlessness.

But the drive for food and the drive to mate could not be
forever confined behind the barrier that divides water and land.
The River of Life is too dynamic. The bigger the fish, the more
crowded and dangerous the place becomes, and the more one
must dare to cross the barrier—even though one's ancestors
from time immemorial considered it insurmountable. The beyond must be investigated to see if new food supplies, safe
from competition, can be found, and also to discover retreats
where reproduction is safe from gliding apparitions, such as
sharks that suddenly appear out of the concealing gloom to
swallow eggs and babies. This necessity set in motion another
order of on the go—the migration of populations.

As we glance back along the corridors of time we see an
appalling spectacle that reveals the power of the drive of the
River of Life to break out of the water and be on the move to
the beyond. Crabs and hippas tossed up on the shore are
struggling in the air; horseshoe crabs, perios, and perches are
creeping on their bellies, wriggling, teetering up the sandy
beach, and many others are peeping out of the mud. This
emigration out of the sea would be incredible if we had to
depend on the fragments of this drama faintly outlined in the
shorthand script of dead fossils.

But all we have to do is to look around and we can see the struggle of ages long past in full swing. The operation of sculpturing new kinds of animals and re-forming them to fit new vital balances is not timed by a stop watch; it never reaches a goal; it is never finished and stopped. It is going on everywhere all the time, adapting some pigeons of the countryside to dodge wheels and legs in the city, some wolves to turn into man's best friend, some snakes to turn into birds—and, behold, they are all live before our eyes, both the before and after models.

This spectacle is revealed not merely in motionless before and after views; we can see it happening. Underwater animals are being driven to cross the barrier to the land before our eyes, and many of them are only half out of the water—to wit, frogs and toads that cannot venture too far away from water as they must not let their skins get dry. These lead double lives, first in the form of fish and then in the form of powerful leapers into the air. Is there any being on earth more astonishing than the double-lived animal, the tadpole and the frog?

The list of the half-outs is varied and exciting, led by horrendous dragons in the guise of crocodiles; there are chameleons and lizards that change their body colors from rich greens to brilliant reds to aquamarine as though they had inherited an idea from the fluid spectral colors of water; the water snake's way of moving has the same action as the patterns of waves and ripples. The water snake hunts at night in the dark depths and climbs out to bask on a warm, dry rock in the sunlight. Moreover, the water snake has caught on to the method used by land mammals for producing living babies inside the body instead of laying eggs. However, it does not reject the basic snake idea of multiple production—forty-four little snakes may wriggle out of their mother in one night.

Turtles are not only half out of water but also their feet are half fins. They use these projections for both swimming and walking. This compromise proves to be a handicap because a fin that is also a foot does not have the flexibility and vigorous action of an exclusive fin, while a foot that is also a fin is weak and awkward. So ever-resourceful protoplasm has built for the turtle a mighty dome of armor under which it can cower for protection in lieu of better mobility.

This is a peculiar example of the lengths to which proto-plasm will go to keep life going. It gave the elephant tonnage, and the dome of armor is the answer given to the turtle to help it solve the problem of how to live a little longer. However, the alternative answer of producing vast numbers which per-mit many to be killed without wiping out the race is more successful than elephant mass and turtle armor, judging by the numbers of flies, ants, and mosquitoes about.

The most fictitious type of halfway animal is the horse's hoof (the horseshoe crab) that creeps out of the water and totters across the gray sand-mud at low tide when you catch crabs and dig clams around the wharf, or is often seen on sand bars facing the open ocean. It reminds you of a small boy who has left his clothes down the beach and is trying to sneak away under an upturned basin.

The horseshoe crab has nothing but basic protoplasm kin-ship to either a horse or a crab. It is an underwater animal that breathes with gills, like a fish; it has pincers like a lobster, compound eyes like an insect, four pairs of legs like a spider. This is the ludicrous combination of the transitional horseshoe crab at this moment of time—a "moment" that, for the horse-shoe crab, is some 400 million years long.

Such success in remaining suspended in time, while seas rise and fall, continents appear and vanish, mountains wear down to plains, and the day grows longer through the drag of the tides slowly applying brakes to the earth's revolution, would seem to indicate an art of reproduction that deserves to be promoted.

The horseshoe crab was coerced across the barrier by the drive to mate rather than by the drive for food. It fills its stomach by plowing through mud and sand under water, rooting up worms and shrimps galore. It lives most all year as a full-time sea-water animal, until June. Then out it comes and starts the trek across the beach to find a sun-warmed hollow to hatch eggs. Its gills are able to breathe air, like those of a toad, on this occasion.

The female dominates the situation. She is much larger than the male, perhaps fifteen or twenty inches across, contrasted to the male's less than six inches. She leads the procession up the beach, advancing with unswerving determination, pulling after her a little male, who holds onto her tail with hooks that have suddenly grown at the tips of his front legs. He does not try to trot along behind her; he concentrates all his energy on holding on, while she drags him unceremoniously up the beach. This grasp on the tail is so strong (it has to be or he would get left behind and horseshoe crabs would have vanished from the earth) that it leaves scars on the female's tail. As the performance takes place exactly once a year in the life of each individual, you can tell the age of a female by counting the scars made by boy friends holding her tail.

Of course there is competition among the males—very fierce competition in fact. Billions of combats of billions of horseshoe crabs must have taken place through the ages involving eager males jousting for the privilege just this once to keep horseshoe crabs extant. Often a reverse harem of males follows the matriarch out of the sea, and, whether they are blinded by passion or whether hope springs eternal, they do not give up when one of their company has a tight hold on the tail. The others then take hold of one another's tails, and thus the female juggernaut bound on her annual mission drags a string of males in her wake, looking like a kite with a live tail.

Possibly the horseshoe crab was the daring pioneer who headed the march of animals out of the sea. If so, the creature seems to have been doing just that ever since—always taking the first steps to become a land animal without ever getting any farther. Because it has fish gills, insect eyes, and spider legs combined with a plastic bowl for a skeleton it may have gotten crossed up, stuck on a pin point of time, without ever becoming a clear-cut classification. For this is a unique model, not belonging to any group but only to itself, although most reference books classify the horseshoe crab with spiders because of the eight legs.

This relationship is odd as it is hard to imagine any two animals more remote in general appearance or in behavior. One lives under water like a fish and gets its food by plowing up the bottom; the other suspends itself in mid-air by glittering threads with which it throws up a fine modern cantilever construction, and catches winged insects, the modern wild animals of our world.

If we are trying to honor a pioneer who has the courage and ability to put across the epoch-making movement from the sea to the land, we should consider the claims of the perio and the anabas, whom we have discovered in a previous chapter, for they are true fish who actually scramble out on the beach, go for a walk, and climb trees, using true fins for walking and climbing.

We can also see the movement from the water to the land taking place in reverse. Some land animals either ran into food shortages or their mates dove into the water too often to escape their pursuers, or most likely their bodies grew too big to support on legs and still keep on the go, so they returned to the water.

Whales are a superb example of a return to the sea when that became necessary for them to survive. Like land mammals, they are warm-blooded, raise young in a womb, and nurse them on milk. They are by far the biggest animals ever to live on earth, outmeasuring the biggest dinosaurs. P. T. Barnum paid ten thousand dollars for Jumbo, the monster from Lake Chad, and spent twenty thousand dollars to transport him. Jumbo stood ten and three quarter feet at the shoulder and weighed six tons. Compare this to the ninety feet of a whale that tips the scales at one hundred and fifty tons.

Instead of trying to put up with the overwhelming trouble of getting around on legs, whales turned from the surge on land to plunge back into the sea. Now they are shaped like fish; they have no fur any more except a dab of hair on the top of the head and around the nose and lips; their ear flaps have disappeared, leaving only the ear hole, and the muscles are still under the skin by which they used to wiggle their ears. Legs are gone, or rather the front legs are remade into paddles, while the back legs are taken away, except that some of the leg bones are left buried in the body; the tail has widened to become a powerful paddle, the famous fluke.

Blubber is the most interesting change made in this sea-living land animal. The whale came down to the sea as a warm-blooded animal and still is. Its body requires warm blood; its babies need warm milk. Not so with fishes, whose body temperature varies with their surroundings; their blood may be warm or cold, according to the water that bathes them.

Land mammals live in freezing winter and hot summer, in the northland and the tropics, but their insides are always about the same temperature wherever they may be or go. Internal balance of mammal bodies is too delicate to be constantly changing with the thermometer, and it was necessary to install thermostatic controls that call for a faster heartbeat in chilly weather and various ways of keeping the blood warm.

This is far more difficult when the body is immersed all its life in cold water, yet whales, with their huge bulk, must maintain warmth. This they do while ranging through the seven seas for tons of food scooped up in huge mouthfuls as they push through the water like submarines and then strain out the one-eyed copepods, called krill. Krill for whales can be compared to our diet of grains, but whales have to get it by plowing thousands of miles of sea water. They especially like the polar seas, where icy water is fertile with krill.

Bears, dogs in winter, white arctic hares, foxes, and musk oxen, which live in cold places the year around, are given long-haired fur that keeps the warm skin from evaporating its moisture, which would cool it off. Whales, which can wear neither fur nor clothes under water, are given a blanket of deep, heat-packing fat, the blubber, which covers their skeleton just under the skin.

This is no mere whim. Life is in deadly earnest. A living being at birth is given every aid for survival. The relentless urge of protoplasm to survive will even send a big fellow back into the sea instead of letting it go forward with the conquering land armies, if that is what it must do to survive.

Getting out of the sea was the first great achievement of the River of Life toward greater scope and freedom. Once bellies were firmly planted on dry land and then raised on legs, a continent was discovered, lands of dreams in which countless models with thrilling, wonderful instruments and equipment could now be begotten, ready to dash off, crawl, run, walk, hop, leap—be on the go across the land.

This was a long, long step from the limitations of an amoeba swelling, contracting, and flowing inside a drop of water. Yet no live action, whether flying or digging, or a fist hard to the jaw, or a squirrel clearing space in the treetop, or the swing of a bat, has ever lost its connection with the same vital force that moves the amoeba. Every cell in the body is patterned on the amoeba, a personification of the River of Life.

Nevertheless, adjustments necessary for life to live on land were so drastic that it is astonishing this could ever be brought to pass. The first out in the air problem to be solved—and if there is a divine board of engineers puzzling over their drawing boards of living bodies, they may have been thwarted for millions of years over this one—was gravity.

Weight is an entirely different problem out of the water than it is under the water. In the case of nonliving weight, such as stone or lead, this doesn't matter because these do not have to move. But it is a fundamental necessity that a body move if it is to live. Therefore, bodies on land had to offset their lack of buoyancy out of the water and get themselves going with an array of propelling devices.

Another problem was to adjust the pressures inside the body to lighter air pressures. Life had become established through countless ages to living under water pressure; its designs were perfected. A thorough overhaul, a fresh and imaginative approach to the problem of different kinds of bodies living in air— yet still based on the fundamental energy concept of the River of Life—was called for, and this challenge was met by protoplasm.

The protoplasm of a single cell has a psyche that makes it itself, able to meet its challenges. This is dramatically revealed in the one-cellers. When billions of cells unite in a many-celled animal, the merger gives that animal the drive and ability to meet challenges of a much greater order of magnitude.

The greatest concentration of this spirit of the living cell is in the cerebral cortex. Thus the human psyche is equal to the greatest challenges of life and it will even be able to cope with the problems of gravity and pressure of outer space. Gravity is mysterious, but it is constant and measurable. We solve the problems it presents in the same way that protoplasm solves them. We are not set apart from nature. We do what protoplasm has always done by using a concentration of the same natural forces.

THE IRRESISTIBLE POWER OF FREEZING WATER

There are other natural forces we are unable to resist. These the River of Life either brushes aside or puts to good use, or they don't matter from the point of view of survival. For example, the force of expanding water when freezing. Most materials get smaller when they freeze, but water gets bigger. It breaks our milk bottles on the back porch, and our plumbing.

It would do no good to make milk bottles of iron and pipes of rock. This force is so great it has never been accurately measured. One inquisitive man burst a cast-iron cannon by filling it with water and letting it stand outdoors in zero weather.

It is estimated that freezing water exerts a force of fifteen tons to the square inch. This would mean that a four-inch pipe, a foot long, filled with water, when freezing would be pushed outward with a force of more than two thousand tons. Protoplasm easily avoids this destruction in fish and hibernating animals by changing the density of blood so that it doesn't freeze so easily as pure water. In the case of plants which live through a bitter-cold winter, the body is constructed to allow for expansion without any harm done. For example, tree trunks and evergreen needles are built with spaces between cells to accommodate expanding water crystals, and thus trees do not explode in the northland in winter. Lakes and ponds are spread out wide, and there is always plenty of room to expand around the shores and upward without any threat to life. In such ways nature outwits adversity, and so do we, by draining the pipes or keeping the house warm, or else we must call the plumber.

THE FAIRY TADPOLE

MacMillan's Arctic schooner was anchored in the harbor of Thule, North Greenland. Two officers of the Air Force brought aboard a cupful of the most energetic water animals that I have ever seen. Each was three quarters of an inch long, with a bowl-like shell suggesting a baby horseshoe crab (which it could not be because this creature had a hundred legs instead of eight), a powerful tail, and all legs whipping and going at terrific speed while the body twisted and bent in the agony of its urge to go somewhere.

It is unthinkable that such life is possible in a temporary fresh-water puddle at the face of the great Greenland icecap, fifteen degrees from the North Pole. The puddle is melted water caused by twenty-four hours per day of sunlight on the glacier's surface. It is icy cold and has but a few weeks of existence; it will suddenly freeze solid and be hard as steel for thirty-six weeks of the year. Yet this inhospitable water contained these lively things fashioned with leaflike swimming feet which also act as gills. In itself this is a marvel; yet how does the creature survive months and months of the polar night, when temperatures are forty, fifty, and sixty degrees below zero? How did it get there? How does it escape the crushing expansion of the freezing pool? Where does it go with all those feet to take it?

The animal is a fairy tadpole, an excellent name for an evanescent, wiggly little specter. This fascinating animal is a lively example of how far the River of Life goes in giving its creatures power for survival.

The fairy tadpole's life span from birth to death is compressed into a few weeks. When you recall that the life of a worker bee is only six weeks, it does not seem unusual for protoplasm to speed up an animal's biological time six hundred times faster than a man's. But this is a different proposition. The worker bee is solely a worker; it does not have to take time or worry over mating and reproducing. The next generation depends on the queen bee, who lives for years. Moreover, all bees live in a land of milk and honey, with unlimited supplies of the purest energy brewed by sunlight. The fairy tadpole has no alternative but to be on the go in clear ice water clinking with ice cubes. For some strange reason it does just this.

Life begins for the fairy tadpole in the mid-July sun-melt. Then the delicate shell of its egg bursts and the fairy tadpole matures in a day or so. If it is a female it looks around for a male, which it promptly embraces with a hundred legs, or whatever number of them it chooses. Then the couple swims around locked in each other's legs for several days. After that the female fairy tadpole carries a clutch of eggs in a fan-shaped pocket on segment number eleven of her abdomen for a day or so. Then she drops these eggs to the bottom and immediately goes after another mate. The eggs hatch so fast that sometimes the contents break out and are on the go before the eggs have time to leave the fan-shaped pocket of segment eleven.

The fairy tadpole has to move fast, so if no mate is encountered she makes eggs anyway and puts them in her pocket and drops them. This is another rare case (reminiscent of the aphids which had to lay such myriads of eggs to keep ahead of death they had no time for sex) in which young are produced without benefit of a male, but everything is thrown into the hopper or goes by the boards to save the fairy tadpole. By using both polygamy and independence the fairy tadpole can lay six clutches of eggs in several weeks and up to two hundred and fifty eggs per clutch. So life goes on with the fairy tadpole.

Soon comes the end of this tour de force. The signal comes in late August at the moment when the midnight sun first dips below the northern horizon. Then a shadowy specter passes across the reflections of the pool, and in its wake the water stiffens. The sole inhabitants of this outpost of life dive. The female mixes some dark-brown stuff like fast-drying glue with the egg shells of the last clutch. She drops them between stones, from which the water will drain before it freezes, so that they will not be crushed by ice, and she vanishes as the limpid water above her suddenly becomes rigid, having succeeded in this frantic last moment in creating the most indestructible seed of animal life known on earth.

Put fairy tadpole brown eggs to the test; try their resistances. You can cook them at two hundred degrees Fahrenheit—only twelve degrees below boiling—for an hour, and the embryo lives. You can glaciate them at three hundred and sixty degrees Fahrenheit below zero—a mere hundred degrees from absolute zero—and the embryo lives. You can keep these helpless, dead-looking little brown eggs in an air pressure of .000001 millimeters—only a whisper away from a complete vacuum—and the embryo lives.

If anything alive on earth indicates the possibility of animal life on other planets, where pressures are drastically different and temperatures are cruel, it is the dark-brown, thick-shelled winter eggs of the fairy tadpole. They can rest in crevices and under stones with a slab of thick ice overhead to keep out drying winds, using an infinitely tiny trace of water and oxygen, while sleeping for nine sunless months in deep, sub-zero temperatures, until ice water bathes them again. Then another incongruous animal with a hundred legs will burst out of each egg, grow like mad, and go hell bent to find a mate, drop eggs, find another mate, drop more eggs, and so on—so that another flock of fairy tadpoles will be able to carry on the same routine next July and August, and for hundreds of years.

Life must go on.

Chapter 18

Time

TIME IS THE ONLY FORCE of nature which man can do nothing about. He can control gravity, though, like time, gravity is omnipresent and man can neither increase nor diminish it. He can use light to his ends, switching it on and off at will; and he can do the same with heat, a quality of light which creates all life and makes it move. He can cope with weather, producing the weather he likes locally; he can even tamper with rain by seeding clouds and study the stratosphere mixing bowl of weather, whose winds have always been his servants—though when they knot their muscles he cowers. By concentrating his imagination, man has even figured out how to use the infinitely great power in the infinitely small atom.

But this tremendous thing called time can hardly be studied objectively. Science can pit all its facts, all its mathematics, all its experience against time and have nothing to say about what it is made of, its qualities, its derivations, its nature. Though every scientific experiment is paced by time, time itself is assumed, taken for granted, or turned over to the realm of philosophy. There is no definition of time because this mysterious force that is so much a part of our everyday lives is un-explainable in terms of any human concept. The dictionary cannot define it except by words like "duration," which does not define time because it is only a synonym.

All life is lived on a point of time, called the present moment, that moves at a constant rate out of the past and into the future. Yet it is almost impossible to measure time precisely.

Civil engineers of the eighteenth century were clockmakers. Their timepieces fired the imagination and became the keynote to progress. Before that, astronomy and navigation stirred men's minds. Today technical progress is paced by communication and control with electronics.

But remarkable as clock mechanisms are, they are makeshifts. Their periods of time mark the rate that a spot on the earth's surface whirls all the way around and comes back to the same position toward the sun. This is convenient but it doesn't fit the universal dimensions of time.

We try to pin time to our provincial thinking by saying that a day on another planet which rotates at a different rate is longer or shorter. This runs into trouble everywhere in the sky. A day on Mercury is eighty-eight times longer than on earth. On Venus it is two hundred and twenty-five times longer. A day on Mars is closest to ours, but even there each day is forty-one minutes longer. On Jupiter it is two and one half times shorter. Even more confounding in this unit of time for which man has built his clocks is that Mercury and Venus keep one face permanently toward the sun. This leaves us with the realization that by linking time to the rate of the earth's rotation, we are still unaware of the true nature of time.

Actually, the sundial is never in pace with the rotation of the earth. It is four minutes off every day—sometimes longer, sometimes shorter. We try to adjust our thinking to this by forcibly changing the hands of the clock, which brings us such frustrations as daylight-saving time. We try to adjust the printed calendar by making some months thirty, some thirty-one, days long, and before we can ever learn which is which, February pops up with twenty-eight or twenty-nine. Such an absurdly fluctuating unit as a day or a year is only a rubber yardstick of time.

A universal timepiece has recently been discovered that shows the timelessness of time. The vibration of atoms inside a molecule is as constant as anything known, and this is true on Mars, in the sun, throughout the universe. A frequency to an accuracy of one second in three hundred years has been measured, and this is four hundred times more accurate than our ticking clocks. The handiest of these timepieces, in case you want one in your office, is the ammonia molecule. It is formed as a pyramid with three hydrogen atoms at the corners of the base and a nitrogen atom at the summit. The nitrogen atom drops down toward the base and up again; occasionally it shoots through the base to a position on the other side without ever changing its rate. This timepiece is unrelated to the earth's rotation. It is the pulse beat of the universe.

The rotation of the earth has been measured by the ammonia molecule and found to be unsteady. Before you sell your possessions and have a final fling I hasten to add that this wobbling of our earth's rotating time unit is routine procedure. Because of the drag of the ocean tides combined with the braking effect on the earth's rotation by the crust of the earth slipping a bit over the melted metal that underlies it, the length of the day changes as much as one and one quarter seconds per year. Sometimes longer, sometimes shorter, the jerks and gives under the stresses are never rhythmic.

The effect of this caper is to slow down the show on the average of one thousandth of a second per century. Female horseshoe crabs that were dragging their males out of the sea and across the beaches before the Coal Age were living in a day five minutes shorter than our day. Not much to worry about, but how many five minutes are there in eternity? We can have no insight as to when time may come to an end, or what it will be like when it does, because we have no insight as to what time is.

Time seems to flow as does light; it appears to exert constant pressure in a way similar to gravity. Yet nobody can be sure that it flows always in the same direction, or if so, in what direction. It is impossible to imagine any part of the universe where there is no time. Our feeble periods of time vanish in the long perspective just as stars vanish in the long distance. An impenetrable mist of time and space walls in our universe. Is there any end to time and space? We cannot imagine. If there is no end, what amounts of time and space lie beyond? What sorts of worlds with what sorts of lives are there? From somewhere time reaches us, permeating life, causing the growth of a body with the same power that spells its death.

LIFE-SPAN TIME

How much time does each individual have? You might say that a baby has more time than an old person. Does a baby then possess a greater wealth of time?

The body grows with a succession of well-synchronized increments until the act of reproduction is reached. At that moment the torch of personality is passed to a new individual with a fresh allotment of life-span time. For the new individual the vital, the dominant fact of life, which determines its thinking and feeling, its outlook on the world, is its full allotment of life-span time. This personal measure of time is far more interesting and important to a being than astronomical time. We have sunrises and sunsets as colorful spectacles; we love birthdays as an annual opportunity for the ego to be on the receiving end of presents and greetings; but one's awareness of the passage of time gives more heed to the milestones of infant, youth, adolescent, young married, maturity, and ripe old age.

In the first chapter we saw a diagram of life-span time when a fat, feverish little bee became five different kinds of being in succession according to a timetable. During its six weeks from birth to death, it was foreordained to be cleaning woman, trained nurse, lady in waiting, housebuilder, nectar-fetcher, honey-maker. It was presented by its protoplasm with the various skills and tools as each moment arrived to perform a different duty. Paced with time, its growth was timed to bring it to the right size and strength for the various roles of its life span. At the right time it acquired a certain shape to fit certain flowers, and the power needed to fly with a heavy payload.

This bee lives as do we, according to the rising and setting of the sun. It is keyed to astronomical time, pacing the lengths of daylight and changes of seasonal temperatures with the flowering of plants. Its moment in eternity is measured by the same yardstick that measures ours. Only ours has six hundred times more days for living than the bee's.

Time carries life in a two-wheeled cart. One wheel is the rotation of the earth, by which plants and animals revolve through the ages. The other wheel of time's vehicle is a life cycle. This is a weird cart with a standard-sized wheel on one end of the axle, and on the other end the wheel has a great variety of sizes, tiny or huge.

I am sure that the May fly which lives one day doesn't consider itself cheated by life. Doubtless the bee's six weeks is a full and satisfactory life from its standpoint, while the Mauritius turtle looks upon one hundred and fifty years as a proper time to live. The wren lives three years, the dog three times the wren, the horse three times the dog, the man three times the horse, and each accepts its life as the right length for living.

Every individual possesses at birth the life-span time of its kind. But this carries no guarantee. It is a precarious inheritance.

Each animal, instinctively aware of this uncertainty, takes fervent steps to keep personally its share of life-span time. Although man can do nothing about time, he can, within the narrow limits of his moment, fight for the full share given to him. He desperately tries to rescue part of his life-span time from being stolen from him by traffic, worries, and overeating and has assembled a vast, expensive army of physicians and drug houses to his cause. The passion to hold onto life is instinctive. A snake, a Japanese beetle, a mouse, a duck, an aardvark, all have the same violent and irrepressible impulse to hold onto their life-span time as does man.

This creates a battle—chiefly waged between the same kind of creatures, where competition is keenest. The battle for life-span time is fought between different kinds of beings only when one is obviously threatening to steal life-span time from the other. Or one creature will slay another kind for a feast without a pang of conscience. This is a remarkable basic principle of life and has no moral aspect whatsoever. If animals didn't eat animals, this would be an entirely different living world. However, it seems to me that so-called civilization is debased when somebody kills a deer that looks at you with big round eyes or kills for fun a duck that is writing a poem in the air. No other animal treats other animals that way. They either eat them, shoo them off, or ignore them.

The essence of time is that something new is always happening. All living bodies, whether elephants or bees, live by the same astronomical time as it flashes past with the rising and setting of the sun, while each kind of body develops at entirely different rates of speed. Beings live a "short time" or "a long time," but the funny side of this is that each considers its particular time as the right time for living.

Age influences the operating speed of the cells of a mammal's body. The cut finger of a child under ten heals five times more quickly than the cut finger of a man of sixty. This means that it takes five times as many days for the same progress in the man's body. Because he makes mental adjustments for this slowing down of his body, he feels that time goes faster. It is well known that time seems to pass much more rapidly as people grow older. In the same proportion that movements and reactions become slower, the passing of external events from day to day is speeded up.

Expenditure of energy also influences life-span time. When its cells are working fast a child can expend a lot of energy because the mechanism for supplying more is in high gear. Older people mutter, "Where does young Andy get all that energy?" But when an aging adult expends energy, it takes longer to replace with slower working cells. The human animal has the advantage of consciously sensing inside wear and tear and voluntarily balancing bursts of energy with periods of rest.

An adult bee does not reduce its expenditure of energy as it grows older. Feverish activity makes every second longer for the bee, and its whole life is stretched out in relation to outside events. The bee's day is six hundred times longer than man's according to their respective time scales.

Because energy is heat, the temperature of the body influences the sense of passing time. A person with a high temperature feels time passing more slowly. A fly will buzz a lot harder in a hot room and automatically shorten its astronomical life even without getting slapped. On the other hand, a body that doesn't go at top speed all its life will have much more time for living. Whether or not it enjoys this is another question.

The Mauritius turtle, supposed to have one hundred and fifty years, grows big because it lives so long. But size is not the important point. The little sea anemone that you can hold in one hand neither runs nor swims, uses little energy, and lives to be sixty-six years old or more. The spider (not the jumping spider) that spends most of its time sitting still while its prey catch themselves may count fifteen years. The vulture, with one hundred and eleven years, seems to be an exception because we think of its screaming swoop and the activity of its prey to get away, but actually it is a lazy bird, gliding and floating more than it flaps its wings.

Statistics have turned up which give a hint of why each kind of animal considers that it has lived the right amount of time—in a sense, the same length of time. Heartbeats are counters of energy expenditure. They are a gauge that everybody can hear and feel. The little mouse's heartbeat goes *squish-squish-squish-squish* so rapidly that in a mouse's life-span time of three and one quarter years its heart scores 1,110,000,000 beats. The elephant's heartbeat goes *squzem-wham, squzem-wham, squzem-wham,* for seventy years, scoring 1,012,000,000 beats. The two totals are surprisingly close, but it may be coincidence. I do not know of anybody who has counted the heartbeat of the giant clam, the spider, or the sea anemone. That offers an opportunity for interesting research.

Time plays such a physical part in life that it is like a peculiar chemical added to bodies. Protoplasm copes with time, which it cannot stay, by using its genius to throttle down bodies. It reduces energy expenditure and increases living time with time out for living through sleep, hibernation, or pupation, in which an individual like a caterpillar will seal itself in a sort of coffin and stay dead, to all outward appearances.

This caterpillar sort of time out for living is linked to one of protoplasm's master tricks of legerdemain. The caterpillar, after having been sealed in its coffin for some time, will suddenly start to live again, break out, and emerge not as a caterpillar at all, but as an utterly different sort of creature with enormous wings. To cause an individual to take a number of different forms—in reality, to live the life of several animals, one after the other—is such an imaginative way to lengthen life-span time that only protoplasm could have thought it up.

Chapter 19

Transformations

THE SLEEP or hibernation recourse for time out for living is given to all the higher nervous systems from frogs and wrens to mice and monkeys. Fish and all underwater animals, except mammals which returned to the water from the land, enjoy a version of hibernation which is not geared to the rhythm of day and night, or to seasons, but is merely pausing and being quiescent. Since these creatures live subconscious lives and are stirred only by the drive for food and the drive to mate, their time out is just a case of wavering between action and inaction according to mood and impulse.

In the case of the insects, protoplasm dreamed up an entirely different way to have more time for living. This consists of putting an individual through a series of lives, letting it live as different kinds of creatures, one after another. It enjoys the way of life of a certain kind of animal, using its shape, size, color, and behavior for a length of time appropriate to that animal, and then it turns into an entirely different kind of animal, to lead another life. Transformations to lengthen life are so incredible we can consider the subject soberly, instead of as sheer hocus-pocus, only because such transformations are in full swing around us in the everyday world.

Some people get the notion that life on this planet is commonplace, less exciting, not so peculiar, as life on another planet would be. That is a terrestrial version of provincial thinking. Of course we shall expect new dimensions, undreamed-of powers, unrecognizable and weird kinds of life when taking a rocket trip to other worlds. Meanwhile, right here under our noses is vigorous living that bears little resemblance to the usual pattern of being born, growing up, reproducing, and dying.

I think the reason we are so fascinated by a legend of monsters or mites with supernatural powers in other worlds is that imaginations in the protoplasm of our minds are limited by actual experience, yet they have innate impulses to cross barriers. It is the nature of protoplasm in cerebral cortexes never to be satisfied but always to want more.

Science, which spearheads this basic drive, works from one obvious and tangible fact to another in hidden and out-of-the-way places. Usually these paths are privy to the scientists; they explore, in the laboratory or calculate in mathematical terms that other people can't know about or appreciate. But the sky is obvious to everybody, and today it influences everybody's life because millions who are not scientists taste the freedom from earth bonds by riding in airplanes. Yet, though the tantalizing spaces of the sky are spread out over our heads, they are not truly tangible but a great mystery toward which science is now trying to find steppingstones of one tangible fact after another.

This procedure necessarily makes scientists solemn and literal, as it does all of us except the poets and musicians, so that if there were no starry sky, nothing to see up there but blue by day and black by night, any suggestion of other worlds would be ridiculous, and this planet would be a finality in a fog. By the same token, if there were no transformations of beings here on earth to be seen, any suggestion of such a plan

10*

for being alive would be considered a myth. Protoplasm is more fanciful, more bizarre, more "unreal" than human imagination. I believe that there is more truth and reality in poetry than in the calculations of science.

The plan to have an individual born (or hatched), grow up, distill its personality into a microscopic nucleus, pass this to a descendant (who in a sense is the same person all over again or rather a compound of two persons), and die, is all right for relatively big and long-living animals such as fish, birds, and mammals, who have plenty of astronomical time to develop as individuals along these lines, and who can skip time with hibernation and sleep detours.

However, little things like insects don't always have time to grow up and distill their personality nucleuses on their very brief astronomical schedules. So their protoplasm accomplishes this result by putting them through a series of different kinds of beings. Out of the egg comes a caterpillar, a vegetarian with a healthy appetite and lots of leaves to feed on. No animal is more fortunately set for an abundant and happy life than a caterpillar animal. But the caterpillar has no female organs—it cannot reproduce. It is a larva animal. ("Larva," as already mentioned, is Latin for "specter.") The caterpillar animal with no drive to mate would vanish from the earth if it were to die.

Protoplasm's answer to this challenge is as remarkable as its making an animal that can't reproduce in the first place. It decrees that a caterpillar animal doesn't die, barring arsenic, accidents, and getting on the menu of birds and others. This is a wonderful fact, even though farmers and gardeners may not be thrilled by it. Instead of dying, the caterpillar animal stops trotting around, pulls in its feet, loses its colorful, bristly hairs, makes a waterproof cell in which to curl up and be undisturbed in the darkness and becomes as immovable as a "dead body"—that is, outwardly immovable compared to an animal on the go, but all the food that was packed into that caterpillar is now supplying the energy for a complete remodeling. The body is changing its form. The organs are re-arranging themselves. Mouth, eyes, legs, antennae are all new and different; even size and shape are utterly changed, and a most astounding innovation for an animal that had so recently been creeping around as lowly as a worm is the appearance of resplendent wings with a complex nervous and muscular system to take this animal into the air.

Neither sleep nor hibernation changes other animals. When they emerge they look and act as they did before, but when the caterpillar awakes where is it?. It is not to be seen. It hasn't died and there is no body. Is this butterfly the caterpillar? Any way you want to answer this question is the right answer. At this point the individuality of life slips through our fingers as did time and space. We are seeing an aspect of the immortality of protoplasm, a peculiar alternative to the immortality in genes.

The caterpillar-butterfly animal (remember it has not been compounded out of genes, and nothing was added from the outside; it grew that way from inside out) can now proceed to reproduce. The path of survival is now clear. It can copulate and lay eggs.

This is a diagram of the way insects are given more astronomical time. The idea is variously applied, with and without cocoons, but basically it consists of putting an individual through a succession of different kinds of lives. Sleep intervenes to give time out for living to others, but this multiple animal has its own peculiar kind of time out, during which its protoplasm works the legerdemain of transformation.

The idea of transforming a being from one kind of animal into another kind so as to keep it going on a different level of existence is an old story under the water, where all life began. For example, the oyster specter is a sexless little ball of an animal, called a spat, that swims around for several days by wriggling its body and waving hairs. When it feels the touch of copper the spat settles to the bottom. A penny dropped in the water will cause spats to cease their on the go and settle down. Because river water has more copper than sea water, oyster colonies usually settle in bays and estuaries.

Before giving up its active life forever the quaint spat looks for a hard surface, so oyster farmers "plow their fields" by throwing overboard blocks of cement, crates filled with rocks, or oyster shells. The spat feels around for a good spot, and as soon as it has found one, it makes two big shells, turns on its side, cements the left shell to the hard surface, and proceeds to transform its body into what we regard as an oyster. The foot vanishes; everything is moved around and this that was a swimming animal turns into what you see on the half shell in a restaurant. There are two kinds of animals in this case—the spat and the oyster. The spat has a few days of life and freedom of action, and the oyster has years of life but no on the go and no fun.

A nice philosophical question is: Which does the most living? The oyster part of this spat-oyster animal lives almost entirely on time out for living. It can be considered as hardly ever waking up, although of course it must stir in its sleep enough to eat what comes along in water currents and to reproduce. As it is cemented firmly to one spot for life the oyster is prevented from going to look for a mate. In this extremity males release their sperms in the water, and these float around until they are captured by the female in the same way she gets her food. This is a reminder of the way many plants are fertilized by throwing out their sperm (pollen grains) to travel in the wind and be caught haphazardly by the female pistils. The result is fruitful. A big old lady oyster can lay a half billion eggs in one season.

A barnacle is a triple sequence. Its swimming specter is known as a nauplius. It took science a long time to discover that this was the same being as a barnacle. The nauplius has one eye, three pairs of legs, and one shell. It is on the go for food, never pausing an instant, until suddenly, after a few days, it stops short in its tracks, crawls under something, sheds its outer garments, and emerges with two eyes, six pairs of legs, and two shells. This new animal is called a cypris.

The weird cypris now goes on a prowl like an insect with antennae, which it uses to feel around for a place to settle down, often on a rock just below the high-tide line. Or it may by chance attach itself to a ship's bottom or even a whale. It cements its head to the spot and, standing on its head, throws away the two shells, mixes cement, and makes the little round fortress which everybody calls a barnacle.

The animal inside is now utterly unlike the nauplius I and II. It closes its eyes forever, while its legs are turned into feathers for catching food and sperm. I don't know whether anybody has discovered how long oysters and barnacles live, barring accidents or being eaten by starfish and people. They bear no signs such as tree rings or horse's teeth to tell their age. Oysters are in the prime of life when, after three to five years, they are hoisted up for the menu. As far as I know, they never die a natural death. Neither do barnacles. Who has ever seen an old barnacle? Time out for living puts an echo of immortality into their sleepy lives.

Of course, a popular example of the double-life plan is the tadpole-frog creature. That an animal can be like a little fish at one time and have an entirely different body that takes great leaps with long legs at another time is just as marvelous in its way as the caterpillar-butterfly operation. The latter may seem more magical only because the tadpole doesn't become living-dead but turns into another animal before our eyes.

THE RIP VAN WINKLE OF THE ANIMAL KINGDOM

A dramatic example of time out for living with insect transformation is that of the seventeen-year locust. This gives the time out to the specter, while reproducing is handled by the on-the-go animal, which is short-lived and very noisy. This reverses the spat-oyster and the nauplius-barnacle plan and shows the versatility of the River of Life in the way it uses various proportions and combinations of the same ideas to introduce the utmost life into the various living spaces of the earth.

The seventeen-year locust is a robust bug measuring one and three quarter inches from its squared-off head, which is shaped like a hammer, to the tips of its strong parchment wings. It is heavy, powerful, looks as though it is built for a long life of fierce conquest, and can make more noise than any other insect on earth. When a large number of seventeen-year locusts turn on their buzz saws at the same time, they can drown out the sound of city traffic or the roar of a train. This uproar is the cry of the males for their mates; the females are silent. Locust mechanism is the most complicated sound machine in the Animal Kingdom, not excepting those which cause the trumpeting of an elephant, the howling of the howler monkey, the barking of the dog, or the babble of the human cocktail party.

Two plates cover an air chamber at the base of the abdomen. Beneath these is a diaphragm with a muscle attached underneath to its center. This muscle is stretched across the air chamber and penetrates another diaphragm, which acts as a sound mirror. Using the muscle to vibrate the outer diaphragm and magnifying it with the inner, the animal can make the most raucous noise. Many small boys have tried the same idea with waxed paper stretched tightly over the open end of a tin can, making it vibrate by pulling the fingers along a string attached to the center.

The net result is that the seventeen-year locust enjoys a few days of energetic mating, lays eggs, and dies. These animals are air-borne in a heavy buzzing way like the dytiscus, but they spend their entire brief lives aloft. To lay eggs they make deep cuts in the twigs of trees and if these happen to be fruit trees of an orchard, the result brings a call for help to the Department of Agriculture.

In six weeks eggs hatch and the sexless specters creep out. The damage to the limb is often enough to make it break and fall, but if it doesn't fall the seventeen-year locust babies drop to the ground anyway and creep through cracks into the blackness of the soil, spurning the sunshine for seventeen years.

The individuals that had been so big, so noisy, and in such appalling numbers have died a natural death, and everybody forgets the whole affair. Years pass, while the invisible specters live in the lush, moist soil that has been called the most effective digestive system known. Every four years these weird little animals stir in their sleep, break their outer garments. Finally, unless a real-estate development has come along or a concrete highway has been built overhead during the seventeen years, a big and husky version of the animal builds a mud chimney, comes out of the top of this, spreads a fresh pair of wings, flies to the branches, pulls on its noise-box muscle, as its father did seventeen years before, and people think that a plague of locusts has suddenly struck again.

As we go about our business all unsuspecting, this life is being prepared on schedule, silently and hidden in the ground. A coming-out party will occur around New York City in 1962 of the creatures which dropped from the trees and went underground in 1945. Indiana and western Ohio have a coming-out party scheduled for 1970 from the 1953 brood. Down in southern Ohio, Kentucky, and Tennessee they will have a coming-out party in 1957. So life goes on, with time out for living, for the seventeen-year locust.

Chapter 20

Time Out for Living

THE SPECK OF PROTOPLASM that flows around and around within its cell wall is a mixing bowl of creative and positive immortality. Evidence of its genius is seen in the shapes, sizes, and devices that enable things to live under all sorts of conditions and circumstances. In the long epochs when mountains were pushed up and worn down flat, and the continents and oceans were taking entirely different shapes, animals and plants were also being converted in revolutionary ways. Today this operation is going on around us without a pause, so those animals we see are just a short sequence out of the reel of time. And somehow each kind has found a secret for conquering time.

For example, through evolution life enjoys an immunity to destruction by changing climates and conditions. This is a kind of immortality that needs no time out for living.

New forms emerge, not suddenly out of a clap of thunder, but deliberately, by evolving slowly from one form into another form.

Man's physical body is that of a monkey, and the bodies of both man and monkey have the same basic pattern as the body of a dogfish. Dogfish and man both have skulls to house their brains, jointed backbones to house spinal columns, hearts in corresponding positions, stomachs, livers, kidneys, spleens, ovaries or testes.

A dogfish breathes with gills and a man with lungs, so in that respect the dogfish keeps an exclusively underwater organ. Otherwise, without adding anything new, the dogfish can be squeezed and poked into a good model of a mammal. The similarity includes microscopic details, such as the way nerves and arteries branch. This is also true of the toad, the titmouse, and the turtle. It shows the kinship of all animals, both water-breathing and air-breathing.

There is supreme strength and direction back of life, in contrast to an operation that is incoherent and cryptic. This is the handiwork that lifted life across the barrier from the sea to the land. Organisms were altered with great ingenuity, while all breathe oxygen, eat, and multiply.

It is within the bounds of reason that when the next vital barrier is crossed and beings surmount the stratosphere and spread over the fresh pastures of the solar system, life's basic skill of immortality will evolve undreamed-of shapes for animals. In that case, our descendants on other planets may be unrecognizable as relatives of those left on earth.

The efforts being made today toward breaking the gravity barrier are instinctively similar to the efforts of the underwater creatures which first crept out onto the beach. The men who pioneer the first flights beyond will be like the tree-climbing fish or frogs that, while sojourning out there, must keep "their skins wet" with the ancestral medium and hurry home to get a good breath of oxygen.

The physical aspects of immortality are the genes. An individual body dies, but its life units—the composition of its personality—live on in its offspring, and the body of the corporation is intact. In a sense an individual is merely a carrying case that has a life packed in it and conveys that life along the course for a while, and then renews its youth by turning its genes over to another.

The amoeba, the simplest diagram of an individual, has not yet achieved the resource of genes, yet even this blob of a being doesn't die. It renews its youth when old age is upon it by breaking in two, and two amoebas march off. If that can be called death, where is the body?

A similar immortality is enjoyed by the sea anemone, which can reproduce by stepping out in opposite directions with such determination that it breaks in two. This is a living demonstration of the saying "he flung himself on his horse and galloped off in every direction." The halves of the anemone ooze off in their separate ways, each soon growing to full size, and there are two fresh, young anemones ready with a full quota of life-span time.

When you look at the population of First Zooers in a drop of water, the most striking fact is their activity. They are on the go pell-mell. They never stop to rest. That is because microscopic life has microscopic time, living in seconds, whereas bigger bodies live in days and years. You might say that the First Zooers do not have time for sleep, but it would be more accurate to say that they don't need sleep for time. And there is another reason why primitive life doesn't need sleep; it is due to the nature of sleep itself, as we shall see.

SLEEP

Sleep is such a common event that we lose sight of how exciting it is and how marvelously it works. Sleep is a great fact of life that decrees the pattern and pace of living, the interrelations of animals, and all their habits of feeling and acting.

So powerful is sleep that it can hush the hubbub of a great city. I have never forgotten once in college days, when night life was a must, standing on the corner of Fifth Avenue and

Forty-second Street, considered one of the most crowded corners in the world, at 3:00 A.M. and seeing not a sign of life in any direction, until a single taxi hove in sight five blocks away, doubtless taking home a passenger sound asleep.

Surprisingly little is known about the nature of sleep. Books on animal life and even standard biology textbooks ignore the subject. I have searched them in vain. Sleep is a mystery to most of us, like the great enigma of time to which it is related.

People enjoy sleep. It has a charm all its own. It is a nirvana with which we may indulge ourselves without shortening earthly existence—in fact, just the opposite. Nightly sleep has the fascination of a new hand of bridge or another hole of golf in the way it starts you off with fresh opportunities and puts a bad day behind you. It does this by ironing out the skin, the feelings, and the worries. Moreover, it restores judgment, which is the most important voluntary asset for living of the human animal. You have an important question to settle, a problem rests on your shoulders which may involve not only your own but other people's lives. You throw it around all day, growing ever more uncertain about the answer. When you sleep, the subconscious thinking machine may take over the problem and sometimes does a better job than the conscious. At such a time baffling crosscurrents seem to be suppressed, the main current of thinking flows freely in the subconscious, and when you wake up the answer is there, beautifully depicted in your conscious thoughts. This is the creative power of good sleep.

Yet so little is known about the nature of sleep that all sorts of superstitions and fallacies have clung to it throughout time. This is a result of the witchcraft of dreams, when subconscious sensations stored up in the cerebral cortex while awake return to haunt you in visual true-life guise. There is no sense of time in a dream, and events are unconnected with anything outside the body, so they have an ethereal, magical quality.

They may be either delightful and romantic or nightmarish and scare you awake if the subconscious network of nerves is overloaded so that their volleys of impulses collide. Sleep carries romantic lore on the one hand and frightening phobias on the other.

Even scientific inquiry was so thwarted by sleep that it turned up a misconception. It was thought that during sixteen hours of conscious living poisons formed in the body and acids accumulated in muscles when they were used energetically. Then eight hours of sleep were needed to purge the body of these chemicals. This led to the dogma of the rhythm of sixteen hours awake alternating with eight hours asleep.

What matters is the proportion of sleep to waking, not the number of hours of sleep. You can lead a singing, soaring life on a four-to-two or an eight-to-four basis. The sixteen-to-eight cycle is imposed by long-standing social custom that began with the cave men, before nights were illuminated with pink electric-light bulbs. It is one of the habits imprinted in the nervous system, a logical and normal habit because it roughtly fits the daylight-and-darkness routine where the majority of people live.

However, sleep is a great gift that protoplasm makes to an individual. With sleep a big active body can burn up energy during the day and then revoke time by taking time out. By nature, sleep has nothing to do with daylight and darkness.

I saw no stress and strain on the nervous systems of the crew of MacMillan's arctic schooner when polar daylight was continuous. Men simply slept when they wanted to. But if the proportion of sleep is less than one to two the body gets tired. If with the sun shining all the time, you are stimulated to look for walrus and polar bear and collect brilliant polar wild flowers and don't want to miss anything of this high adventure, at last you will be stricken unconscious with sleep. Sleep comes with a damping of the vibrant volleys discharged in the nervous system. This control can be held off for a while by strong stimulation. But after two or three days awake and active, I venture to say that not even a radiogram saying that you have just inherited a million dollars could keep you from going to sleep.

You don't have to go to the polar regions to see that sleep is independent of night and day. Just watch the human animals sleeping in airplanes and railroad trains. Boredom puts you to sleep—that is, boredom in the sense of a damping of excitement inside you, a loss of curiosity or interest. This occurs regardless of whether your system needs sleep. Look at your dog, or cat, or any animal, or a human baby that hasn't yet been imprinted with the sixteen-to-eight social habit. Their bodies wake up only briefly, when an internal alarm system sounds that a function necessary for living must be performed. A baby expresses its displeasure by yelling. Then, as soon as it is fed, it goes to sleep again. The normal condition is to be asleep; it is an emergency to be awake. Evidently, the inborn impulse to wake up and live leads to consciousness; consciousness leads to interest, curiosity, thrills. This activity extends nerves, excites them more and more, creates new and marvelous channels for their impulses, and in one animal— namely, man—has grown into the marvelous conscious thinking and enjoying mechanism we call the cerebral cortex. This is the seat of sleep. Until its vibrations are damped it will keep you in the special condition of consciousness. Sometimes sleep-producing fatigue is so great that its pressure overflows into other circuits, sending sensations into the brain to keep you from sleeping. Overtiredness then works in the same way as pain.

The consciousness by which you alone enjoy life started as an emergency. Most animals, including the bee, the dytiscus, the perio, the dogfish, have probably not much beyond the instinctive level of mental activity. I doubt whether that can be called consciousness as we think of it. They sense a situation, but thinking it over or enjoying it is doubtful, except perhaps in monkeys, dogs, horses, and animals that have established habits of alertness.

An earthworm can be trained to take a path to the right instead of to the left at a fork in its tunnel. This isn't intelligence, although it may be a rudimentary seed of intelligence. This is habit formed by repetition of a certain nerve impulse circuit. Does an earthworm sleep? It is asleep all the time in its way and only bestirs itself at an internal summons, as the human baby does.

In other words, the earthworm has a nervous system so simple that its muscles act only on direct stimulation. The earthworm doesn't stand at the fork of the tunnel and figure, "Now let's see which way is the best bet." Its body has been trained to lead it by touch in the direction it is trained to go. Protoplasm leads it by the hand. It works as automatically as Dr. Wiener's electronic machines that can run around the room, avoid collision with table and chair legs, find the door, go out into the hall, turn to the left and run down the hall. A cybernetics machine does not say, "I will not be bossed. I resent this," and turn and go the wrong way, any more than does the earthworm.

The nerve system of the earthworm, simple as it is, is well suited for a luxurious and productive life. The earthworm census gives us a population of from two hundred fifty thousand to two and one half million earthworms per acre in rich farmland. The last figure bestows on the farmer more pounds of earthworms per acre working for him than the weight of all his domestic animals put together. Worms can be bred to the tune of three thousand worms per cubic foot of soil. These statistics suggest that earthworms have a secret for getting food and for reproducing that is bewilderingly successful. They can be considered as one of the most efficient designs for living among land animals. They love the land—it is their food supply. An acre of earthworms eats more than two hundred tons of good dirt per year.

The reproductive secret of the earthworm is strange indeed. Its protoplasm has figured out how a smooth, tube-shaped body that is blind and glides along in the blackness of a tunnel which exactly fits the diameter of its body can still enjoy the time-honored custom of passing genes from one individual to another. How to find a mate under these circumstances, how to recognize the opposite sex, how to do anything about it if recognized, would surely baffle our cerebral cortexes.

The earthworm secret of success lies in the abolishment of mate hunting by creating all earthworms alike—each is both male and female. But though an earthworm is both male and female, it cannot fertilize itself.

Every earthworm has a raised, dark-colored band about one third of the way along its body from the front end. A poet would call this the earthworm's wedding ring. Two earthworms projecting from adjacent tunnels will bend over and glue themselves together by this ring. Then they reciprocate. Each endows the other with sperm. When they separate, the glue of the bands loosens and becomes a sort of plastic bag. Each worm now peels this off over his-her head. As it slips along the body it collects eggs, which are then sealed up, by a sort of drawstring, in the bag, along with the sperm. The plastic bag thereupon acts as an ovary in which, outside the bodies of the parents, the sperm and the eggs join, and after a little while, on a rainy day, tiny earthworms dissolve the end of the bag and wriggle out, eager for their first dinner of good dirt.

Up to a certain point our nervous systems operate like the earthworm's, especially when we are asleep and our bodies are running on the timeless subconscious level. We can have dreams because our cerebral cortex conjures up pseudoconscious pictures out of vibrations that overflow from an overloaded nervous system. I doubt whether an earthworm has dreams in its subconscious life, but I suppose, from barkings and growlings in sleep, that a dog has dreams. He has a cerebral cortex too, although not nearly so big as ours.

A CLOSE LOOK AT THE CEREBRAL CORTEX

Few people have any idea what a cerebral cortex—the machine that enables them to stay awake and enjoy life—looks like. Its nature is so miraculous that this stay-awake or thinking machine can think about itself.

It is a very thin (one sixteenth to one eighth of an inch) film of pinkish, coral gray matter covering masses of white fibers. This film undulates with swellings and folds, for in this way protoplasm can spread out a much greater surface without making the head bigger. It would take a head many times larger to lay out a smoothly rounded surface of gray matter, so it builds this superb command post with many convolutions.

The cerebral cortex is the most exciting and creative of the inventions of the living cell, and is second only to the heart in importance. (The heart is the cornerstone of animal life. It turned the bodies of animals from stationary open systems, like that of the sponge, in which circulation is set up by waving hairs, into closed systems which can carry around their sea water in the form of blood within their bodies and thus are free to go places. Sea water and blood are chemically similar, with almost the same degree of saltiness.)

The cerebral cortex is the inspiration and impetus of life. Yet there could be a kind of vigorous and colorful life on earth without it. We see it in the reflex actions of bees, flies, fishes, and earthworms. Without a cerebral cortex, even a mammal has enough reflex nerve controls to walk, run, avoid obstacles, as does the cybernetic machine. I once witnessed hideous proof of this when a man carrying ammunition had his head blown off by a bursting shell yet proceeded at a trot toward his destination for about fifty feet before dropping dead.

The cerebral cortex is a double-barreled action. It handles the subconscious, reflex controls and also raises certain nerve impulses out of the mysterious depths of no-thought and turns them into ideas that become consciousness and imagination—the chief ingredients of human living. The cortex also blends the subconscious and the conscious. Some people are only half awake. They operate on a serene, routine basis, free of worry. They are placid people who might be considered a little dumb.

When the cerebral cortex takes an idea circuit out of the subconscious and flashes it on the screen of the conscious, we speak of intuition, flashes of genius, inspiration. This co-operation between the two systems of control, bringing intercommunication between thoughts and feelings, is one of the great gifts of the cerebral cortex.

The smooth-running operation gives no hint of the immense complexity of the cerebral cortex and the incredible marvel of the way it quietly sorts out billions of tiny electric circuits and presents them instantaneously for our consideration. The whole cerebral cortex is not active all the time. It avoids confusion by choosing this or that set of vibration patterns while others are damped out of consciousness. You can think of only one thing at a time, although the idea machine works with such lightning speed that you can think of a variety of subjects by jumping around. Jumping around is the normal way for the cerebral cortex to work, because it gives the mind a chance to rest in spots.

In fact, we use very little of our minds in the normal course of events, for most circuits are resting or lolling around in the subconscious. It is easier to let the thoughts jump around, which is what they do in the relaxed or half-awake state, or in day dreaming, while the effortless, instinctive circuits carry on. It takes effort and uses up energy to concentrate, and it takes effort to recollect circuits, dredge them up from the subconscious, and put them together to produce creative thinking. Thinking uses almost as much energy as hard muscular exercise; you get hungry writing a book.

Underlying the thin film of gray matter is white stuff consisting of a mass of nerves receiving impulses from all over the skin, from muscles throughout the body, and from the senses. A nerve is a cable of countless nerve fibers bound together so tightly that in cross section they make hexagon patterns like the beehive. Each nerve fiber is a single cell drawn far out long and thin. This infinitely slender fiber is not solid like a wire, but it is a cell in the shape of a long, soft tube or immensely long, thin bag. Such a form for the basic living cell, normally shaped like a battered shoe box, is a wonder.

A nerve fiber, like other cells, can expand under pressure. It is filled with a fluid. If it is severed it will grow out with the movement of an amoeba, elongating by the strange force inherent in a living cell. It forms a waxy lining like paraffin and this is lined with protoplasm, but the fluid inside the cylinder, which carries messages boosted along by electric discharges, is not protoplasm. Electric impulses are fast but not continuous. When discharging, they make a microscopic tattoo with a strength of around one fifty millionth of a volt. This is feeble on our gross electric scale, but this nerve fiber is a million times more sensitive than any other sense in our bodies. The electricity generated in the nerve is either a by-product of its activity, like sparks from an emery wheel, or it is a vital booster of nerve messages along their course. The speed of the mysterious nerve impulse or message is not nearly so fast as electricity; it averages about three hundred and thirty feet per second.

A nerve nas an independent existence. It can go on discharging impulses when not inside the body. As a structure and in behavior it does not seem any more weird and strange than other parts of the body. It is endowed with special powers that no one can explain, but so are all living cells—so are the heart and lungs. It is what happens to these impulses when they are poured into the cerebral cortex that is the miracle. It is the way they are sorted and combined to give guidance and control to muscles, and to produce thoughts.

The subconscious department makes the body function by

xix. *When you sleep, the subconscious thinking machine may take over a problem and sometimes do a better job than the conscious.*

BERNARDA BRYSON

PLATE XIX

causing you to jerk back your finger from burning, jump aside from an oncoming car, dodge people on the street—which everybody does very deftly even on a crowded sidewalk without thinking about it. At such a time signals from your eyes, feet, skin, nose are all pouring into the subconscious levels of your cerebral cortex, which sorts them out, sizes them up, and sends back rapid-fire orders to various muscles. While this subconscious operation is going on you can be thinking about the World Series or the girl you are going to meet.

If there is no crowd on the sidewalk and you are proceeding on your course thinking your thoughts, the subconscious part of your cerebral cortex may signal that another person is approaching head-on. At just the right moment to avoid collision, both of you get a signal to step aside, but one cortex chooses the left and the other the right. The result is that you still confront each other, so both cortexes signal the opposite direction, and you both step to the other side, still confronting each other and unable to break the rhythm of these instinctive signals. The poor cortexes are doing their best, but when it doesn't work out in the emergency, they call for your conscious part to wake up and think about what you are doing. You and the other pedestrian both feel silly doing a jig on the sidewalk, and so you both think up a way to break the subconscious control in order to avoid the collision and be on your way.

The subconscious or reflex department of the brain is the most important part for living in all animals. Even in the case of the human animal it is the bulk of his life, although he doesn't realize it. But in human life it is the conscious department of the cerebral cortex that counts the most. It is there that we have our thoughts, fun, fellowship, worries, and suffering. By blending the conscious and the subconscious departments, we can feel the thrill of art or close the eyes to enjoy music, and love.

The cerebral cortex started with reptiles and birds, which seem to have flashes of intelligence, hints of consciousness.

Toads, however, have no cerebral cortex, and all their actions are subconscious, like those of fishes and insects. Before the cerebral cortex was invented, these subconscious controls were distributed through the nervous system. The cerebral cortex concentrated the impulses, grew bigger and heavier with mammals, and reached its climax in man's masterpiece.

All animals have different amounts and qualities of brain power according to the weight of the white mass of nerve fibers and the expanse of the cerebral cortex as seen in the depths and curves of convolutions. The chimpanzee's cerebral cortex is closest to man's, although much smaller. The Indian elephant, the dog, and the horse rate next and have well-developed cortexes for animals. The beaver, lion, and bear are not far behind. The rhinoceros is the dumbest of all the large land mammals, with a depression where other animals have a well-rounded brow.

His subconscious system sends the rhinoceros on a rampage in your direction at the least sound of a snapping twig. Your cortex tells you to step aside at the charge of the monster, and you are saved because he will not turn back but will forget the whole affair in a few steps and go wandering off. We can suppose that the rhinoceros is somewhere between the earthworm and man on the brain scale.

HABITS

The nervous system's ability to form habits is basic necessity for the River of Life. It applies to eating and sleeping and every way of life; it makes conventions, and it is the foundation of social relationships. It is also the cause of nationalist feelings and of hostility between groups with different habits. Animals below man are strongly stereotyped. They are thoroughly creatures of habit because similar nervous systems produce similar impulses for action, communication, and mannerisms.

It takes effort to break a habit. This is the effort and agony of growing up. A baby starts with only the subconscious habits of the body of a primitive animal. It takes effort to create new circuits for new habits and fresh ideas. People find it much easier to repeat the same habits; there is a kind of gravity in the nervous system that is forever leveling. Man alone of all the inhabitants of the world has been able to resist this leveling of life, although the tides of regimentation have caught vast populations and carried them into the sea of helplessness.

The ability of a circuit to repeat, and each time it is repeated to grow stronger, as though etching a grooved path through a maze of interlocking nerve channels, is a provision for surviving, for damping the strain in nerves, which grow tired when overloaded. Habits are the lubrication of the nervous system.

At the same time the mass of white fibers underlying the cerebral cortex is a mystical mixing bowl. It can sort out, choose, reject, from the flood of signals arriving from outside and inside the body. Then swiftly it improvises a special circuit, setting up a path that flashes a fresh idea on the cortex, or causes its animal to act instinctively in a way which it has never acted before. Incidental circuits are used constantly for incidental situations—in conversation, when crossing the street, picking up something from the floor. Each is a little different from every other situation ever encountered.

This readiness of the nervous system to produce special circuits all the time for special action is the emergency side of the nervous system—and, happily, in man it is also available for new ideas.

In other animals, setting up special circuits in the subconscious nerve system is common practice—training your dog, horse, or the cows to come home for milking. Breaking a habit without the assistance of conscious thinking is very difficult. A bird lover in Dunbarton, New Hampshire, caught a baby white heron that staggered into her yard in the teeth of a storm. She saved its life by persuading it to eat sardines when standing on her arm. This was a joy—to rescue such a beautiful bird. That was two years ago, and the bird lover has not taken a vacation since, because the little white heron will eat sardines only when standing on her arm, and not when the saucer is placed on the ground.

The Nations in the Tree

THE TREE OUTSIDE MY WINDOW is mottled with shadows which, from a little distance, look like entrances to dark caves behind the sunlit surfaces of the leaves. I just saw a chickadee vanish in a split second by shooting in between two leaves with a flip of his wings.

When I stand under the crown of the tree and look up, I see, instead of black caves, a space beautifully lighted with a sun-flecked glow, formed like a big upside-down basket behind the tapestry of leaves. This is a curious sort of place, suspended above the ground, crisscrossed with branches and twigs, protected from wind and rain, filled with fresh air of moderate and steady temperature. It would be hard to imagine a place in the world more pleasant to live in. And it would be hard to find a creature more suitable than the chickadee to be an inhabitant of such a place.

The chickadee is perfectly designed to fly around in the basket of the tree crown, where there is by no means clear flying space. The chickadee body is bullet-shaped, with a round head snuggled into it instead of projecting on a neck. A compact tail is attached to powerful muscles at the hind end of the body by an amazing hinge that flips it through half a circle. This fast-acting rudder steers the chickadee more quickly than thought, so the chickadee avoids collision with twigs when flying inside the basket of the tree. Very short wings snap closed and hug the body, without the tips sticking out, then spring out to vibrate for an instant of flight. Other birds must come in with momentum from the outer air and shoot through the canopy with folded wings, or glide to a perch on outer branches.

Because of the peculiar nature of this happy hunting ground of the chickadee, there is no right side up or upside down for him. The paths between branches are twisted labyrinths. To swim through them calls for diving down or rocketing up at steep angles: whirling, somersaulting, describing figure eights, turning suddenly at right angles. The chickadee defies the law of gravity with a nervous system planned with short communication lines, rotary blood circulation, and a spherical arrangement of organs. Whether perching on a branch or clambering on the trunk, the chickadee may be head up or head down or sidewise.

For the same reason, storms with high winds that upset the equilibrium of other birds do not upset chickadees. People out in the rain see the acrobatic chickadee always headed into the wind to prevent rain or snow from being blown under his feathers from behind. In winter, when other birds have taken refuge, he comes out of his nesting hole in the trunk and frolics in a snowstorm. He will zip over to a dripping icicle and, without any support except the sensitive mechanism of wings and tail, catch the drops as they fall off the end of the icicle more neatly than you and I can drink from a fountain.

The chickadee looks like a "little darling," instead of the crafty hunter that he is. He can snap up an insect while turning a somersault in mid-air; he has a trick of whipping a caterpillar over a twig and then, ducking under, he takes hold of both ends of the caterpillar and does a giant swing. He can scrape up and swallow caterpillars at the rate of three per minute—that is, he can do that with smooth, moist caterpillars, while caterpillars with stiff bristles take a little longer. The problem of a bristly caterpillar, like the woolly bear, is solved in typical chickadee fashion. When a python swallows a porcupine head-first, it glides down the alimentary canal with quills folded toward the tail. But caterpillar bristles don't fold, so the chickadee puts a foot on him to hold him down while he picks out the meat with his nut-pick beak and leaves the bristles, like bones of a shad on the plate.

The busiest, fastest-moving inhabitant of the tree basket needs an enormous supply of energy. Indeed, when the chickadee is about to lay eggs, she eats her body weight in meat every day. At such a time, instead of saying "chickadee," she says "phoebe," with the high clear note of a boy soprano.

To the chickadee, the tree basket is a beautiful arrangement exclusively for chickadee living. But the deeper we look the more we discover countless nations and cultures everywhere in the tree world. Hidden within this familiar object of our everyday world dwell stranger and more unbelievable beings than any we can imagine.

THE NATION IN THE ROOT JUNGLE

The nation of the tree which is least known or suspected lives in a weird white jungle deep in the blackness of the ground. Both jungle and inhabitants, bathed in the vital essences of the soil, are terrifically animated.

The tip of a root consists of a few tough cells welded together to form a spike that wedges, pushes, and twists its way between tightly packed pebbles and soil particles. This thing that looks so flabby and tender possesses immense power. The cells of the spike do not move forward, although, by expanding back of the point, they act like a wedge. They move by elongating the way a rubber balloon moves forward from your

lips when you inflate it. While the irresistible spike is winning
new ground, its power is constantly renewed through its cells,
which divide to keep ever fresh cells out in front pushing
farther and farther. As older cells are stalled and left behind,
the inherent power that had thrust them forward now causes
them to grow in a peculiar way. Each bulges out with a
nipple at right angles to the forward movement of the whole
root. The nipple lengthens swiftly, becomes a long, slender,
white hair. This is unlike an ordinary hair on a leaf or an
animal body—it is an extension of the body of the living cell
itself and has protoplasm flowing within it. This marvelous
hair is a finger that can explore and absorb nourishing fluids
in the neighborhood.

In this way, just back of the growing tip of every root the
white jungle appears like a puff of felt. This is the fastest-grow-
ing part of the tree. The dense thickets of these hairs bubble
out forward and get taller and deeper aft. Then suddenly they
shrivel and vanish, while fresh ones are springing out up in
front. The mass and height of a tree betokens the immensity
of this operation, of food gathering by astronomical numbers
of microscopic hairs.

It is impossible even to guess at how fast the roots of a tree
grow or what their total length is. If you tried to heave up a
great tree out of solid ground with a bulldozer you would
never, with all the clamor and confusion, be able to find and
separate the vast root system with which that tree has so
quietly permeated the soil. By watching them in a microscope
you can see the great speed of root hairs.

A single grass plant of winter rye was grown from seed in
a wooden box a foot square and twenty-two inches deep. This
gave it a little less than two cubic feet of dirt all to itself. At
the end of four months it produced a plant about twenty inches
tall. When its roots were painstakingly measured with the most
accurate instruments, they were found to have grown at the
rate of more than three miles per day. But that is only a small

part of the story—the grass roots were outstripped by their root hairs with fifty miles of new length per day. The total score for the four months of this single plant reveals (with traumatic effect) how strenuously and intimately a living thing can explore its portion of the earth's surface for food to live by. The winter rye reached out with two million feet of roots, and these bubbled out with six thousand miles of root hairs—*sic*!

Countless numbers of fanciful, tiny creatures live in this white root jungle and travel with it through the ground. Thread worms tie themselves in knots, millipedes run through soil tunnels on two hundred and thirty legs, earthworms swell and extend their muscular bodies. The most populous and important inhabitants of the place are the minute units of life which we call bacteria, beings invisible to the eyes of men, insects, and birds. They are utterly different from other animals and plants in the way they eat raw elements and convert these almost instantly into the droplets of their living bodies.

The bacterium during its life incessantly soaks up minerals locked up in the soil and brews them in its body juices. Bacteria are being born and dying every twenty minutes, so their generations are like ripples of life. The white threads of the roots of the tree world pick up the elixirs in the bodies of the dead generations of bacteria and pass them into the river of sap, to become mysterious life forces we call proteins, enzymes, and hormones. Thus the nations in the root hairs make living chemicals that are the cornerstone of all the life of the tree world.

THE NATION IN THE LEAVES

A vast distance away from the white jungle, at the other end of the tree world, a green leaf flutters in the sun. It seems as though any inhabitants of that leaf would find themselves in a situation similar to that of a dinghy tossed in a rough sea.

But there is a population living snugly in a wide, vast, low-ceiling room between the upper and lower surfaces of the leaf. Green, sausage-shaped cells hang in great numbers from a transparent ceiling, and the light that filters through lends the place a soft, emerald glow. Below these hanging sausage-shaped cells, the room is loosely filled with spongy cells, between which fresh air circulates from vents in the floor. This is the food factory, where the tree makes energy out of water, air, and sunlight, for root elongating, bud opening, seed packing, trunk expanding. This energy is made in such quantities that there is plenty left over to power all the animal life of the tree world.

A unique nation have moved into this lush, air-conditioned place where they are closer to the source of food all processed and ready to eat than all other beings on earth. They are invisible to outsiders, well sheltered, and have no food transportation problem, no water shortage. They are called leaf miners because they spend their lives running tunnels inside the leaf.

Leaf miners are the specters of certain kinds of beetles, moths, and flies who look so different from one another in the outer world, where we see them buzz, flutter, or streak like sparks of sunlight. But the specters of these beetles, moths, and flies that live inside leaves all look and act in about the same way, because conditions in the leaf are the same for all of them.

They got inside after their mothers had laid eggs about the leaf. The fly mother used a saw to slit the edge of the leaf and put in her eggs. Another used a hypodermic needle to puncture a hole and shoot in the eggs. A third sowed rows of eggs along a vein, and when they hatched, the babies bit a hole and climbed in.

Leaf miners are flat or slender cylinders. They are moist so that they may slip along easily. They often have wedge-shaped heads to push open a path among the sponges and sausages. Legs, if any, are reduced to knobs on which the creature slides. The specter of the fly inside the leaf has a plastic body of no definite shape. It can take the form of a ribbon to squeeze through narrow places between leaf veins and compress its body flat to pass through a shallow place between the juicy cells of the leaf room, becoming round again when pressure is removed. One leaf miner has stiff bristles mounted in ball sockets scattered over its body which can be moved individually in any direction by strong muscles in the skin. This animal poles its way, with its body in any position at all, through the sponges and sausages that fill the room.

Eating equipment of leaf miners is remarkable. Some have sharp, hollow needles to puncture the cells and suck the juice freshly made that instant out of air, water, and sunshine. Others are equipped with scissors on their jaws and hedge-clip a path, swallowing cells whole as they go. Another wears a sharp, curved blade with which it cuts a swath through the green cells like a reaper. Hedge clippers and scythes cannot cut with broad strokes up and down in such a shallow place, so the larvae which use them turn their heads at a right angle and reap the harvest with horizontal strokes.

I have often been fascinated by the sinuous, serpentine paths of leaf miners, as you see these paths traced in white on the outside of the leaf, when the green cells have been eaten for the tunnels underneath the surface of the leaf. This indicates extremely lazy miners who do not bother to cut the hard, woody cells of the veins, but wander around without direction among the softest and juiciest cells in the paradise of delight.

THE NATIONS ON THE LEAF SURFACE

The praying mantis, the giant of the leaf surface, looks like a wistful clown, with big round eyes set in a little triangular face, but it behaves like a steel trap. Most of the time it holds its body frozen still while only its head turns slowly as it

follows a caterpillar or a walking stick with its gaze. This is
the only insect that can revolve its head all the way around to
look directly behind without moving its body. At a carefully
calculated instant its arms, which have been folded like a
monk's in prayer, flash out with a blow that never misses. If the
katydid climbing over the edge of the leaf is lucky enough to
catch sight of the steel trap and ducks down or flies away, the
praying mantis simply waits. It seldom bothers to move; it
just waits and waits, vanishing in the shadows as a good-sized
twig.

City people looking for a quiet night in the country have
been driven almost mad by *"katydid, katydidn't."* I have heard
it resound from a half mile across the valley. The lonely male
takes a stance on a leaf and rasps from that spot hour after
hour, frustrating scientists trying to record how long the
katydid can make a noise without stopping. An English
authority reports that his katydid said "katydid" from one
spot near the top of a tree for more than a week. This pitilessly
strident sound is made by two wings that look like green leaves.

A color slide I made showing the veins of a katydid wing
is always mistaken for a leaf. A single vein curving across the
broadest part of the left wing has microscopic teeth along its
entire length. Opposite this file vein a section of the right wing
is sharp-edged, and when scraped across the file it vibrates,
and this operates as a terrific amplifier. The wings are hinged
so that the katydid can play on its wings as with a violin,
drawing the edge of one across the vein of the other. The katydid looks so much like a green leaf he would hardly ever be
seen or known except for his violin playing.

You will often see the measuring worm proceeding across a
leaf with the most absurd locomotion of looping up and flat-
tening out. This buffoon imitates both leaf and twig. In early
summer when leaves are bright green, the measuring worm
is bright green. When it walks half its person is always
standing still. This is done by abolishing legs in the middle of

the long, slender, caterpillar body. The front end walks forward, stretching it out; then the front end stands still while the rear end walks up, causing its middle to rise in the beautiful loop. After a few weeks, the well-fed measuring worm gets lazy, turns the color of a dark-brown twig, and, taking a mighty grip with its hind legs, stiffens and stands out at an angle, even copying the little bumps and irregularities of a twig. The strength of a grip that permits a solid inch of caterpillar body to stand out at right angles passes understanding. Imagine grasping a small tree trunk and having the power to hold yourself at arm's length horizontally for hours.

APHID MULTITUDES

The great paradox of tree-world life is the way leaves teem with aphids even though an aphid is so weak and defenseless you can hardly pick one up without killing it and has ruthless enemies organized for mass destruction, stalking it relentlessly across the leaves.

An aphid looks like a delicate, long-legged fly or a tender little bug, according to whether it happens to be wearing wings. You are most apt to see it in the bug form, and it is green, black, or red in color.

The aphid secret of being lies in streamlined multiplying. From spring to midsummer males are banished, and thirteen generations of females are born in a few weeks at the rate of a hundred eggs per aphid. Children grow up so fast they become grandmothers in twenty-four hours. This is meat production by the ton. It has been calculated (by serious authority) that, in twelve generations, the tonnage of aphids starting from one female would equal the weight of five hundred million human beings—if all the aphids lived.

This miracle of reproduction is performed by the elixir of life in the currents of sap gathered by the root hairs down in the fecund soil. The aphid carries a fine sucking needle folded

11*

against her breast while she shifts a bit, looking for a good place. Then she plunges this in and drinks for days without moving. When eggs start coming out, she merely takes a few steps to make room for children that trail out behind her.

The drop of sap that one aphid sucks is of no consequence to a tree, which can quickly replace the nourishing juice by its food-making powerhouse. But aphids are sometimes deployed in armies that total a tremendous sap pump which can kill a tree. The multitude stands tilted forward, with sucking needles thrust in to the hilt, blissfully unaware of anything except the delicious drinking. Here and there some individuals are so punch drunk they lift their hind feet in the air. Give one of these a shove, and his hind legs drop, up comes his head, withdrawing the sucking needle, and he scrambles away. In so doing, he must stumble over his fellows, who, without pausing in their drinking, violently let go their hind legs, like mad mules, and literally kick the disturber off the reservation.

In late summer something happens in the aphid nation. Both males and females appear; they sprout wings, jump off their leaf surface, and fly away on a honeymoon. In a few weeks a deserted bride returns to her tree and deposits one big strong egg in a crack of the bark, where it will survive the winter until the following spring.

THE LION THAT CHASES APHIDS

It is clear that aphids do not inherit the tree world. If they did, it would lead to the instant suicide of their race because there would soon be no more leaves to pump. They are so vigorously dealt with that aphids are usually hardly more than a sluice which diverts saps into the bodies of other fine and wonderful creatures. For example, ladybird beetles, those polished, oval, yellow or red gems with black spots, or black gems with red or yellow spots. The three colors are constant but interchangeable between base colors and spots. Ladybird beetles have a voracious taste for aphids, scooping them up ten at a time and eating sixty in an hour.

There is a lion at large in the leaf pasture with as great an appetite for aphid meat as the ladybird. Lion is his true name and, in the eyes of an aphid, he is as fierce as the king of the jungle and far uglier, with a pair of incurving sickle blades on his head that puncture prey when they snap closed.

Nature is always dreaming up versions of Beauty and the Beast. The mother of the lion is a fairy with golden eyes and cloudy, blue-green wings. Their delicacy gives this mother of lions the name lacewing. She climbs out of a round hole in a ball of silk during the summer, and you'll find this exquisite creature walking on a leaf. The lacy wing membrane, more delicate than any tissue paper we can imagine, is stretched on a framework of veins that is an exquisite miracle of engineering. She touches the leaf with a medicine dropper at the rear end of her abdomen, depositing a sticky droplet of "rubber cement." Then she lifts the tip of her abdomen, drawing up a vertical thread of the clear, viscous fluid. In the second of time this takes, the thread hardens and stands up like a fine, vibrating wire a half-inch tall. Now, touching the top of this with her eye dropper, she deposits one egg. She takes a few steps and repeats; soon the leaf has a miniature orchard of straight pins, each with an egg for a head.

If the lion mother laid her eggs in rows or clumps the way other insects do, when the baby lions hatched, these gruesome creatures would eat each other. As it is, after climbing down to the leaf surface, the baby lion immediately goes after aphids. The pin device saves a vast population of lions, for a single tiny lion bags thirty aphids the first week; then, as it grows, sixty the second, ninety the third. When it has eaten around a hundred aphids, it spins a silk ball and goes to sleep.

A MAGNET FOR ALL KINDS OF LIFE

The shadowy nooks and crannies of the tree are packed with food in every corner. No other living place in the world is higher in proteins and calories manufactured on the premises.

These caves and hiding places draw birds out of the air and tempt animals to leave the ground and run up. There is room for squirrels, possums, monkeys, even a kangaroo, to live in the tree world. Snakes, toads, and chameleons quit the ancient haunts of their ancestors in soil and water and mount trees, to spend their lives high up in the air. Snails slide along slippery paths up the trunk to make their homes in high perches in the tree. Even an eight-inch fish, as we have seen in an earlier chapter, is drawn by the tree to break the surface of the water, turn himself into an air-breathing fish temporarily, and climb the trunk.

To the animal who lives in the trunk, his hole is his castle. The first one to move into a hole, whether chickadee, woodpecker, squirrel, raccoon, possum, bat, or owl, becomes the owner of a fort with strong, soundproof walls. Everyone instinctively respects such ownership—unless the one in the hole is good to eat, which is a different matter. Perhaps this respect for the property of another developed through generations of raiders taking one look at the dour pie face of an owl staring out of the hole of a tree trunk.

The river of sap of the tree world has its source in the clear water of the soil in which life-giving minerals are dissolved, and its mouth in myriads of twig points bathed by fresh air and touched by the dynamic power of sunshine. No matter how many years, or thousands of years, the wood built along its rivers of sap may stand, the life of a tree is forever young. Its buds have opened and new leaves unfolded fresh this year. It is truly the fountain of youth for all its inhabitants.

xx. *The tarsier, the loneliest individual in the United States.*

PLATE XX

BERNARDA
BRYSON

The Little Old Man in the Tree

FOR A LONG TIME they didn't know he was still alive on earth. Until a few years ago no white man ever saw him at large in the jungle, but now we know that he has been living in South Sea jungles in the Philippines, Borneo, and the Malayan Islands. At this writing one is living at the Philadelphia Zoo, mateless, and the loneliest individual in the United States.

I went to call on him and found a furry body the size of a chipmunk asleep on a bare branch. Although this branch was at a steep angle, the *Tarsier* snuggled his body and forearms against it, taking a firm hold with an opposing thumb and four long, slender fingers. His toes are shorter than his fingers and do not grasp so firmly, but he squats on his haunches, a position which young children and Orientals without chairs have never given up. A slender but solid and comparatively heavy tail is twice as long as his body. This is hairless except for a tassel at the tip that gives a little more air resistance for better steering without adding too much weight to the tapering point. The tail is held out from the branch at an angle and sways almost imperceptibly, constantly, instinctively ad-

justing the balance. The tarsier is a beautiful example of serene
balance, perfect for the tarsier style of body, in which the long,
slender tail is used for balancing in the same way as the long
pole of a high-wire walker.

When aroused, the tarsier, lifting his round head, with a
good skull for a brain and two little shell-shaped ears, turned
a pug nose toward his visitor and stared with big, round eyes.
It could have been a funny little old man.

Looking into those beautiful eyes, you forget everything else
about him, and you wonder whether he is reproachful or disdainful, or feeling wide-eyed astonishment at what fifty million
years since his day has brought to earth in animal form.

Somebody had to make the first move and that was definitely
myself, because the little old man in the tree gave every appearance of never again moving a muscle so long as he could
stare into eyes that were about the same size as his. So, after
a long time, a small stick was used for a small poke. The result
was like that of a moving picture which gives a wink and the
scene moves over and continues exactly as before. The tarsier
had translated himself to another branch, where he now clung
in the same position, staring with those big, round eyes and
the same expression on his face. This wink of a leap had no
preliminary movement, such as loosening his hold or adjusting
position to get poised. His hind legs, working with the same
action as the long-hinged legs of a frog or a kangaroo, had
sprung him across the space so fast that the eye could hardly
follow; and suddenly arriving at the other branch, there was
no apparent need for adjusting or shifting. In his home trees he
can clear eight feet in a flash from a squatting start, and one
who has peered closely says that in mid-air his tail sticks out
behind and, with head up, face straight ahead, hair streaming back, he looks like a witch on a broomstick.

A pair of good eyes is needed for a performance like this.
These eyes are better when they roll, or the neck must turn,
or both. This reminds us of ourselves, although the tarsier is

not the only tree animal which acquired a turning neck. We have seen how the praying mantis for one could revolve his head to look over his shoulder, but the mantis is an insect, while the tarsier is a little old man in a tree.

With good sight, the tarsier does not need so keen a smell, and in accordance with nature's process of body building, the long snout of this wistful tree animal is shortened to a pug nose. His top lip bears a neat mustache. Since he chews instead of gnaws, his teeth are lined up like ours. He has blue eyes at birth, and his eyelids are edged with a row of long lashes. There is a little beard at the angle of the chin—not like a professional goatee in the center of the chin but a crescent of hair dipping with the line of the chin in Amish style. He has a whorl of hair on the nape of his neck. And his sperm resembles a man's.

It is not as though one animal turned into another until the tarsier was perfected and then it was only a step until we were completed. Body building calls for assembling all sorts of parts, trying them out, selecting some for this animal or that, rejecting parts not needed, until various members of the Animal Kingdom were put together to fit various conditions. Nevertheless, the tarsier is a fine figure of a man.

The tree world conjured up another dramatic being who, accepting his inheritance of limbs like the tarsier, proceeded to use only his arms for going places by swinging, and thereby developed the longest, strongest arms in the tree world, while his tail shrank and vanished. The name of this distinguished relative of the tarsier is *Hylobates hoolock*, the "tree walker." Walking through trees using arms alone develops them very long and strong. The arms must hold and swing the entire weight of the body. The hoolock represents the high point of arm development, and we may have him to thank for the length of our arms and proud biceps. In that case, we owe the hoolock all the fun we have with our arms—golfing and wrestling, swinging an ax, boxing and hugging. The hoolock dispensed with a tail, and we can suppose, looking at him, that man lost his tail before he came down from the tree—except for the bump at the base of the spine.

We don't have wings because we don't have to fly, while our fellow mammal, the bat, turned his arms into wings. We don't have tails like the tarsier because we don't balance on branches or need them for rudders when jumping across space. But the tail was a great idea, widely used in the tree world. The spider monkey developed the most wonderful tail of all because he swung by it, using its tip as a lasso to grasp branches. Such a tail is an extra arm and hand. The possum has a great tail, which it wraps around a tree limb, and the sloth abolished the tail but kept claws instead of fingernails to hang on with upside down from the tree limb.

Running on two legs has been well tried out by other creatures than ourselves. Birds use their light, springy, two-legged mechanism for landing and running. One of the oldest examples of two-leggedness is the lizard in Australia that walks on all fours most of the time, but impulsively, when excited, rears up on his hind legs and takes to his heels across the sand exactly like a scared boy. The opposing-thumb idea perfected by the tarsier was tried out also by birds that put one claw on the opposite side of the branch and clamp this grip so that they don't fall off when they go to sleep.

Big eyes, accurate sight, co-ordination of nervous system and muscles were so perfect that they have held the tarsier in vital balance in his tree world for millions of years. Others of his kind who were ambitious and daring eventually turned into the hylobates hoolock. Still others in the hylobates' manner, ambitious and daring, came down out of the tree, ate berries and grains, and turned into people.

In the person of the tarsier we first see our eyes and ears among the branches, the human nose, revolving neck, hair style, and long arms clubbed with five digits, of which the opposing thumb is very important, and fingernails and soft pads of the palm and fingertips to fit and hold against rounded or uneven surfaces. And, when straightened out, the long hind legs for squatting and jumping are like ours.

All the odds were against it from the start. A fish, a crocodile, a tree, or a tarsier—each is the product of one in a billion, billion chances. But the overwhelming fact of existence is that time is eternal; it cannot be measured by any yardstick or described in any terms, and, within time, opportunities are infinite.

When a life form came into being, it possessed a relentless hunger to absorb the elements and use their energy to re-create more like itself. This urge, with the increase of life, became a terrible power of reproduction. For countless ages this power flowed through animals and plants as mechanical and involuntary as gravity, although constantly channeled through new forms, until the tree world appeared with its vivid contrasts and peculiar combination of forces.

Before the rise of the tree world, bodies were shaped by water. Although those ancient haunts of life teemed with fantasies of forms, none among underwater bodies could ever look like a man or woman. Many creatures of the water world reproduced without radical changes down the ages in the stable conditions of the sea, until, fascinatingly, they show us what life was like before a tree ever grew on earth. Bodies are apt to be long, slender, and smooth under water; fat and furry on land.

The first legs that marched across the water barrier belonged to reptiles. Future lengthenings of stubby crocodile legs would be used to climb into the tree world of the future. The reptiles staggered or wiggled out of shallow pools and swamps to lie on sun-warmed rocks, but because they did all their feeding under water they were overcome with drowsiness on land. Sun-bathing calls for little energy, and such a situation was not conducive to developing speed and alertness. However, life is so eternally urgent that it would have been no special miracle for a reptile body to have acquired, perhaps in a much later age than ours, respectability and ideas. Then the "human race" might have been styled with tough, leathery skin, long noses, or what not, instead of the upstanding, long-legged torsos that we are. If the tree world had not appeared on earth!

The tree world offered life new terms. It brought to the water's edge its special challenge—to exchange underwater eating tools for an entirely different set of tools, to give up swimming equipment as surplus and discover what arms and legs can do. The tree world held out alternatives so that life would no longer be so involuntary and automatic. The tree world called for the sharpening of sight and hearing, and the making of decisions—which eventually would lead to dreams. Thus, the conformity of the underwater type and the sultry resignation of the crocodile type could be replaced by a new kind of body activated by voluntary effort, surprise, interest, wonder, and eagerness.

In the tree world the shock of trifles makes animals more free, more lonely, more independent, and bereft of ties. An animal must find a mate, must see farther and more clearly to pluck a fruit, must sharpen its wits to seize a prey. Such pressures make it jump a greater distance or swing a little farther, or turn its head, or decide to go or stay. More intense and longer life makes death more touching, and gives time for building a tradition.

While the bodies of a shark, crocodile, chickadee, or man are equal miracles, another quality which cannot be described in any laboratory was also accumulated step by step, through the call of the tree basket for extra-special sight or touch or— memory. From there, jumping the gap between beast and man, we find *imagination*.

With imagination, we may hear the music of the tree world in the pattern of a tree. It starts with the high, silvery notes of fluid entering myriads of white root hairs. That magnitude of sound is far beyond the reach of our ears, but sound there must be for the same reason that air passing through organ pipes becomes a sounding medium. In the background you hear the rapid rhythm of the dance of the molecules of minerals dissolved in the water, the Brownian movement which we can see with our own eyes through a microscope. Then comes a deeper resonance as the sap moves upward through the longer tubes in the heavy wood of the trunk. Its symphony rises to a crescendo when the tree is stretching in the spring of the year, accented by the expanding cells, the crystallizing of new wood, the cracking of bark. After that comes the third movement, which repeats with variations the theme of the first. The tempo changes, the pitch grows steadily higher as the sap flows through the tapestry of the branches and through finer and finer tubes of the tiniest twigs and leaf veins—and fades into sunlight. This is the melody of the tree's challenge to life.

To us the human body is the greatest masterpiece of animal styling. We spend a great deal of money to save its natural lines and smooth skin and make it the subject of the highest arts. But we do not usually regard it as a part of nature. "Nature" is everything else on earth but us. We are so biased on this point that we refuse to concede that our bodies are assembled out of other animal parts. This denial prevents us from seeing the revelation of immortality as one of the great facts of life, not merely a dogma. It is the inherent quality of protoplasm, a reservoir of life shared alike by all living things, that it constantly renews its youth along the infinity of time by passing again and again through the original state of the raw elements.

The physical bodies of individuals, even individual species, do not count in the past and the future; they are but milestones in the flow of immortal life. However, each living animal has the power to alter the capacity of its drop of life stuff, to bend its instinctive heritage a tiny bit in a certain direction, until out of involuntary and subconscious action there can grow wisdom or a capacity for beauty or that resolution of the conscience that lies in worship or the faculty to create—or, on the other hand, to lose these qualities and revert to the purely indifferent and blind. The aggregate result spells civilization, true happiness, divine vision, a golden age—or else a dark age, Neanderthal brutality, destruction of a cathedral. Or, it is conceivable that, after all the trees are destroyed and the earth is scorched, there may be a return to the stability of the automatic and involuntary life in the sea.

Looking out from inside our masterpiece, we see that all other animals are odd, fanciful, or funny—with the exception of some dogs, horses, and pussycats that are a bit civilized and seem to share our admiration of ourselves.

On the other hand, the giraffe, who is a remarkable product of the tree world, glancing down from the top of his stepladder where he is chewing the leaves, would doubtless think that the human body is very funny with such a short neck. The chickadee would be justified in his opinion that a man is ridiculous in the way he struts around on the ground, and the housefly would get a laugh out of man's contraptions for flying. In the judgment of an owl, a man's eyes are much too small in proportion to his body. If you and I had eyes measuring up to the owl's standard, they would weigh ten pounds. What do we suppose the walking stick would think of buttocks and breasts? Isn't it possible that an aphid, which can produce fifty babies at a clip without a male, would regard two people kissing as a ridiculous way of making an odd sound?

Of all creatures, though, we alone have the capacity to enjoy the show.